TIME FOR POETRY

compiled by May Hill Arbuthnot

Illustrated by Arthur Paul

A representative collection of poetry for children,

to be used in the classroom, home, or camp; especially

planned for college classes in children's literature; with

an introduction for teachers and parents on reading poetry

to children and using poetry in verse choirs

Scott, Foresman and Company

Chicago   Atlanta   Dallas   Palo Alto   Fair Lawn, N. J.

General Edition

TIME FOR POETRY

Revised

To friends all over the United States

who have discovered the delight

of reading poetry aloud

and who are sharing it with their children

Library of Congress catalog card number: 61–5724

CONTENTS

PREFACE TO
THE REVISED EDITION

The question may well be asked, why should a book that has enjoyed as wide and happy acceptance as *Time for Poetry* need to be revised? The first reason for the revision springs from the fact that over the last decade there has been an astonishing increase in the use of poetry with children. It is pleasant to think that perhaps *Time for Poetry* itself and the seven chapters on poetry in *Children and Books* are having something to do with this growing interest. But whatever the cause, the increased use of poetry has been matched by an equally surprising increase in the publication of delightful new books of poetry for children.

This is the first reason for the revision of *Time for Poetry:* the desire to introduce children and grownups to new poems by such poets as David McCord, Gwendolyn Brooks, William Jay Smith, Harry Behn, Frances Frost, John Ciardi, and Robert Frost. Selections from their books—varied in subject matter and fine in quality—will, it is hoped, send children and grownups scurrying to the library or bookstores for the books themselves.

Second, because upper grade teachers suggested that the earlier edition paid more attention to the primary grades than to the later grades, this revised edition has added more poems for the middle and upper grades—selections that will both challenge and delight older boys and girls.

With these various additions, *Time for Poetry* now has 735 poems, ranging from the nursery school and primary levels through junior high school.

Third, the increased use of poetry in schools throughout the country has resulted in many inquiries about and experimentation with verse choirs or choral speaking. To answer these questions and to help adults launch this work, a new section on verse choir techniques has been added. (See p. xxiv.) The methods recommended are as practical and down to earth as long years of conducting verse choirs with both children and adults can make them. Additional help is provided by detailed analyses of many poems for choral speaking. This new section should enable any grownup to approach verse choir work with confidence. Given an ear for rhythm and for natural, sensible phrasing, anyone can follow these directions and carry a group of children from first experiences in speaking together to the point where they thoroughly enjoy their verse choirs and speak a variety of fine poetry with intelligence and spirit.

These, then, are some of the reasons for this revision and for the new materials that have been included.

May Hill Arbuthnot

Cleveland, 1960

READING POETRY TO CHILDREN

With the child's world overflowing with brightly illustrated books about everything from puppies to atoms, fairy tales to biography, and here-and-now adventures to adventures on Mars, it is reassuring to hear teachers and parents ask, "What about children and poetry? When and how should it begin? Is it possible today to develop in children a permanent liking for poetry when other books, radio, television, and moving pictures all seem to crowd it out?"

The oral approach to poetry

Young children make it possible to answer these questions optimistically because in the years before they learn to read, they get their poetry as men first got it—through their ears. And, like their unread ancestors, children respond to verse with every evidence of enjoyment and almost immediate participation. When a grownup reads *Mother Goose* to small children their frequent response is "Sing it again," which the willing slave does until presently the children join in and chant with him. They may mark time with their heads or hands, or jounce gaily with their small bodies, or begin to chant the words for themselves. These responses are precisely the responses children make to that other aural art, music, because poetry is like music. It tickles their ears with its tunefulness and rhythm, and promotes a joining-in response just as music does.

This is a first clue for the happy introduction of poetry to children and young people—it should be spoken and heard in order to be wholly understood and enjoyed. The Irish poet William Butler Yeats wrote:

I have just heard a poem spoken with so delicate a sense of its rhythm, with so

perfect a respect for its meaning, that if I were a wise man and could persuade a few people to learn the art I would never open a book of verse again.[1]

By this he implies that reading a poem silently from the printed page is to miss its music and perhaps even its meaning. If this is true for grownups, it is doubly true for children, who encounter so many reading difficulties in the printed form of poetry that they come to suspect it as queer and hazardous. But when they hear it read with sincerity and vigor, they enjoy its swing and readily catch its meaning. If children are to develop a genuine liking for poetry, they must hear quantities of it read aloud from their earliest years, and, simultaneously, begin to speak it, and, later, read it aloud for themselves.

This places the responsibility for the development of a growing taste for poetry upon the grownups who guide children's literary experiences. It is the grownups who must choose and read poetry to children in the years before they can read it for themselves. And, since adults are sometimes as afraid of poetry as children are, a few first aids to reading it aloud may be in order.

When the small child commands "Sing it again," it shows that he recognizes music when he hears it, whether it is made with an instrument or with words. For the first appeal of poetry is through its melody and movement, and when it is read, these must be preserved and even emphasized. Walter de la Mare calls these qualities "tune and runningness" and they are the qualities which distinguish poetry from prose. Nor are they merely ear-tickling devices. They serve a

[1] William Butler Yeats, *Ideas of Good and Evil* (New York: Macmillan, 1907), p. 16.

variety of purposes. The melody and movement of a poem sometimes suggest the action the poet is describing. Sometimes they help to establish a mood or feeling. And sometimes they underscore or clarify the meaning. Since this is true, it is well to know what is meant by melody and movement in poetry or "tune and runningness" or music and rhythm, however you wish to designate these qualities.

The melody or tune of poetry

Let's consider the tune of poetry first. This refers in part to the sound of the words. That is, a poet chooses words not only for their precise shades of meaning but also for their peculiar vowel or consonant sounds, which actually reinforce the mood or meaning he is trying to express. Melody in poetry may stem from rhyming words at the conclusion or within the lines, but rhyme is only a part of the music. Vowel or consonant combinations, the explosiveness or smoothness of the lines, the clipped brevity or sonority of the words, these are also involved. For instance, half the fun of Laura Richards'

> Riddle cum diddle cum dido,
> My little dog's name is Fido,

turns upon the ear-tickling sounds of those explosive consonants. And, by the way, it is interesting to notice how often nonsense verse depends for its effects upon the staccato beat of consonants. "One misty moisty morning," "Husky hi, husky hi," "Godfrey Gordon Gustavus Gore," "The Pirate Don Durk of Dowdee" are all funnier because of their absurd sounds. And you know something humorous is under way the moment you read the titles of T. S. Eliot's poems about his nonsensical cats—"The Rum Tum Tugger" and "Macavity: the Mystery Cat." So, when you have nonsense verse to read, watch for the funny-sounding consonants and make the most of them.

Lovely vowel combinations produce subtler and more beautiful melodies.

> Oh, fair to see
> Bloom-laden cherry tree,
>   Arrayed in sunny white;

> An April day's delight,
>   Oh, fair to see!

is like a clear, sweet tune because of the beauty of its vowel sounds. *Mother Goose*, with her "Blow, wind, blow" and many others, develops early the child's sensitivity to the melody of words. Eleanor Farjeon has two poems, "Boys' Names" and "Girls' Names," whose charm lies in the unique tone color produced by the vowel sounds of certain first names. These vowels must be given full value, not only to bring out the music of the lines but to enhance the humor of the surprise endings, which turn upon a sharp contrast in sound.

Perhaps these examples suffice to illustrate the principle that to read poetry aloud effectively and meaningfully, the reader must give careful thought to the sound values of words. Ignore this melody of verse, whether it is sonorous or clipped, harsh or sweet, staccato or flowing, and you lessen the impact of the poem on yourself and your listeners. Give the vowels and consonants their full values in roundness or crispness and you enhance both the melody and the meaning of the poem.

Rhythm and movement in poetry

Mother Goose is a good first source of "runningness" for children. Her pages are full of bouncy rhythms that hop, skip, jump, gallop, walk, or swing as gently as a lullaby. "Ride a cock horse" is as unmistakably a gallop as "Hippety hop to the barber shop" is a skip, and "To market to market" an everyday, off-to-the-grocery sort of a walk. Movement in verse is its swing and lilt, its sledge-hammer beat, or its soporific softness. These are the result of meter and the rhythmic patterns of words and lines. Like melody, they differentiate verse from prose.

Small children usually like their rhythms well marked and contagiously gay, in poetry as well as in music. When a small boy in Utah heard Dorothy Baruch's "Merry-Go-Round" for the first time, he immediately responded by waving one arm in a big arc, going faster and faster as the carrousel gained momentum, and slowing down until he and the poem came to a full stop together. Some little girls thought Kate Greenaway's children were jumping rope in her "Jump —jump—jump," so they tried it themselves. And the children soon discover that the words in Mr. Milne's "Hoppity" hop right along with Christopher Robin.

Presently, the grownup who reads many poems to children discovers subtler movements in poetry than the obvious examples just cited. For instance, in Stevenson's "Where Go the Boats" there is a flowing-water movement throughout the lines, for all the world like the surge of the river in the music of Smetana's "River Moldau." Or in Walter de la Mare's "The Cupboard" there is a gay, tripping rhythm, almost syncopated, that is like the jubilant prancing of the small boy who is about to receive some "Banbury Cakes and Lollipops." To read this poem heavily with a singsong emphasis on the metrical beat is to destroy completely its gaiety and fun.

Meter and rhythm

This brings up a ticklish problem in reading verse aloud. Because of the nature of poetry and the exciting effect of its movement, it is agreed that this quality of rhythm must be preserved and emphasized. Yet that very emphasis may result, both with children and adults, in singsong which can reduce a poem to meaningless patter. To avoid this, the reader must recognize the difference between rhythm and the metric beat of poetry. Meter is the precise number of syllables or the organization of feet to a line, while rhythm is the larger flow of cadences, the rise and fall of sound. It might be said that the metric beat of poetry is like the beat of the metronome in music. If you play a musical composition with the precise beat of a metronome, you have music as mechanical as a hurdy-gurdy. So, if you read poetry with a precise marking of the metric beat, the results will be singsong and meaningless patter. To avoid this, think carefully of the meaning the words must convey and speak them in the rhythms of natural speech while respecting the larger flow of the lines as well. The metric beat often obscures meaning where the natural rhythm will clarify it. Take the first two lines of "The Cupboard." The metric beat would make it read:

I knów a líttle cúp board
With a tee ny tíny kéy,

But such reading is nonsense. No one tells an interesting bit of news in any such singsong patter. The rhythms of natural speech would find the child telling his exciting news like this:

I know a little *cupboard*
With a teeny tiny *key,*

Those last words are not overstressed, but they do stand out as the very center and focus of a delightful secret. And the metric pattern is not upset by this reading. There is a due regard for lines and rhymes, but the mechanical tick tick tick of the metronome gives way to the natural rhythms of storytelling in verse form.

Functions of melody and movement

Actually, melody and movement in poetry are not two separate qualities but inseparables, one an integral part of the other. That is, the vowel and consonant sounds of words help to make the swing and movement of the lines, and these, in turn, are a part of the melody or tune of the poem. Together, these essential characteristics of poetry serve three purposes: melody and movement may suggest the very action the poet is describing; they may help to establish the mood of the poem; or they may even clarify or emphasize the idea—what the poem is about.

For example, in the words and short lines of Eleanor Farjeon's "Mrs. Peck Pigeon," there is actually the bobbing, teetering motion of a pigeon "picking for bread." In Herbert Asquith's "Skating," the lines swing and swoop with the skater. The galloping rhythm of Stevenson's "Windy Nights" goes on and on like the mysterious wind-rider galloping farther and farther away and then coming back again. "Texas Trains and Trails" gives the "chuck-a-luck, chuck-a-luck" movement of trains to perfection, ending with a burst of speed and a "whoop," which the children love. These are only a few of innumerable examples wherein the music of poetry suggests the action being described.

The power of poetry to evoke a mood is evident as you speak or read it aloud. The quiet sound of "This Happy Day" induces a mood of gentle serenity. "Where's Mary?" is an amusing study in mounting irritability. The words and lines pile up with an accumulative, staccato beat that makes the reader feel like the peevish woman who is speaking. In contrast, there are quiet and peace in the plain words of "Evening Hymn." This poem has no patter, no swinging rhythm, but it uses simple words, rich in associative values, and its melody is like plain song, almost monotonous in its austere simplicity and its power to comfort and reassure. There is a mood of hushed mystery in "Some One," sheer gaiety in "The Little Whistler" and "Jill Came from the Fair," sober reflection in "House Blessing," and fun and nonsense in "Timothy Boon." These are only a few examples of the power of melody and movement in poetry to evoke a mood.

Even more surprising is the discovery that when you speak or read poetry aloud, the unique music of a particular poem may help to emphasize or clarify the meaning. For instance, if you understood no English and heard someone read "Firefly," you would know that it had to do with something small and frail because the words are little with no sonorities, and as vanishing in sound as the "little bug all lit" is in sight. Or, if you heard "The sea gull curves his wings" without understanding the words, you would still catch the feeling of contrasting ideas in each verse. The first couplets in each are smooth, slow, and melodious. The second couplets are harsh, staccato, like a cry of warning, which they really are. Understanding the words of these two poems, you are likely to forget how much the effectiveness and even the clarity of the idea in each is due to the tone patterns in which they are expressed. These examples can be multiplied. The sledge-hammer beat of T. S. Eliot's "The world turns and the world changes" actually serves to hammer in the grave importance of his message. And all through James Stephens' "The Snare" there is a sense of hurry and pressure which is the very essence of the idea or significance of that poem.

It is true that in order to read poetry aloud or to speak it effectively the reader must understand its meaning. And it is also true that the process of aloudness forces the reader to know what he is saying. If his words are not making sense as he reads aloud, he quickly becomes aware of it. But there is an additional point—namely, that as he reads a poem aloud, its tune and movement will, over and over again, supply the reader with clues to meaning which are entirely lacking when the poem is read silently.

Here lies the chief reason for the oral (and aural) approach to poetry. If it is read silently, the reader may miss its unique musical pattern and he may also be blandly unaware of how little of its meaning he is getting. This is driven home the moment he tries it aloud and he is forced to go back, to find out what he is really saying. This means that every unfamiliar poem, of any degree of complexity, must be explored orally so that its music may have a chance to supply clues to meaning and increased enjoyment. It also means that the child's taste for poetry will develop in proportion to the amount of good and suitable verse which he hears vigorously spoken, has a chance to speak for himself, and, later, as his reading skill matures, to read from the printed page also.

Sensory and emotional response to poetry

When you read poetry aloud to children and catch its tempo, tone color, and cadence, you discover that these qualities evoke other reactions which are also essential to understanding and appreciation. These reactions are sensory imagery and emotional response. Sometimes the interpretation of a poem depends upon visual imagery—a picture of trees bowing down their heads as the wind passes by. Sometimes it demands auditory imagery—the rain playing "a little sleep-song on our roof at night." Kinesthetic imagery is especially prominent in poems for small children—the feel of going "Hippity hop to bed," or galloping to "Husky Hi." Even smell, touch, and taste sensations are evoked in the varied poetry offering for children. For instance, the galloping rhythm of "Windy Nights" helps to rouse a feeling of eerie excitement over that galloping wind-rider who comes and goes so mysteriously. This example suggests the close relationship between sensory imagery and emotional response. It might be said that the more vivid the sensory imagery aroused by the lines of a poem, the deeper the emotional reaction to that poem will be. And it might be added that without sensory imagery and emotional reaction there can be no real understanding or appreciation of a poem.

This point is so basic to the whole literature program, both poetry and prose, that it will bear amplification. When, for instance, a child hears a story or a poem for which there are no illustrations, it is quite possible that he will enjoy it only in proportion to his ability to create his own mental pictures of the characters, action, or situation. Hilda Conkling's "Little Snail" will have slight reality for the child who has never seen a snail. That child needs the help of experience or pictures or both before "his house on his back" means anything to him or before there is any humor in the concluding lines of that poem. Walter de la Mare's simple little jingle "The Huntsmen" never says in so many words that it is about three little boys riding their hobbyhorses up to bed. But if children do not understand this and do not see the picture clearly in their minds, then the "clitter clatter" of those wooden sticks on the stairs, and indeed the whole meaning of the poem, will be obscure. If the American child translates "Banbury Cakes and Lollipops" into his favorite chocolate cakes and popsicles, then his sensory imagery of luscious-tasting sweets will illumine the words, and he will share the delight of the boy in the poem.

The grownup's responsibility for interpretation

This is where the grownup comes in. It is his function to help the child translate a poem into his own experience until he shares the vivid sensory imagery and feels a lively emotional response to the selection. This can be done either by preparing for any possible obscurities in a poem before reading it or by talking it over afterwards and taking time to savor its charm. Nowadays, so many children are urban and so much of our poetry is rural that the combination invariably calls for first aids to understanding and enjoyment. Think, for instance, of the peculiar picture a city child must visualize when he hears how Chanticleer "shakes his comb." This is sheer nonsense unless he knows both Chanti-

cleer and his topknot. And, for city children, you may be sure that "the strong withered horse" evokes the peculiar picture of a wrinkled old horse unless the meaning of this expression is cleared up in advance. The ballads are, of course, full of strange words that must be defined before understanding is possible.

But all of these are fairly obvious examples of first aids to meaning. The preparation of a poem may call for something more subtle than attention to unfamiliar words or situations. The adult who has prepared a poem by reading it aloud before she presents it to the children knows the varying moods of poetry for which preparation is often needed. Over and over, the poetry of Walter de la Mare demands some word of explanation in advance. For example, she might say: "This poem 'Some One' is a mystery. Who came knocking? I don't know. See what you think." Or, "Before I read you this poem about 'Tillie' I must tell you something queer. Fern seeds are supposed to work magic on people. Something awful happened to poor old Tillie after she swallowed some." It would be fun, by the way, to follow this poem with "Midsummer Magic" by Ivy Eastwick, where fern (bracken) seed also works its spell. Or, in Elizabeth Coatsworth's " 'Who are you?' asked the cat of the bear," children are much more ready to catch the fun of that poem if you furnish them with one clue in advance—"This poem is a conversation between a cat and a bear. The bear is boasting of his size and his strength, but notice the way the little cat manages to take him down." The condensation in the ballads, together with unfamiliar words, makes it almost necessary to tell the story in advance or at least to furnish the children with definite clues to the main points of the narrative. Then these poems will grow in richness with each rereading.

With many poems, it is better to read them first and then mull them over informally, and reread them. For small children, "Minnie and Mattie" is easy enough to follow but they usually miss the rather amusing detail that one of the old mother hens is guarding a brood of ducklings instead of chickens. That can be brought out casually in the discussion of the poem, and then it is more interesting to them when the poem is reread. "Falling Star" invariably elicits a burst of personal experiences with falling stars and wishes. At an older level, "To Beachey, 1912" calls for amplification until the children sense the wonder and admiration we should all feel when, lying snug in our beds, we hear planes overhead and think of those unknown pilots winging their way through storms and darkness. The ballad stories need to be talked over and speculated about. Why did the wife in the "The Raggle, Taggle Gypsies" run away from her fine hall and husband? Could she have been a gypsy too? What about the maid in "The Wife of Usher's Well?" What has she to do with the story? Certainly, the poems in the last section of the book, "Wisdom and Beauty," call for quiet discussion. These poems are obviously for older children, but, even so, they will often need to be translated into terms of the children's own lives to be really understood. By the way, these should never be used as a group, but slipped in occasionally, one at a time, along with other poetry.

Such preparations for the meaning and mood of a poem and such honest, simple, informal discussions at its conclusion should heighten both understanding and appreciation. Needless to say, the atmosphere of poetry time, whether by the fireside, at bedtime, around a campfire, or in a schoolroom, should be kept informal, happy, and completely comfortable. Not all children will like all of the poems you select, and that is to be expected and is quite all right. Start where your children are, with nonsense verse, probably, and story poems, and you may be sure they will want many of both. But help them at the same time to explore a wide variety of poems. Their enjoyment will increase as they begin to say their favorites with you and learn them in the process. Choral speech or verse choirs may add enormously to their zest for speaking verse and they will learn an astonishing amount of it. A detailed discussion of verse choirs follows this introduction on page xxiv.[2]

How to use this book

Time for Poetry is a collection of poems to be read aloud in schoolrooms, on vacations, by campfires, and in homes. The verses are grouped under large subject matter heads with subdivisions under each. For instance, "The Animal Fair" begins with dogs and cats, progresses to birds and beasts of all varieties, and includes the animals of the forest, the farm, the circus, and the zoo. "Animals" is a good group to illustrate the organization. In general, the poems progress, under each topic, from easy to hard, or for young children 4 to 6 to older children 12 to 14. But such a plan means that at the conclusion of a mature poem about a *dog*, suitable for a twelve-year-old child, the unwary reader may find himself confronting a *Mother Goose* jingle about *cats,* suitable for a five-year-old. Even so, it seems best to keep this easy-to-hard plan of organization for the convenience of the teacher or mother who wants a group of cat or rabbit poems all together, so that she can scan them at a glance and choose the ones simple enough or mature enough for her children. There are poems here to fit the seasons, the festivals, and most of the units of the school year. But there are many others which are included just for fun, for variety, or for sheer beauty. These are quite as important as the poems which "correlate" with school subjects, and they will do much to promote the child's emotional and literary growth.

In reading these poems to children, you may wish to begin with the subject that is uppermost in your school activities or in the child's interests, and find a group of verses to fit. The child may love pets or wild animals, or you may be working with community helpers, or modes of travel, or Indians, or colonial heroes. Autumn may be splashing the hillsides with color, or spring working her heady enchantment. Poems may be found to add beauty and fresh meaning to all of these subjects or experiences. But sometimes, when you and the children are bogged down with routine or a general dullness, and such days do occur now and then, why not take a fling at nonsense verse, or a blood and thunder ballad, or a curious whimsey like "Sam" or "Macavity: the Mystery Cat," or end the day with "Evening Hymn" for quiet beauty? Poems may be found which fit the subjects and interests of school and home, but look also for poems in contrast to these, poems which breathe a new breath of life into the everyday world.

[2] *See also May Hill Arbuthnot,* Children and Books *(Scott, Foresman, 1957)* , Chapter 9. This whole chapter *deals with verse choir techniques*

With a book that has as wide an age-range appeal as this one and as great a variety of poetry types, it would seem essential that you know in advance what you are going to read. Explore the unfamiliar poems by reading them aloud, of course, in order that you may interpret their melody adequately, know their sensory and emotional appeal, and discover what you wish to clear up in advance or talk over afterwards. Actually, this preparation should not be too onerous. The reading aloud is the one essential. With the children, you can feel your way. If you watch them, it is easy to sense their blankness, and you can amplify, reread, or translate the poem into their own everyday experiences. You can also sense their delight when they chuckle, or their eyes shine, or they sit hushed and breathless, or they ask you to read it again. That is your triumph and your goal—a continuous, day-after-day growth in their liking poetry and wanting to hear more.

For help in reading these poems to children occasional footnotes have been placed at the bottom of the page to be out of your way when you are reading but they are italicized in the hope that they will catch your eye before you read. These footnotes accomplish several purposes. Sometimes they throw additional light on the meaning of the poem. Sometimes they afford first aid to good oral reading or interpretation. Frequently they call attention to the unique musical pattern of a poem or suggest its possibilities for choral speaking. In addition to these footnotes you will find in May Hill Arbuthnot's *Children and Books* (Scott, Foresman and Company, 1957), seven chapters on poetry in Part 2: Sing It Again. These chapters are "Mother Goose," "Ballads and Story-Poems," "Verses in the Gay Tradition," "Poetry of the Child's World," "Singing Words," "Using Poetry with Children," and "Verse Choirs." You will gain much help from using *Poetry Time* (Scott, Foresman and Company, 1951), an album of records in which Mrs. Arbuthnot demonstrates with her own readings her theory and methods of using poetry with small children.

The miracle of the poems in this book is that they take many of the experiences of the child's everyday world and give them a new importance, a kind of glory that they did not have when they were just experiences. "Not the rose, but the scent of the rose" says Eleanor Farjeon about this curious distillation of experience to its essence, which is poetry. And so, because it heightens, deepens, and enriches experience, it becomes a shining armor against vulgarity and brutality. Here are the small animals that the child loves—puppies, kittens, snails, fireflies, butterflies, rabbits that

> ". . . dance hungry and wild
> Under a winter's moon."

In these poems a child goes "Skipping Along Alone" by the sea, or he watches "Boats of mine a-boating" and wonders "Where will all come home?" He finds it pleasant to say "Good morning to the sun" and not unusual to converse with fairies or to hear a goblin arguing with a nymph. These poems carry him from skips and gallops to dreams and aspirations. *Time for Poetry* should be a time to lift young spirits and give them something to grow on, for poetry lovers do grow in grace and in reverence for life because

> "Loveliness that dies when I forget
> Comes alive when I remember."

And children remember poetry.

USING POETRY IN VERSE CHOIRS

A verse choir or choral speaking group is composed of children or adults who speak literature together. A choir usually has three sections of blended voices that may be combined or not as the selection seems to require. Ordinarily such groups speak poetry, but sometimes they use prose when the prose selections are effective spoken in choral form. As a matter of fact, there is such a variety of selections suitable for choral speaking that the choice becomes a matter of choir skills and the individual taste of the leader.

BACKGROUND FOR CHOIR WORK

Launching a verse choir sounds like a formidable undertaking, but actually, in the schoolroom, choral speaking almost starts itself. Wherever there is a teacher who knows and loves poetry, there will be children who love it, too. When the teacher reads aloud to her class, there are always favorite poems the children demand over and over. An observant teacher will presently remark, "I believe you almost know that poem. You are saying it to yourselves right along with me. Let's see if you really know it. I'll read it slowly and softly and you say it with me." Two or three repetitions on two or three consecutive days, and the children will know the poem by heart. They learn poetry as readily as they learn songs, and in no time at all they will have memorized a lot of poetry in just this casual, effortless way. A most desirable outcome!

If the class is a big one, let half the group speak a poem while the other half listens. Then reverse the process, but to keep the listening half on the alert, see if it can come in right on the beat when the first half finishes. Mark the time with your hand or finger as you do when the children sing together, and be sure to keep the voices light and pleasant to hear. Stop them at once if they become loud or harsh or if they are sing-songing or racing along without thinking. Any of these undesirable things may happen when children or even adults begin to speak together. But when half the group listens, it begins to develop an ear for clear, understandable speech, good timing, and agreeable voices.

A dialogue or a narrative poem with one or more choruses gives the children another chance to listen critically to each other and you begin to get such comments as these: "That was too fast," the listening group says, or, "That was just right. We could understand every word." "That sounded real nice," refers vaguely to both voices and diction. "They kept together," means good timing and unison. Such comments show that the children are unconsciously acquiring good ear training and a feeling for timing, diction, and unison speech.

They should also be developing a sense of speaking for meaning. For instance, in "Oh, Susan Blue" (p. 11) are there one or two persons speaking? The group must decide whether a friend greets Susan Blue and Susan replies hesitatingly, or whether one person speaks the whole six lines. The answer to this decides the way the lines will be spoken. The first interpretation is almost inevitable once the poem is read aloud. "Pussy-cat, pussy-cat" (p. 48) is simple enough for the four-year-olds to speak glibly, but the sixes are capable of deciding whether Cat is telling a tall tale as an excuse or whether he really did see the Queen. Does Cat's Owner believe the runaway? On the answer to these questions depends the way in which those cryptic lines, by Cat and by Owner, will be spoken.

In this preliminary stage, it is just as well to choose practice verses that are not too easily spoiled—Mother Goose for the youngest and nonsense verse for the older children. Here are a few suggestions for this beginning work:

PRELIMINARY SPEAKING TOGETHER
[UNISON]

Children 4–8

THE GRAND OLD DUKE OF YORK (p. 94), a brisk marching rhyme, when repeated may grow louder and nearer and then fade gradually away.

ROCKABYE BABY, a lullaby as peaceful and quieting as "The Grand Old Duke of York" is martial.

HOPPITY (p. 94), a genuine hop with staccato words from the diaphragm.

HOW MANY DAYS HAS MY BABY TO PLAY? (p. 173), a jig if ever there was one.

JONATHAN (p. 127).

Children 9–12

MASTER I HAVE, AND I AM HIS MAN (p. 95), a tremendous gallop requiring lots of breath control to carry that old dun horse through to the end.

HUSKY HI (p. 95), guaranteed to wake up everyone; another gallop, pure nonsense, but wonderful staccato from the diaphragm.

JOG ON, JOG ON, THE FOOT-PATH WAY (p. 78), a regular Boy Scout sort of walking tune.

BELL HORSES, BELL HORSES, WHAT TIME OF DAY? (p. 164), refers to a clock tower where horses prance out.

GRIZZLY BEAR (p. 121).

[DIALOGUE]

Children 4–8

PUSSY-CAT, PUSSY-CAT (p. 48), a subtle conversation between Cat and Owner.

BOW, WOW, WOW! (p. 44), big bully of a dog and little new dog.

Children 9–12

OH, SUSAN BLUE (p. 11), two little girls, over the gate asking, what shall we do?

OLD WOMAN, OLD WOMAN, SHALL WE GO A-SHEARING? (p. 126), not too subtle and good fun.

[CHORUS]

Children 4–8

MY DONKEY (p. 117), the way the chorus is spoken indicates the faking quality of the donkey's ailments.

Children 9–12

A FARMER WENT TROTTING UPON HIS GRAY MARE (p. 116). Each chorus heightens the pleasant or disastrous or laughing events described.

By second or third grades—if the children have heard a variety of poems, can think what they speak, can read dialogue with spirit and understanding, and can distinguish between clear and muddled speech, they are ready to begin work on choral speaking in organized form. It is challenging, it is exhilarating, and it is fun. Let's begin.

GROUPING FOR A VERSE CHOIR

Simply speaking a poem in unison is not verse choir, nor does saying dialogue poems with two groups, or a narrative poem with a single voice reading the story and the group coming in on the chorus constitute true choral speaking. A speaking choir, like a singing choir, requires a tonal grouping of like voices. Instead of having the soprano, contralto, tenor, and bass of a singing choir, a speaking group generally has the three divisions—high, medium, and low voices (H, M, L). With children the range is not so great as with adults, but there *is* a range and the divisions are not too difficult to make. Any teacher who listens to her children talking and reading day after day knows some of the extremely high voices and the surprisingly low voices in the group. Explain to the children that they have been speaking their poems so well that it seems a good time to begin a verse choir. For such a choir they will need high voices, low voices, and some in-between voices to blend the two.

Start by finding some of the high, sweet voices and some of the low, rich voices. Take two or three children at the high range and have them speak some Mother Goose jingle together—"Jack and Jill" or "Little Miss Muffet" or "Jack be nimble"—any ditty that can't be spoiled by repetition. When you have four or five voices that blend nicely in the high range, repeat the process with the low voices. Then try the remaining children for the medium choir, adding as you go to both the high and low groups. There will be a range within each division, but curiously enough there comes to be a blending of voices with a like timbre that the children themselves can recognize. Often they will say, "Oh, Mary belongs in the low choir," or, "John should move up to the high choir."

There is, by the way, no grouping by sex. There is the whole range of high to low among boys as well as girls. Be sure to stress the desirability of having a voice in any of these groups—high, sweet, and light; low, deep, and rich; or medium and pleasant to hear. Children are extremely sensitive to anything in themselves that is out of the ordinary and so there must be sincere praise for each kind of voice. And as for that occasional problem voice that is harsh or nasal, place it in the back of its group and you may need to say now and then, "You have such a strong, carrying voice, Virginia, you can speak just a bit more softly than the others and still be heard." Console yourself with the knowledge that choir work may help that voice.

The moment you have your three groups, let them try—in divided choir form—some poem they already know so that they can hear themselves and sample the curiously exciting effect of the three different choruses. The usual arrangement of the three choirs is shown in the diagram below.

Low   Medium   High

The children stand for both practice sessions and actual performances. As a start take something easy and familiar, perhaps "Chanticleer" by John Farrar (p. 68), for the young children. Have the low voices speak the first two lines, medium voices lines 3 and 4, high voices lines 5 and 6, and conclude lines 7 and 8 with the low voices. And by the way, you will have to transcribe these markings to the poem itself. For the older children, you might use Langston Hughes' "April Rain Song" (p. 160)—line 1 M, 2 H, 3 L—line 4 M, 5 L, 6 H, and the concluding line 7, which is almost like a sigh, may be spoken by the low choir or the whole group of three choirs, speaking together as softly as a breath. When the children first hear the three choirs and the entirely different effect each one gives to a line, they are astonished and delighted. Invari-

ably they want to try more, so be ready with poems that will lend themselves to a variety of choral speaking forms.

CASTING A POEM FOR VERSE CHOIRS

Casting means not only assigning lines to certain choirs but also deciding whether to do a poem in antiphonal style or in unison or perhaps line-a-child. The question of which is the best way to cast a poem cannot be answered conclusively. Probably no two leaders of verse choirs would cast a poem in precisely the same way. Indeed, teachers say that using the same poem a second year with another group of children often leads to a change in the assignment of lines.

However, there are a few general principles which may help a new director. Usually high voices ask a question, unless the questioner is male or definitely on the gruff side. High voices also give a lift to lines and speak the little tripping words or the gay singing words that are bright and clear. Low voices generally answer a question, unless the answer is spoken by a woman. Low voices also take the lines with sonorous, big-sounding words, the grave or ominous lines, or those in the minor key. The medium choir blends the high and low and is most effective for narrative portions of a poem or for opening lines or lines that state an idea. Look back now at "Chanticleer" and "April Rain Song" and, as you read them aloud, see if you can feel why the lines were assigned as they were.

One other general principle: the younger or less experienced the choirs are, the more difficult it is for them to break off or come in briskly at the end of one line. A two- or three-line assignment is safer for beginners than a single line because the choir that picks up the next line must come in precisely on the metric beat. Older children with experience can do this but never the youngest or the beginners. The teacher who is starting this work with her class should read and reread a poem aloud before she decides on the form. Her own interpretation of the lines, her feeling for the quality of the words—grave or gay, brisk, small words or sonorous, big words—these are her clues to casting the poem.

Unison speech

In the British handbooks for choral speaking, unison speech is pointed up as the crowning achievement of well-trained choral groups. But in this country, as we suggested earlier, unison speech is used informally as a starting point. It is unfortunate that many groups never go any further, since there is nothing more monotonous than a whole program of poems spoken in unison. In such programs, the children generally over-enunciate to make up for the mob, or use extremes of high and low voices, or over-dramatize their material. It is natural and desirable to let children speak some of their favorite poems together and in so doing learn to keep their voices light and sweet and to follow the time beat of their leader. So used, unison speech is a good background for choir work until the children are old enough to accept the practice and careful discipline of the latter.

After this preliminary work, when the children have achieved some degree of precision and beauty in their choirs, short poems are often enhanced by fine unison speech. In addition to the verses suggested for "Preliminary Speaking Together," here are other verses that require disciplined practice. All of those listed for the younger children are also acceptable for the older groups.

UNISON

Except for "Good Night" and "This Happy Day," the poems for the younger children offer no particular difficulties. The latter may be spoken in unison, but if the group of children is large, let half speak the first verse and the other half the second verse. The higher voices speak the first verse cheerfully and, if you like, a solo voice may speak the last line "Good morning Sun!" The lower voices will speak the second verse with a serene, smooth, sustained tone that is as peaceful as twilight. The last two lines should be spoken quietly and reverently. It is a little prayer of thanksgiving, child-size.

"Who has seen the wind" may also be divided between two groups, each speaking one verse in unison. It calls for sweet, light voices and a slow even, sustained tone throughout.

Be sure the children get the hop into the words when they speak this all-staccato, Christina Rossetti poem:

> And timid, funny, brisk little bunny,
> Winks his nose and sits all sunny.

The suggested poems for older children are a challenge and will reveal that unison speech, if it is to be a finished performance, is far from easy. Take Rossetti's "Oh, fair to see"—it calls for a sustained, even tone and sweet, light quality. When the children first speak it, they may not notice the important contrasting words in the two verses—"bloom-laden" and "fruit-laden." In each case, a lovely description follows. These contrasted verbal pictures need not be unduly emphasized but must come through clearly, and the final "Oh, fair to see!" sings with a special warmth. It is a Gloria!

Kipling's "Seal Lullaby" requires perfect timing. The slow tempo and rocking movement that run throughout the poem must be maintained unbroken to the end. To avoid monotony, there is a light, tender touch in the two lines beginning "Where billow meets billow" and climaxing in the charming "Ah, weary wee flipperling, curl at thy ease!" Then, the slow, even, rocking movement resumes with the wonderful reassurance of the last line that comes out warmly.

One of the most beautiful poems to speak in unison with an experienced choir is "The Noise of Waters." It calls for predominantly low, rich voices speaking slowly, gravely, almost in a monotone. Notice in the first verse the long *o* sounds with *m* or *n* which, by prolonging the nasals ever so slightly, give almost the effect of a moaning wind. In the second verse, the words *blowing, flowing, go, below, fro* bring a rich, round, melody that is beautiful to speak and to hear. The children should make the most of these sounds which give contrast to the two verses and the whole melodic pattern of the poem. But don't let them mouth their words unnaturally.

To console the high voices who were left out of the last poem, let them say lightly "The Rains of Spring" and "Daffodils." In the first poem the lines move along in conversational style, building up to the charming climax of the last line. In "Daffodils" there is a similar pattern, except that the last line is in distinct contrast to the dismal first line and should be spoken as a happy surprise.

The chief problems in unison speaking are to keep the timing exact, to avoid monotony, a heavy tone, or a heavy metric beat, and above all to so interpret meaning that the poem is enhanced by such choral work. It is wonderful training for the children, and these selections are well worth memorizing. Remember always, however, that in a program of choral speaking, unison selections are scattered among other types of choir work.

Dialogue or antiphonal choir work

Like unison speech, dialogue or antiphonal choir work may be a natural starting point and it may also culminate in subtle and disciplined interpretation of poetry. A dialogue poem is, of course, a conversation. A poem that falls into two parts—the two parts often contrasting—is read antiphonally. For example, for the youngest, "Oh, Susan Blue" is dialogue. The friend speaks

the first three lines and Susan answers, somewhat hesitatingly, with the last three lines. On the other hand, the contrasting effects in "Blow wind, blow, and go mill, go" (p. 153), make it a good example of an antiphonal poem, with half the children speaking the sonorous first two lines, and the other half coming in briskly and trippingly on the other three lines. Here are some suggested poems for the two age groups.

DIALOGUE OR ANTIPHONAL

Children 4–8

WHAT DOES THE BEE DO? Christina Rossetti, p. 4

OH, SUSAN BLUE, Kate Greenaway, p. 11

BLOW WIND, BLOW, AND GO MILL, GO, Mother Goose, p. 153

MOON-COME-OUT, Eleanor Farjeon, p. 169

"TALENTS DIFFER," Laura E. Richards, p. 51

OPEN THE DOOR, Marion Edey and Dorothy Grider, p. 172

CONVERSATION BETWEEN MR. AND MRS. SANTA CLAUS, Rowena Bennett (also enjoyed by older group)

PUPPY AND I, A. A. Milne, p. 45

Children 9–14

MOMOTARA, Rose Fyleman, p. 129

OVERHEARD ON A SALTMARSH, Harold Monro, p. 143

HALLOWEEN, Marie Lawson

"WHO ARE YOU?" ASKED THE CAT OF THE BEAR, Elizabeth Coatsworth, p. 50

IT IS RAINING, Lucy Sprague Mitchell, p. 160

GYPSY JANE, William Brighty Rands, p. 14

HOLIDAY, Ella Young, p. 154

COLD WINTER NOW IS IN THE WOOD, Elizabeth Coatsworth, p. 188

THE SEA GULL CURVES HIS WINGS, Elizabeth Coatsworth, p. 54

The first group for the younger children offers no particular difficulties. "Moon-Come-Out" might well be thought of as a unison poem, but the nice little contrast in the two verses suggests the antiphonal form: the first verse for the low voices, a bit slow and sleepy; the second verse brisk, bright, and gay with high voices. "Talents Differ" goes along in a regular pattern, high voices asking the question, lower voices answering, until the last verse where the tables are turned and the high voices come out triumphantly.

"Open the Door" is delightful dialogue with all sorts of variations possible. The high choir certainly asks the question each time. For the answers, it is fun to use not more than five children, a different group for each verse, or the answers spoken by different solo voices if you prefer.

This poem by Rowena Bennett is a delightful dialogue poem for the youngest:

CONVERSATION BETWEEN
MR. AND MRS. SANTA CLAUS
(*Overheard at the North Pole
Early Christmas Morning*)

"Are the reindeer in the rain, dear?"   High
Asked Mrs. Santa Claus.
"No. I put them in the barn, dear,   Low
To dry their little paws."

"Is the sleigh, sir, put away, sir,   High
In the barn beside the deer?"
"Yes, I'm going to get it ready   Low
To use again next year."

"And the pack, dear, is it back, dear?"   High
"Yes. It's empty of its toys,   Low
And tomorrow I'll start filling it,
For next year's girls and boys."

The selections for the older children range from the simple "Momotara" and "Gypsy Jane" to some rather subtle and beautiful poetry. Marie Lawson's "Halloween" is an eerie dialogue, almost scary until the last two lines in which the child admits—*what?* That she was fooling all along, or that strange, eerie things *do* appear on Halloween? Let the children discuss this and upon their decision will rest the interpretation of those last two lines. The child's lines belong to the high choir. Granny is matter-of-fact, a complete skeptic, and her lines belong to the low voices. The poem may also be spoken by only two children.

"Conversation Between Mr. and Mrs. Santa Claus" by Rowena Bastin Bennett in *Jack and Jill*, December 1947. Copyright 1947 by the Curtis Publishing Company, Philadelphia. By permission of the author.

HALLOWEEN

"Granny, I saw a witch go by,   High
I saw two, I saw three!
I heard their skirts go swish, swish, swish——"

   "Child, 'twas leaves against the sky,   Low
   And the autumn wind in the tree."

"Granny, broomsticks they bestrode,   High
Their hats were black as tar,
And buckles twinkled on their shoes——"

   "You saw but shadows on the road,   Low
   The sparkle of a star."

"Granny, all their heels were red,   High
Their cats were big as sheep.
I heard a bat say to an owl——"

   "Child, you must go straight to bed,   Low
   'Tis time you were asleep."

"Granny, I saw men in green,   High
Their eyes shone fiery red,
Their heads were yellow pumpkins——"

   "Now you've told me what you've seen,   Low
   WILL you go to bed?"

"Granny?"   High

   "Well?"   Low

"Don't you believe——?"   High

   "What?"   Low

"What I've seen?   High
Don't you know it's Halloween?"

"Overheard in a Saltmarsh" is a dramatic dialogue that children from second grade to high school speak well. The goblin's lines are spoken by low-medium voices. Keep the "No" down to conversational level until the last; let that come out decisively with emphasis.

"The sea gull curves his wings" is also subtle antiphonal work for older children. The first two lines of both verses are smooth and easy, suggesting the sailing flight of the gull. The second two lines of each verse are a sharp cry of warning.

"Halloween" by Marie A. Lawson in *Child Life*, October 1936. Copyright 1936 by Rand McNally & Company, Chicago. Reprinted by permission of the Estate of Marie A. Lawson.

THE SILENT SNAKE
Author unknown

High   The birds go fluttering in the air,
       The rabbits run and skip,
       Brown squirrels race along the bough,
       The May-flies rise and dip;
       But, whilst these creatures play and leap,
Low (at creeping pace, in creepy tone) The silent snake goes *creepy-creep!*

High   The birdies sing and whistle loud,
       The busy insects hum,
       The squirrels chat, the frogs say "Croak!"
       But the snake is always dumb.
       With not a sound through grasses deep
(at creeping pace, in creepy tone) The silent snake goes *creepy-creep!*

RING OUT, WILD BELLS
Alfred, Lord Tennyson

High (slowly, exultantly; "sky" not "sky-ee") Ring out, wild bells, to the wild sky,
Medium   The flying cloud, the frosty light;
       The year is dying in the night;
High   Ring out, wild bells, and let him die.

Medium   Ring out the old, ring in the new,
Low   Ring, happy bells, across the snow;
Medium (or all choirs) slowly, gravely, but not loudly The year is going, let him go;
       Ring out the false, ring in the true.

For both dialogue and antiphonal speech it is well to divide your three choirs into two groups in this way:

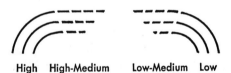

High High-Medium Low-Medium Low

Narrative poems with a chorus

Narrative poems with a chorus are a third possibility for beginning choral work and, like unison and dialogue, may be simple and easy or may require rather subtle interpretations. For instance, "The Christmas Pudding" (p. 182) is simple enough to swing the four-year-old along with gusto. Half of the children speak narrative lines and the other half come in with a vigorous "Stirabout, stirabout, stirabout." Although "A farmer went trotting upon his gray mare"

(p. 116) is equally simple, it calls for a more subtle performance. The two choruses may be spoken by two different groups or one choir may speak both. In either case, the chorus underscores the change of mood—in the first verse all is serene, in the second all is catastrophic, and in the third the villainous crow is laughing and the chorus is spoken just on the edge of laughter.

Here are a few possibilities:

NARRATIVE POEMS WITH CHORUS

Children 4–8

A FARMER WENT TROTTING UPON HIS GRAY MARE, Mother Goose, p. 116
MY DONKEY, Rose Fyleman, p. 117
THE BABY GOES TO BOSTON, Laura E. Richards, p. 78
KINDNESS TO ANIMALS, Laura E. Richards, p. 116
WHAT TO DO, William Wise
WAKING TIME, Ivy O. Eastwick

Children 9–14

RING OUT, WILD BELLS, Alfred Tennyson
THE SILENT SNAKE, Unknown
OPEN RANGE, Kathryn and Byron Jackson, p. 30
COTTONWOOD LEAVES, Badger Clark, p. 31
I WILL GO WITH MY FATHER A-PLOUGHING, Joseph Campbell, p. 192
WAKING TIME, Ivy O. Eastwick
FAITH, I WISH I WERE A LEPRECHAUN, Margaret Ritter, p. 150

In "The Baby Goes to Boston" there are two choruses which, as in "A farmer went trotting upon his gray mare," may be spoken by one or by two choirs. These also reinforce the mood or the tempo of the narrative: slowly and easily in the first verse, more briskly in the second, really fast in the third, more slowly in the fourth, and slowing to a stop in the last verse. The poem has two choruses that are amusing tongue-twisters the young children enjoy saying.

"What to Do" may be cast in various ways. It may, of course, be spoken antiphonally. The first and fourth lines of each verse may be spoken by a narrative group made up of a blend of voices, or by a solo voice each time, a different voice for each verse. The chorus to each verse is almost like an echo and may well be carried all the way through by the medium choir. The poem ends jubilantly. Here is "What to Do" by William Wise.

WHAT TO DO

What to do on a rainy day;
What to do
What to do.
There must be a new kind of game to play;
I wish I knew
I wish I knew.

Sister is dressing her dolls again;
They're fine for her
They're fine for her.
Cat and Kitten are washing themselves,
Cleaning their fur
Cleaning their fur.

"What to Do" from *Jonathan Blake* by William Wise. Copyright © 1956 by William Wise. Published by Alfred A. Knopf, Inc., New York, reprinted and used with their permission.

What to do while it rains outside;
Where to go
Where to go.
I've already eaten, I've already napped;
And the time goes slow
The time goes slow.

But now I see some blue in the sky;
I see some blue
I see some blue.
The clouds are parting, the wind has changed;
And the rain is through
The rain is through!

And soon I'll be out of the house again;
I'll run and shout
I'll run and shout.
I can think of a dozen things to do,
When the sun is out
When the sun is out.

"Waking Time," by Ivy O. Eastwick, might be cast in this way:

WAKING TIME

At four o'clock in the morning,	Medium
The cockerels wake, they do,	
With a "Cocker-doo-dle,	High
Cocker-doo-dle,	
Cocker-doo-dle-doo!"	
At five o'clock in the morning,	Medium
The thrushes wake, they do,	
With a "Pretty-sweet!	High
Oh, pretty-sweet!	
The sky is rose-and-blue!"	
At six o'clock in the morning,	Medium
The blackbirds wake, they do,	
With a 'What's to eat?	High
Oh, what's to eat?	
I'd like a worm or two!"	
At seven o'clock in the morning,	Medium
The mothers wake, they do,	
With a "Here's the honey,	Low
And here's the bread,	
And milk all sweet and new!"	

"Waking Time" by Ivy O. Eastwick. Reprinted by permission of the author from *Jack and Jill*, June 1946. Copyright 1946 by the Curtis Publishing Company, Philadelphia.

At eight o'clock in the morning,	Medium
The children wake, they do,	
With a "Where's my sock?"	Low
And "Where's my smock?"	
And "I can't find my left shoe!"	

For the older children, the poems are more difficult.

"I Will Go with My Father A-Ploughing" is a beautiful poem that should be spoken with complete simplicity and sincerity. The first two and last two lines of each verse constitute a chorus of great importance. High voices may speak the first two lines, low voices the last two in each verse, while the medium choir carries the narrative throughout. This poem requires care both in the interpretation and in the diction.

"Cottonwood Leaves" is even more difficult. Let the high voices carry the narrative of the first two verses, with the medium choir speaking the choruses, lines 2 and 5. On the third verse, have the medium choir speak the narrative and the high choir the choruses, lines 2 and 5. Low voices will speak the narrative of the last two verses and the medium choir will resume the choruses. This poem is so rich in onomatopoetic words that it requires much practice and drill. The "clap, clap" almost *is* the sound of cottonwood leaves, and every verse is full of words whose sound, as well as meaning, conjures up the picture the words are describing. This is a thriller recited beside a camp fire—even a stage campfire. The last verse is ghostly and ends in a wail.

Line-a-child or line-a-choir

Line-a-child or line-a-choir interpretation of a poem marks a more advanced form of choral speaking, but one that is challenging and greatly enjoyed. Speaking a couplet instead of a single line is about as fast as beginners are able to pick up on the beat and keep both the rhythm and the meaning. With the youngest groups try "Little wind, blow on the hill-top" (p. 152) in couplets until they catch the idea of coming in on the beat and then try it with one child speaking the first line, another the second line, a third the third line, and all three speaking the last line together. Or try it a couplet-a-choir and then a line-a-choir with all three groups speaking the

last line joyously. Here are some other interesting possibilities (some of the poems have appeared in earlier lists):

LINE-A-CHILD OR LINE-A-CHOIR

Children 4–8
EIGHT O'CLOCK, Christina Rossetti, p. 10
THE LITTLE RED SLED, Jocelyn Bush, p. 101
JUMP OR JIGGLE, Evelyn Beyer, p. 96 (by couplets)
FOR, LO, THE WINTER IS PAST, Bible, p. 191
TRAINS, James S. Tippett, p. 80 (by couplets)
FINIS, Sir Henry Hewbolt, p. 171 (by couplets)

Children 9–14
AMY ELIZABETH ERMYNTRUDE ANNIE, Queenie Scott Hopper, p. 8
GIRLS' NAMES, Eleanor Farjeon, p. 6
BOYS' NAMES, Eleanor Farjeon, p. 6
BUNCHES OF GRAPES, Walter de la Mare, p. 7
THE FALLING STAR, Sara Teasdale, p. 169
WRITTEN IN MARCH, William Wordsworth, p. 192
LEISURE, William Henry Davies, p. 203 (by couplets)
SPRING, Harry Behn, p. 191
HIE AWAY, HIE AWAY, Sir Walter Scott, p. 89

The words "by couplets" following the poems in the list above mean that it is safer to have younger children and beginners speak two lines rather than one, until they have mastered the art of coming in right on the beat.

In "The Little Red Sled" the first two lines should be spoken by one child or choir, but the other lines singly. In this poem, it seems desirable to end by repeating the first line.

The children enjoy the exciting movement of "Trains," but they will run away with it unless you mark time for them. Don't let them begin to gain momentum until the last verse, when all may come in on the final line.

For the older children there are so many possibilities it is hard to select a few. "Amy Elizabeth Ermyntrude Annie" is great fun for them, either with choirs or with single children speaking the lines individually. Again, it may be well to speak couplets to begin with and then single lines. For that poem, let all the voices speak the first and last couplets together, the first simply, introducing the idea, the last on a note of happy triumph.

Two of the loveliest poems for line-a-choir and for subtle tone color in the voices are Eleanor Farjeon's "Boys' Names" and "Girls' Names." These are equally possible for both primary and upper-grade choirs and are superlatively effective.[1]

Scott's "Hie Away, hie away" is also delightful to speak chorally. This is definitely smoother in couplets, either by single children or by choirs. All voices speak the first and last two lines, H choir speaks lines 3 and 4; M, lines 5 and 6; H, lines 7 and 8; L, lines 9 and 10.

Group work

Group work using three or more choirs is the major part of choral speaking because inducting all the children into the pleasure of speaking poetry is, of course, the goal. So many poems lend themselves to this work that it is possible to suggest only a few to represent the range and variety.

GROUP WORK

Children 4–8
THE LITTLE KITTENS, Elisa Lee Follen, p. 113
TAKING OFF, Unknown, p. 81
HAVE YOU WATCHED THE FAIRIES? Rose Fyleman, p. 136
MERRY-GO-ROUND, Dorothy Baruch, p. 109
SONG, Eugene Field, p. 185
JONATHAN BING, Beatrice Curtis Brown, p. 132
APRIL RAIN SONG, Langston Hughes, p. 160
JUMP OR JIGGLE, Evelyn Beyer, p. 96
VALENTINE FOR EARTH, Frances M. Frost

Children 9–14
SONG FOR A BLUE ROADSTER, Rachel Field, p. 86
DOGS AND WEATHER, Winifred Welles, p. 47
HALLOWE'EN, Harry Behn, p. 176
TO BEACHEY, Carl Sandburg, p. 82
THE LITTLE FOX, Marion Edey and Dorothy Grider, p. 60
SKATING, Herbert Asquith, p. 93
UNTIL WE BUILT A CABIN, Aileen Fisher, p. 169
HALLOWEEN, John Ciardi
THE RIVER IS A PIECE OF THE SKY, John Ciardi

[1] See *Children and Books*, pp. 217–218

Frances M. Frost's "Valentine for Earth" is a delightful and easy poem for beginning choirs. Let the children speak the verses choir by choir until the last verse when all of the children will speak the final two lines gently but fervently. The order of assigning the verses may vary—this form is only a suggestion. Notice that in verses 3 and 4 the questions carry over to the following verses.

VALENTINE FOR EARTH

Oh, it will be fine	Medium
To rocket through space	
And see the reverse	
Of the moon's dark face,	
To travel to Saturn	Low
Or Venus or Mars,	
Or maybe discover	
Some uncharted stars.	
But do they have anything	High
Better than we?	
Do you think, for instance,	
They have a blue sea	
For sailing and swimming?	
Do planets have hills	Medium
With raspberry thickets	
Where a song sparrow fills	
The summer with music?	
And do they have snow	Low
To silver the roads	
Where the school buses go?	
Oh, I'm all for rockets	High
And worlds cold or hot,	
But I'm wild in love	All
With the planet we've got!	

"Merry-Go-Round," "Taking Off," "Song," "Jonathan Bing," and "April Rain Song" are thoroughly enjoyed by older children. But with the possible exception of "The Little Fox," the poems listed for older children are far too difficult for the younger ones.

choirs	HALLOWEEN	line-a-child
Low	Ruth says apples have learned to bob.	1st child
Medium	Bob says pumpkins have a job.	2nd
Low	Here's the man from the Witching Tree	3rd
	Ask *him* since you won't ask me:	
High	Do you think Ruth is telling the truth?	1st
Low	"Man from the Tree your skin is green.	4th
Low/High	What night is this?" "It's Halloween."	4th/5th
Low	Ruth, Ruth, you told the truth.	1st
	The man says Apples *have* learned to bob.	
Medium	The man says Pumpkins *do* have a job.	2nd
	The man come down from the Witching Tree	
Medium/High	Says he wants someone. No, not me.	2nd/3rd
High	Says he wants someone good and true—	3rd
All	YOU	All
High	Mother, Mother, Ruth's gone flying!	High (three children)
Medium and Low	*Hush, children, stop that crying.*	One low voice (mother)
High	Mother, Mother, she's up in The Tree!	High (three children)
Medium and Low	*Climb up and tell me what you see.*	One low voice (mother)
High	Mother, she's higher than I can climb!	High (three children)
Medium and Low	*She'll be back by breakfast time.*	One low voice (mother)
High	Mother, what if she's gone for good?	High (three children)
Medium and Low	*She'll have to make do with witches' food.*	One low voice (mother)
High	Mother, what do witches eat?	High (three children)
Medium and Low	*Milk and potatoes and YOU, my sweet.*	One low voice (mother)

Dorothy Baruch's "Merry-Go-Round" is as melodic as carousel music. Let the medium choir introduce the idea in the first four lines. Then the movement of the merry-go-round begins with low voices speaking the next four lines, very low and slowly at first, gradually going higher and faster, until the high choir picks up on the ninth line going with increasing speed and excitement through line 12. Line 13, spoken by medium voices, slows down markedly. Low speaks 14, still more slowly and brings the poem haltingly to a stop just as the old merry-go-round runs down. This poem demands graduation in tone for each choir as well as acceleration and deceleration.

"Taking Off" and "Song" will be analyzed later because both are better with a solo voice.

"Dogs and Weather" (p. 47) is very effectively done in choral form. The words in this poem are lovely but require careful diction, especially the last three lines with all those s's. It will require practice. Let all speak the first 2 lines slowly, reflectively; M, line 3; L, lines 4–7, mak-ing the most of lines 5 and 7; H, lines 8–10; and M, lines 11–14. Those last lines are a challenge. If one choir has better enunciation than another give it the last four lines and change the order of the others.

Another fine poem that is most effective in choral form is Harry Behn's "Hallowe'en" (p. 176). Number the 22 lines and try it in this form: L, lines 1 and 2, mysteriously; M, lines 3 and 4 (don't hiss s's but bite off *tch*'s); H, lines 5–7, eerily; M, lines 8 and 9, hushed; L, lines 10 and 11 (stress long *o*'s); H, lines 12–14; L, lines 15 and 16; M, lines 17 and 18; H, lines 19–21; and 22, all voices in a high squeal. Or try the final verse in this alternate form: L, lines 15–18; M, lines 19–21; H, line 22, in a squeal.

Another Halloween poem—this by John Ciardi—lends itself to many ways of casting for choral speaking. Two possibilities are suggested here. This poem is a conversation, but the speakers are not indicated until the exchange between children and mother in the last five couplets.

Before you cast this poem, read it to the children two or three times. Before you repeat it the third time, say to the children, "What do you think about that last dialogue between the mother and children? If they are youngsters speaking, they are working themselves up to a good scare. Do you think the mother, in that last line, really wants them to be scared, or do you think she might feel this scare-game has gone far enough and so would speak the last line with a smile, almost laughing?" Read it to the children both ways and see what they think.

In the line-a-child interpretation, choose the highest voices in the group for the three children, and let their voices crescendo on their first four lines. But when it comes to the last question, their voices drop to a scared half-whisper. On the other hand, the mother (a low voice) has spoken casually until the last line; then she either intends to scare them or she thinks it's time to let them know this is all a joke. Let the children decide.

Whether this poem is spoken by groups or line-a-child, the interpretation is the thing. The green-skinned man from the Witching Tree evidently speaks the words, "It's Halloween," so choose a high voice that can say those words eerily, hanging on to the "eennnnn" almost like a high wailing wind. Beginning with "Ruth, Ruth," the couplets are spoken light-heartedly, almost chanted. When all the voices say "You!" it should come with a scary little shout (not too loud), and a step forward with everyone pointing to someone in the audience. The last dialogue is really fun. The whole poem requires a thoughtful interpretation of every line.

An easier poem of Mr. Ciardi's to speak is "The River Is a Piece of the Sky." The conclusion offers triumphant proof that sky is sky, not river. For children who know a river in city or country and have looked at it from the middle of a bridge, this poem will mean something. Actually, this poem speaks so simply, that the casting does not really matter so long as small groups of children speak together until the middle five lines. These can be line-a-child for variety and prompt pick up.

THE RIVER IS A PIECE OF THE SKY

From the top of a bridge	Medium
The river below	
Is a piece of the sky—	
Until you throw	
A penny in	
Or a cockleshell	Line-a-child 1
Or a pebble or two	Line-a-child 2
Or a bicycle bell	Line-a-child 3
Or a cobblestone	Line-a-child 4
Or a fat man's cane—	Line-a-child 5
And then you can see	High
It's a river again.	
	Low
The difference you'll see	
When you drop your penny:	
The river has splashes,	All
The sky hasn't any.	

A solo voice with the choir

Sometimes a solo voice with the choir is startlingly effective. Try that little airplane poem, popular with any age group, "Taking Off" (p. 81) —L choir, lines 1 and 2; M choir, lines 3 and 4; H choir, lines 5 and 6; a clear, distinct, single voice, line 7; and all the voices speaking softly line 8. The three choirs should take their couplets in an ascending scale; the solo voice should mark the climax with a high, clear voice, and then the drop to the soft, regretful last line should come in a lower pitch.

Eugene Field's "Song" (p. 185) beginning "Why do bells for Christmas ring?" is much lovelier when a beautiful solo voice asks the questions in the first two lines; the M choir takes lines 3–6; the L choir, lines 7 and 8; the H choir, lines 9 and 10; and then the solo voice takes the quiet conclusion. In this case the single voice may be chosen from any of the three choirs, just so it has a clear, lovely quality. Some prefer to close the poem with all the choirs speaking the concluding couplet softly. Try it and see which way you prefer. The soloist may speak from his place in the group or may step out and stand a little apart.

How well your children speak any or all of these poems will depend upon your own interpretation of them in the first place. After the choirs have spoken them, take out a number of children and let them listen, then another group and another, so the children have a chance to hear the effect of different voices. When the children are up to speaking such poems individually, the listening group is also important—not to criticize, but to appreciate.[2]

THE CHOIR LEADER

The leader of a verse choir must in the beginning be an adult. If a few children develop sufficient skill to lead, now and then it is desirable to let them lead, but children should not lead in the beginning, and not during the learning of a new poem or during the practice periods that must follow if any degree of precision is to be attained. In a verse choir, as in a singing choir, beautiful effects and good teamwork do not happen—they are the result of careful and repeated practice. The leader must have read a poem aloud a number of times, marked it for casting, and studied it for meaning and interpretation before she reads it to the children. When they begin to speak it with her, she will mark the time just as she would for singing, and the tempo and the light, sweet voices must be maintained evenly during the learning process. The leader may gesture with her hand or finger— never a baton—for starting and stopping, for marking the time, and for going from choir to choir. Make this work as natural as possible and develop precision in your directing gestures so that the choirs know what is expected of them. In the beginning the gestures may have to be larger and a little more vehement than is desirable later. As the choirs become more proficient, the gestures should be toned down to the point of being completely unobtrusive and barely visi-

ble to an audience. Indeed, for a finished performance the leader can sit for her directing if she likes and she may limit her gestures to a signal to begin, a signal for the entrance of each choir, and occasionally a gesture to increase or diminish tone.

PROGRAMS BY VERSE CHOIRS

Programs of choral speaking by children should be easy, natural outgrowths of what they have been doing in class. Special costumes are neither necessary nor desirable, and colored lights and dramatic gestures are both anathema. Light, pleasant voices; intelligent interpretation of the poems; and a quiet enjoyment of what they are speaking—these are the essentials of a good performance, whether it is for the class next door or the PTA or visiting celebrities. Anything that smacks of the theatrical is out of place. Poetry is precious because of its melodies, its meaning, its beauty, or its laughter and these rather than choir vestments or elaborate staging are valuable both to the children and to their hearers.

Program selections as in music should represent a pleasant variety, a story poem perhaps, some humorous selections—some charming lyrics, and a serious poem or two. The various ways of casting the poems will also add interest and prevent monotony. On the whole, poems that have marked melodic values lend themselves especially well to choral speaking, but this is not necessarily true. Occasionally a prose selection may be effectively spoken by experienced choirs. Speaking of story poems, "The Pied Piper of Hamelin" (p. 24) has been superbly spoken by solo voices, choirs, and choruses, and in a great variety of ways. Certainly the rhyme, rhythms, and dramatic contrasts in this famous poem make it exciting both to speak and to hear. "The Pirate Don Durk of Dowdee" (p. 133) is also amusing in choir form. One class was divided for that colorful jingle on the basis of sex and made a very funny performance of it. The boys spoke of his wickedness, and the girls replied exuberantly or simperingly, "But oh, he was perfectly gorgeous to see!/The Pirate Don Durk of Dowdee."

[2] Other suggestions for verse choir work are made in the footnotes accompanying these poems: The Raggle Taggle Gypsies (p. 15), The Crafty Farmer (p. 16), Get Up and Bar the Door (p. 17), Stop—Go (p. 85), Momotara (p. 129), Holiday (p. 154), Open the Door (p. 172), Psalms 24, 100, 103, 147, and 150 (p. 178), Here We Come A-Caroling (p. 184), In the Week When Christmas Comes (p. 184), For Christmas Day (p. 185), Song (p. 185), A Christmas Carol (p. 186).

VALUES IN CHORAL SPEAKING

Obviously, successful choral speaking requires considerable preparation on the part of a teacher and practice on the part of the children. Is it worth while? Interestingly enough, the first testimonial of anyone who has worked with choral speaking groups, whether young children, preadolescents, youths, or adults, is that the work is tremendously exhilarating. "It's fun!" the children say. Poetry is therapeutic just as music is. When you are tired, speaking it with others can give you a lift and a sense of renewed energy. If you are keyed up, it can rest you, and if you are dull or stale or just plain discouraged, it can take you out of yourself and make you over. For the children, some remarkable personal changes are often noticeable. The over-aggressive child who monopolizes class discussions or activities is suddenly dropped into the background. If he is an intelligent child, he listens and becomes sensitive to the beauty of group voices speaking together quietly in pleasant harmony. This is a corrective for his exhibitionism. He adds his good voice to the others and the result is pleasing. The over-timid, self-conscious child really comes into his own. As one of a group, he speaks confidently, perhaps aggressively, and is not even surprised at himself. One of these days, the teacher gives him a solo line and he speaks it without thinking twice. A milestone for him! Children who have been roughly treated at home, who have heard coarse, harsh speech and use it themselves, speak gently and quietly in a verse choir, in pleasant voices they hardly knew they possessed. To see and hear rough boys speak richly and longingly "I must go down to the seas again, to the lonely sea and the sky," is to feel the power of words and ideas penetrating the hard crust of youthful bravado to the spirit of youth that somehow or other holds fast its dreams.

Poetry will do much for children's voices and for their speech as well. There is no question that experience in a verse choir is one of the most pleasant ways there is of improving speech.

The leader says, "You know speaking together this way magnifies every sound. The *s*'s hiss and the *r*'s bur-r-r as they don't when we speak individually; so we must soften them a bit. Consonants," she tells the children, "give vigor and crispness to words. Whatever we do, we must be sure the consonants come through with distinctness—especially *t*'s, *ng*'s and all the others except the troublesome *s*'s and *r*'s." Even these are important if not overstressed. Work for pure, clear vowels and strive for the best, the most understandable, and cultured speech of your particular area of the country. New England should not strive for Southern speech, nor the South for a New England accent, nor the West for either—and, of course, Americans should not ape British English. The goal is clear, crisp, vigorous speech with neither affectations nor impurities. Verse choir practice is as painless a method of improving diction as anything we know.

And finally as these children develop personally, and improve their voice quality and diction, they also develop in their range of experience with poetry. Over and over again, children have confided, "Until we started choral speaking, I always skipped poetry in a book. I would never have thought of opening a book that was all poems. Now I read poetry—I even asked for a book of poems for a Christmas present!" This last is, of course, the ultimate tribute. If children begin to read and explore poetry on their own, if their taste has broadened so that they enjoy not merely light verse or nonsense, but fine lyric verse as well, then indeed they have grown. And if they speak it or read it unselfconsciously, trying to bring out its music and its meaning, then they are on the way to being poetry-lovers for life.

One word of caution in conclusion: Be sure you don't endanger these achievements by excessive drill. Choral speaking should be exhilarating and joyous. By way of it, children should grow in their appreciation of good literature and in their sensitivity to beauty and to the power of the spoken word.

THE PEOPLE

Elizabeth Madox Roberts

The ants are walking under the ground,
And the pigeons are flying over the steeple,
And in between are the people.

NEIGHBORLY

Violet Alleyn Storey

My Mother sends our neighbors things
  On fancy little plates.
One day she sent them custard pie
  And they sent back stuffed dates.

And once she sent them angel food
  And they returned ice cream;
Another time for purple plums
  They gave us devil's dream.

She always keeps enough for us
  No matter what she sends.
Our goodies seem much better
  When we share them with our friends.

And even if they didn't, why,
  It's surely lots of fun,
'Cause that way we get two desserts
  Instead of only one!

ALL SORTS OF PEOPLE

Christina Georgina Rossetti

Mother shake the cherry-tree,
  Susan catch a cherry;
Oh how funny that will be,
  Let's be merry!

One for brother, one for sister,
 Two for mother more,
Six for father, hot and tired,
 Knocking at the door.

"SH"
James S. Tippett

"Sh!" says mother,
"Sh!" says father.
"Running in the hall
Is a very great bother."

"Mrs. Grumpy Grundy,
Who lives down below,
Will come right up
First thing you know."

"Sh!" says father,
"Sh!" says mother.
"Can't you play a quiet game
Of some kind or other?"

SHOP WINDOWS
Rose Fyleman

Mother likes the frocks and hats
And pretty stuffs and coloured mats.

Daddy never, never looks
At anything but pipes and books.

Auntie's fond of chains and rings
And all the sparkly diamond things.

Richard likes machines the best;
He doesn't care about the rest.

Nannie always loves to stop
In front of every single shop.

But I don't want to wait for a minute
Till we get to the one with the puppy dogs in it.

SMELLS (JUNIOR)
Christopher Morley

My Daddy smells like tobacco and books,
 Mother, like lavender and listerine;
Uncle John carries a whiff of cigars,
 Nannie smells starchy and soapy and clean.

Shandy, my dog, has a smell of his own
 (When he's been out in the rain he smells
 most);
But Katie, the cook, is more splendid than all—
 She smells exactly like hot buttered toast!

SHOES
Tom Robinson

My father has a pair of shoes
So beautiful to see!
I want to wear my father's shoes,
They are too big for me.

My baby brother has a pair,
As cunning as can be!
My feet won't go into that pair,
They are too small for me.

There's only one thing I can do
Till I get small or grown.
If I want to have a fitting shoe,
I'll have to wear my own.

FATHER
Frances Frost

My father's face is brown with sun,
His body is tall and limber.
His hands are gentle with beast or child
And strong as hardwood timber.

My father's eyes are the colors of sky,
Clear blue or gray as rain:

"The People." From *Under the Tree* by Elizabeth Madox Roberts. Copyright 1922 by B. W. Huebsch, Inc., 1950 by Ivor S. Roberts. Reprinted by permission of The Viking Press, Inc., New York

"Neighborly." From *Child Life*, December 1926. Child Life, Inc., Boston. Used by permission of the author

"Mother shake the cherry-tree." From *Sing-Song* by Christina Georgina Rossetti

"Sh." From *I Live in a City* by James S. Tippett. Copyright, 1927, Harper & Brothers

"Shop Windows." From *Gay Go Up* by Rose Fyleman. Copyright 1929, 1930 by Doubleday & Company, Inc. By permission also of Miss Rose Fyleman, The Society of Authors, and Messrs. Methuen & Co.

"Smells (Junior)." From *The Rocking Horse*. Copyright 1918, 1946 by Christopher Morley. Published by J. B. Lippincott Company

"Shoes." From *In and Out* by Tom Robinson. Copyright 1943 by Tom Robinson. Reprinted by permission of The Viking Press, Inc., New York

"Father." From *The Little Whistler* by Frances Frost. Published by McGraw-Hill Book Company, New York, 1949. By permission of the author

They change with the swinging change of days
While he watches the weather vane.

That galleon, golden upon our barn,
Veers with the world's four winds.
My father, his eyes on the vane, knows when
To fill our barley bins,

To stack our wood and pile our mows
With redtop and sweet tossed clover.
He captains our farm that rides the winds,
A keen-eyed brown earth-lover.

AUTOMOBILE MECHANICS

Dorothy Baruch

Sometimes
  I help my dad
Work on our automobile.
  We unscrew
  The radiator cap
    And we let some water run—
    Swish—from a hose
    Into the tank.

  And then we open up the hood
  And feed in oil
  From a can with a long spout.
  And then we take a lot of rags
  And clean all about.
    We clean the top
    And the doors
    And the fenders and the wheels
    And the windows and floors. . . .
      We work *hard*
      My dad
      And I.

Christina Georgina Rossetti

What does the bee do?
  Bring home honey.
And what does Father do?
  Bring home money.

And what does Mother do?
  Lay out the money.
And what does baby do?
  Eat up the honey.

SONG FOR MY MOTHER

Anna Hempstead Branch

My mother has the prettiest tricks
  Of words and words and words.
Her talk comes out as smooth and sleek
  As breasts of singing birds.

She shapes her speech all silver fine
  Because she loves it so.
And her own eyes begin to shine
  To hear her stories grow.

And if she goes to make a call
  Or out to take a walk,
We leave our work when she returns
  And run to hear her talk.

We had not dreamed these things were so
  Of sorrow and of mirth.
Her speech is as a thousand eyes
  Through which we see the earth.

God wove a web of loveliness,
  Of clouds and stars and birds,
But made not anything at all
  So beautiful as words.

They shine around our simple earth
  With golden shadowings,
And every common thing they touch
  Is exquisite with wings.

There's nothing poor and nothing small
  But is made fair with them.
They are the hands of living faith
  That touch the garment's hem.

They are as fair as bloom or air,
  They shine like any star,
And I am rich who learned from her
  How beautiful they are.

"Automobile Mechanics." From *I Like Machinery* by Dorothy Baruch. Harper & Brothers, New York, 1933. Used by permission of the author
  "What does the bee do?" From *Sing-Song* by Christina Georgina Rossetti
  "Song for My Mother." Anna Hempstead Branch. From

The Shoes That Danced and Other Poems. Published by Houghton Mifflin Company, Boston, 1905
  "Andre." From *Bronzeville Boys and Girls* by Gwendolyn Brooks. Copyright © 1956 by Gwendolyn Brooks Blakely. Published by Harper & Brothers, New York
  "Slippery." From *Smoke and Steel* by Carl Sandburg,

ANDRE

Gwendolyn Brooks

I had a dream last night. I dreamed
I had to pick a Mother out.
I had to choose a Father too.
At first, I wondered what to do,
There were so many there, it seemed,
Short and tall and thin and stout.

But just before I sprang awake,
I knew what parents I would take.

And *this* surprised and made me glad:
They were the ones I always had!

SLIPPERY

Carl Sandburg

The six month child
Fresh from the tub
Wriggles in our hands.
This is our fish child.
Give her a nickname: Slippery.

INFANT JOY

William Blake

"I have no name;
I am but two days old."
What shall I call thee?
"I happy am,
Joy is my name."
Sweet joy befall thee!

Pretty joy!
Sweet joy, but two days old.
Sweet joy I call thee;
Thou dost smile,
I sing the while;
Sweet joy befall thee!

Kate Greenaway

Little Blue Shoes
Mustn't go
Very far alone, you know.
Else she'll fall down,
Or, lose her way.
Fancy—what
Would mamma say?
Better put her little hand
Under sister's wise command.
When she's a little older grown
Blue Shoes may go quite alone.

LITTLE

Dorothy Aldis

I am the sister of him
And he is my brother.
He is too little for us
To talk to each other.

So every morning I show him
My doll and my book;
But every morning he still is
Too little to look.

TWO IN BED

Abram Bunn Ross

When my brother Tommy
Sleeps in bed with me,
He doubles up
And makes
himself
exactly
like
a
V

And 'cause the bed is not so wide,
A part of him is on my side.

LITTLE BROTHER'S SECRET

Katherine Mansfield

When my birthday was coming
Little Brother had a secret:
He kept it for days and days
And just hummed a little tune when I asked
    him.
But one night it rained
And I woke up and heard him crying:
Then he told me.
"I planted two lumps of sugar in your garden
Because you love it so frightfully.
I thought there would be a whole sugar tree for
    your birthday.
And now it will all be melted."
O the darling!

GIRLS' NAMES

Eleanor Farjeon

What lovely names for girls there are!
There's Stella like the Evening Star,
And Sylvia like a rustling tree,
And Lola like a melody,
And Flora like a flowery morn,
And Sheila like a field of corn,
And Melusina like the moan
Of water. And there's Joan, like Joan.

BOYS' NAMES

Eleanor Farjeon

What splendid names for boys there are!
There's Carol like a rolling car,
And Martin like a flying bird,
And Adam like the Lord's First Word,

And Raymond like the Harvest Moon,
And Peter like a piper's tune,
And Alan like the flowing on
Of water. And there's John, like John.

THE TWINS

Elizabeth Madox Roberts

The two-ones is the name for it,
And that is what it ought to be,
But when you say it very fast
It makes your lips say *twins,* you see.

When I was just a little thing,
About the year before the last,
I called it two-ones all the time,
But now I always say it fast.

TIRED TIM

Walter de la Mare

Poor tired Tim! It's sad for him.
He lags the long bright morning through,
Ever so tired of nothing to do;
He moons and mopes the livelong day,
Nothing to think about, nothing to say;
Up to bed with his candle to creep,
Too tired to yawn, too tired to sleep:
Poor tired Tim! It's sad for him.

BUNCHES OF GRAPES
Walter de la Mare

"Bunches of grapes," says Timothy;
"Pomegranates pink," says Elaine;
"A junket of cream and a cranberry tart
    For me," says Jane.

"Love-in-a-mist," says Timothy;
"Primroses pale," says Elaine;
"A nosegay of pinks and mignonette
    For me," says Jane.

"Chariots of gold," says Timothy;
"Silvery wings," says Elaine;
"A bumpity ride in a wagon of hay
    For me," says Jane.

THE CUPBOARD
Walter de la Mare

I know a little cupboard,
With a teeny tiny key,
And there's a jar of Lollipops
    For me, me, me.

It has a little shelf, my dear,
As dark as dark can be,
And there's a dish of Banbury Cakes
    For me, me, me.

I have a small fat grandmamma,
With a very slippery knee,
And she's Keeper of the Cupboard,
    With the key, key, key.

And when I'm very good, my dear,
As good as good can be,

There's Banbury Cakes, and Lollipops
    For me, me, me.

AMY ELIZABETH ERMYNTRUDE ANNIE
Queenie Scott Hopper

Amy Elizabeth Ermyntrude Annie
Went to the country to visit her Grannie,

Learnt to churn butter and learnt to make
    cheese,
Learnt to milk cows and take honey from bees,

Learnt to spice rose-leaves and learnt to cure
    ham,
Learnt to make cider and black currant jam.

When she came home she could not settle down,
Said there was nothing to do in the town.

Nothing to do there and nothing to see:
Life was all shopping and afternoon tea!

Amy Elizabeth Ermyntrude Annie
Ran away back to the country and Grannie.

WHERE'S MARY?
Ivy O. Eastwick

Is Mary in the dairy?
Is Mary on the stair?
What? Mary's in the garden?
What is she doing there?
Has she made the butter yet?
Has she made the beds?
Has she topped the gooseberries
And taken off their heads?
Has she the potatoes peeled?
Has she done the grate?
Are the new green peas all shelled?

It is getting late!
What? She hasn't done a thing?
Here's a nice to-do!
Mary has a dozen jobs
And hasn't finished two.
Well! here IS a nice to-do!
Well! upon my word!
She's sitting on the garden bench
Listening to a bird!

PORTRAIT BY A NEIGHBOR
Edna St. Vincent Millay

Before she has her floor swept
  Or her dishes done,
Any day you'll find her
  A-sunning in the sun!

It's long after midnight
  Her key's in the lock,
And you never see her chimney smoke
  Till past ten o'clock!

She digs in her garden
  With a shovel and a spoon,
She weeds her lazy lettuce
  By the light of the moon.

She walks up the walk
  Like a woman in a dream,
She forgets she borrowed butter
  And pays you back cream!

Her lawn looks like a meadow,
  And if she mows the place
She leaves the clover standing
  And the Queen Anne's lace!

GRANDFATHER WATTS'S PRIVATE FOURTH
H. C. Bunner

Grandfather Watts used to tell us boys
That a Fourth wa'n't a Fourth without any noise.
He would say, with a thump of his hickory stick,
That it made an American right down sick
To see his sons on the Nation's Day
Sit round in a sort of a listless way,

With no oration and no trained band,
No firework show and no root-beer stand;
While his grandsons, before they were out of
    bibs,
Were ashamed—Great Scott!—to fire off Squibs.

And so, each Independence morn,
Grandfather Watts took his powder horn,
And the flintlock shotgun *his* father had
When he fought under Schuyler, a country lad.
And Grandfather Watts would start and tramp
Ten miles to the woods at Beaver Camp;
For Grandfather Watts used to say—and scowl—
That a decent chipmunk, or woodchuck, or owl
Was better company, friendly or shy,
Than folks who didn't keep Fourth of July.
And so he would pull his hat down on his brow,
And march for the woods, sou'east by sou'.

But once—ah! long, long years ago;
For Grandfather's gone where good men go—
One hot, hot Fourth, by ways of our own
(Such short cuts as boys have always known),
We hurried, and followed the dear old man
Beyond where the wilderness began—
To the deep black woods at the foot of the
    dump;
And there was a clearing and a stump—

A stump in the heart of a great wide wood;
And there on that stump our grandfather stood,
Talking and shouting out there in the sun,
And firing that funny old flintlock gun
Once in a minute, his head all bare,
Having his Fourth of July out there—
The Fourth of July that he used to know,
Back in eighteen-and-twenty, or so.

First, with his face to the heaven's blue,
He read the "Declaration" through;
And then, with gestures to left and right,
He made an oration erudite,
Full of words six syllables long;
And then our grandfather burst into song!
And, scaring the squirrels in the trees,
Gave "Hail, Columbia!" to the breeze.

And I tell you the old man never heard
When we joined in the chorus, word for word!
But he sang out strong to the bright blue sky;
And if voices joined in his Fourth of July,
He heard them as echoes from days gone by.

And when he had done, we all slipped back,
As still as we came, on our twisting track,
While words more clear that the flintlock shots
Rang in our ears. And Grandfather Watts?
He shouldered the gun his father bore,
And marched off home, nor'west by nor'.

THE RAGGEDY MAN

James Whitcomb Riley

O The Raggedy Man! He works fer Pa;
An' he's the goodest man ever you saw!
He comes to our house every day,
An' waters the horses, an' feeds 'em hay;
An' he opens the shed—an' we all ist laugh
When he drives out our little old wobble-ly calf;
An' nen—ef our hired girl says he can—
He milks the cow fer 'Lizabuth Ann.—
    Ain't he a' awful good Raggedy Man?
      Raggedy! Raggedy! Raggedy Man!

W'y, The Raggedy Man—he's ist so good
He splits the kindlin' an' chops the wood;
An' nen he spades in our garden, too,
An' does most things 'at boys can't do.—
He clumbed clean up in our big tree
An' shooked a' apple down fer me—
An' nother'n', too, fer 'Lizabuth Ann—
An' nother'n', too, fer The Raggedy Man.—
    Ain't he a' awful kind Raggedy Man?
      Raggedy! Raggedy! Raggedy Man!

An' The Raggedy Man, he knows most rhymes
An' tells 'em, ef I be good, sometimes:
Knows 'bout Giunts, an' Griffuns, an' Elves,
An' the Squidgicum-Squees 'at swallers ther-
    selves!
An', wite by the pump in our pasture-lot,
He showed me the hole 'at the Wunks is got,
'At lives 'way deep in the ground, an' can
Turn into me, er 'Lizabuth Ann!
    Ain't he a funny old Raggedy Man?
      Raggedy! Raggedy! Raggedy Man!

The Raggedy Man—one time when he
Was makin' a little bow-'n'-orry fer me,
Says, "When *you're* big like your Pa is,
Air you go' to keep a fine store like his—
An' be a rich merchunt—an' wear fine clothes?—
Er what *air* you go' to be, goodness knows!"
An' nen he laughed at 'Lizabuth Ann,
An' I says " 'M go' to be a Raggedy Man!"
    I'm ist go' to be a nice Raggedy Man!"
      Raggedy! Raggedy! Raggedy Man!

DOORBELLS

Rachel Field

You never know with a doorbell
  Who may be ringing it—
It may be Great-Aunt Cynthia
  To spend the day and knit;
It may be a peddler with things to sell
  (I'll buy some when I'm older),
Or the grocer's boy with his apron on
  And a basket on his shoulder;

"Doorbells." From *The Pointed People* by Rachel Field. The Macmillan Company, New York, 1930. Used by per- mission of Arthur S. Pederson, Trustee, Estate of Rachel Field Pederson

It may be the old umbrella-man,
  Giving his queer, cracked call,
Or a lady dressed in rustly silk,
  With a card-case and parasol.
Doorbells are like a magic game,
  Or the grab-bag at a fair—
You never know when you hear one ring
  Who may be waiting there!

THE SCISSOR-MAN

Madeline Nightingale

Sing a song of Scissor-men,
"Mend a broken plate,
Bring your knives and garden shears,
I'll do them while you wait.
Buzz-a-wuzz! Buzz-a-wuzz!
Fast the wheel or slow,
Ticker Tacker! Ticker Tack!
Rivets in a row."

Sing a song of Scissor-men,
Sitting in the sun,
Sing it when the day begins,
Sing it when it's done.
Be it hard or be it soft,
Here's a jolly plan;
Sing to make the work go well,
Like the Scissor-man.

THE POSTMAN

Laura E. Richards

Hey! the little postman,
  And his little dog,
Here he comes a-hopping
  Like a little frog;
Bringing me a letter,
  Bringing me a note,
In the little pocket
  Of his little coat.

Hey! the little postman,
  And his little bag,
Here he comes a-trotting
  Like a little nag;
Bringing me a paper,
  Bringing me a bill,
From the little grocer
  On the little hill.

Hey! the little postman,
  And his little hat,
Here he comes a-creeping
  Like a little cat.
What is that he's saying?
  "Naught for you to-day!"
Horrid little postman!
  I wish you'd go away!

Christina Georgina Rossetti

Eight o'clock;
The postman's knock!
Five letters for Papa;
  One for Lou,
  And none for you,
And three for dear Mamma.

THE NEW NEIGHBOR

Rose Fyleman

Have you had your tonsils out?
  Do you go to school?
Do you know that there are frogs
  Down by Willow Pool?

Are you good at cricket?
  Have you got a bat?
Do you know the proper way
  To feed a white rat?

Are there any apples
  On your apple tree?

"The Scissor-Man." From *Nursery Lays for Nursery Days* by Madeline Nightingale. By permission of Basil Blackwell & Mott, Ltd., Oxford

"The Postman." From *Tirra Lirra* by Laura E. Richards. Little, Brown & Company, Boston, 1932

"Eight o'clock." From *Sing-Song* by Christina Georgina Rossetti

"The New Neighbor." From *Gay Go Up* by Rose Fyleman. Copyright 1929, 1930 by Doubleday & Company, Inc. By permission also of Miss Fyleman, The Society of Authors, and Messrs. Methuen & Co.

"Oh, Susan Blue." *Here is a conversation over the garden gate. First the friend speaks, then Susan has the last three lines. This poem is read by May Hill Arbuthnot in the record album* Poetry Time, Scott, Foresman. *From* Marigold Garden *by Kate Greenaway. Frederick Warne*

Do you tnink your mother
Will ask me in to tea?

Kate Greenaway

Oh, Susan Blue,
How do you do?
Please may I go for a walk with you?
Where shall we go?
Oh, I know—
Down in the meadow where the cowslips grow!

AT MRS. APPLEBY'S
Elizabeth Upham McWebb

When frost is shining on the trees,
It's spring at Mrs. Appleby's.
You smell it in the air before
You step inside the kitchen door.

Rows of scarlet flowers bloom
From every window in the room.
And funny little speckled fish
Are swimming in a china dish.

A tiny bird with yellow wings
Just sits and sings and sings and SINGS!
Outside when frost is on the trees,
It's spring at Mrs. Appleby's!

A. A. Milne

Diana Fitzpatrick Mauleverer James
Was lucky to have the most beautiful names.
How awful for Fathers and Mothers to call
Their children Jemima!—or nothing at all!
But *hers* were much wiser and kinder and cleverer,
They called her Diana Fitzpatrick Mauleverer
James.

MISS T.
Walter de la Mare

It's a very odd thing—
As odd as can be—
That whatever Miss T. eats
Turns into Miss T.;
Porridge and apples,
Mince, muffins and mutton,
Jam, junket, jumbles—
Not a rap, not a button
It matters; the moment
They're out of her plate,
Though shared by Miss Butcher
And sour Mr. Bate;
Tiny and cheerful,
And neat as can be,
Whatever Miss T. eats
Turns into Miss T.

from ALL AROUND THE TOWN
Phyllis McGinley

P's the proud Policeman
With buttons polished neat.
He's pleased to put his hand up
When you want to cross the street.
By daylight he protects you;
He protects you through the dark,
And he points the way politely
To the playground or the park.

and Company, New York and London, 1910.
"At Mrs. Appleby's." From *Child Life*, February 1945. Child Life, Inc., Boston. Used by permission of the author
"Diana Fitzpatrick Mauleverer James." From *A Gallery of Children* by A. A. Milne. David McKay Company, Inc., New York, 1925
"Miss T." *If you really bite your consonants off distinctly when you speak this poem, you'll discover prim, prissy*

Miss T. in the very sound of the words. From *Collected Poems, 1901–1918,* by Walter de la Mare. Copyright, 1920, by Henry Holt and Company, Inc. Copyright, 1948, by Walter de la Mare. Reprinted by permission of the publishers
"P's the proud Policeman." From *All Around the Town.* Copyright 1948 by Phyllis McGinley. Reprinted by permission of J. B. Lippincott Company

THE POLICEMAN

Marjorie Seymour Watts

He never used to notice me
When I went by, and stared at him.
And then he smiled especially,
And now he says, "Hello there, Jim."

If he becomes a friend of mine,
And I learn all I ought to know,
Perhaps he'll let me turn the sign
And make the people Stop! and Go!

He and I are friends, you see,
And he always smiles at me.

Once I wasn't very good
Rather near to where he stood,
But he never said a word
Though I'm sure he must have heard.

Nurse has a policeman too
(Hers has brown eyes, mine has blue),
Hers is sometimes on a horse,
But I like mine best of course.

MY POLICEMAN

Rose Fyleman

He is always standing there
At the corner of the Square;
He is very big and fine
And his silver buttons shine.

All the carts and taxis do
Everything he tells them to,
And the little errand boys
When they pass him make no noise.

Though I seem so very small
I am not afraid at all;

THE BALLOON MAN

Dorothy Aldis

Our balloon man has balloons.
He holds them on a string.
He blows his horn and walks about
Through puddles, in the spring.

He stands on corners while they bob
And tug above his head—
Green balloons and blue balloons
And yellow ones, and red.

He takes our pennies and unties
The two we choose; and then
He turns around, and waves his hand,
And blows his horn again.

THE DENTIST

Rose Fyleman

I'd like to be a dentist with a plate upon the door
And a little bubbling fountain in the middle of
   the floor;
With lots of tiny bottles all arranged in coloured
   rows
And a page-boy with a line of silver buttons
   down his clothes.

I'd love to polish up the things and put them
   every day
Inside the darling chests of drawers all tidily
   away;
And every Sunday afternoon when nobody was
   there
I should go riding up and down upon the velvet
   chair.

THE COBBLER

Eleanor Alletta Chaffee

Crooked heels
   And scuffy toes
Are all the kinds
   Of shoes he knows.

He patches up
   The broken places,
Sews the seams
   And shines their faces.

MANUAL SYSTEM

Carl Sandburg

Mary has a thingamajig clamped on her ears
And sits all day taking plugs out and sticking
   plugs in.
Flashes and flashes—voices and voices calling for
   ears to pour words in
Faces at the ends of wires asking for other faces
   at the ends of other wires:
All day taking plugs out and sticking plugs in,
Mary has a thingamajig clamped on her ears.

MELONS

Mary Mapes Dodge

Melons! melons!
   All day long
Joe's mother sits
   Selling melons.

"Ho! ripe and rich!"
   Is her song,
All day long
   Selling melons.

Melons! melons!
   All day long
Joe walks the street
   Selling melons.
"Ho! ripe and sweet!"
   Is his song,
All day long
   Selling melons.

THE SHEPHERD

William Blake

How sweet is the shepherd's sweet lot!
From the morn to the evening he strays;
He shall follow his sheep all the day,
And his tongue shall be filléd with praise.

For he hears the lambs' innocent call,
And he hears the ewes' tender reply;
He is watchful while they are in peace,
For they know when their shepherd is nigh.

A PIPER

Seumas O'Sullivan

A piper in the streets to-day
Set up, and tuned, and started to play,
And away, away, away on the tide
Of his music we started; on every side
Doors and windows were opened wide,
And men left down their work and came,
And women with petticoats coloured like flame.
And little bare feet that were blue with cold,
Went dancing back to the age of gold,
And all the world went gay, went gay,
For half an hour in the street to-day.

"Manual System." *This is an amusing picture of a tele-phone switchboard operator.* From *Early Moon* by Carl Sandburg, copyright, 1930, by Harcourt, Brace and Company, Inc.
"Melons." *From* Rhymes and Jingles *by Mary Mapes Dodge, Charles Scribner's Sons, 1874*

"The Shepherd." From *Songs of Innocence* by William Blake.
"A Piper." From *Collected Poems* by Seumas O'Sullivan. Orwell Press, Dublin, 1940. Used by permission of the author

GYPSY JANE

William Brighty Rands

She had corn flowers in her hair
    As she came up the lane;
"What may be your name, my dear?"
    "O, sir, Gypsy Jane."

"You are berry-brown, my dear."
    "That, sir, well may be,
For I live more than half the year,
    Under tent or tree."

Shine, Sun! Blow, Wind!
    Fall gently, Rain!
The year's declined, be soft and kind.
    Kind to Gypsy Jane.

BEING GYPSY

Barbara Young

A gypsy, a gypsy,
Is what I'd like to be,
If ever I could find one who
Would change his place with me.

Rings on my fingers,
Earrings in my ears,
Rough shoes to roam the world
For years and years and years!

I'd listen to the stars,
I'd listen to the dawn,
I'd learn the tunes of wind and rain,
The talk of fox and faun.

A gypsy, a gypsy!
To ramble and to roam
For maybe—oh,
A week or so—
And then I'd hie me home!

DARK DANNY

Ivy O. Eastwick

Dark Danny has eyes
As black as the sloe,
And his freckles tell
Where the sunbeams go!

Dark Danny has hair
Like a raven's wing,
And his voice is gay
As the thrush in Spring.

Dark Danny will show
You the first wild rose;
Where the earliest violet
Blooms—he knows!

Where the red fox hides,
Why the nightingale sings . . .
Dark Danny knows all
These lovely things.

MEG MERRILIES

John Keats

Old Meg she was a Gipsy,
    And liv'd upon the Moors:
Her bed it was the brown heath turf,
    And her house was out of doors.

Her apples were swart blackberries,
    Her currants pods o' broom;
Her wine was dew of the wild white rose,
    Her book a churchyard tomb.

Her Brothers were the craggy hills,
    Her Sisters larchen trees—
Alone with her great family
    She liv'd as she did please.

No breakfast had she many a morn,
    No dinner many a noon,
And 'stead of supper she would stare
    Full hard against the Moon.

But every morn of woodbine fresh
    She made her garlanding,
And every night the dark glen Yew
    She wove, and she would sing.

And with her fingers old and brown
    She plaited Mats o' Rushes,

"Being Gypsy." From *Christopher O!* by Barbara Young. David McKay Company, Inc., New York, 1947

"Dark Danny." Taken from *Fairies and Suchlike,* by Ivy O. Eastwick, published and copyright, 1946, by E. P. Dutton & Co., Inc., New York

And gave them to the Cottagers
  She met among the Bushes.

Old Meg was brave as Margaret Queen
  And tall as Amazon:
An old red blanket cloak she wore;
  A chip hat had she on.
God rest her aged bones somewhere—
  She died full long agone!

THE FIDDLER OF DOONEY

William Butler Yeats

When I play on my fiddle in Dooney,
Folk dance like a wave of the sea;
My cousin is priest in Kilvarnet,
My brother in Moharabuiee.

I passed my brother and cousin:
They read in their books of prayer;
I read in my book of songs
I bought at the Sligo fair.

When we come at the end of time
To Peter sitting in state,
He will smile on the three old spirits,
But call me first through the gate;

For the good are always the merry,
Save by an evil chance,
And the merry love the fiddle
And the merry love to dance:

And when the folk there spy me,
They will all come up to me,
With 'Here is the fiddler of Dooney!'
And dance like a wave of the sea.

THE RAGGLE, TAGGLE GYPSIES

(Old Folk Song)

There were three gypsies a-come to my door,
  And downstairs ran this lady, O.

One sang high and another sang low,
  And the other sang "Bonnie, Bonnie Bis-
  kay, O."

Then she pulled off her silken gown,
  And put on hose of leather, O.
With the ragged, ragged rags about her door
  She's off with the Raggle, Taggle Gypsies, O.

'Twas late last night when my lord came home,
  Inquiring for his lady, O.
The servants said on every hand,
  "She's gone with the Raggle, Taggle Gyp-
  sies, O."

"Oh, saddle for me my milk-white steed,
  Oh, saddle for me my pony, O,
That I may ride and seek my bride
  Who's gone with the Raggle, Taggle Gyp-
  sies, O."

Oh, he rode high and he rode low,
  He rode through woods and copses, O,
Until he came to an open field,
  And there he espied his lady, O.

"What makes you leave your house and lands?
  What makes you leave your money, O?
What makes you leave your new-wedded lord
  To go with the Raggle, Taggle Gypsies, O?"

"What care I for my house and lands?
  What care I for my money, O?
What care I for my new-wedded lord?
  I'm off with the Raggle, Taggle Gypsies, O."

"Last night you slept on a goose-feather bed,
  With the sheet turned down so bravely, O.
Tonight you will sleep in the cold, open field,
  Along with the Raggle, Taggle Gypsies, O."

"What care I for your goose-feather bed,
  With the sheet turned down so bravely, O?
For tonight I shall sleep in a cold, open field,
  Along with the Raggle, Taggle Gypsies, O."

"The Fiddler of Dooney." From *Poetical Works* by William Butler Yeats. Copyright 1906, 1934 by The Macmillan Company and used with their permission. By permission also of Mrs. William Butler Yeats and The Macmillan Company of Canada

"The Raggle, Taggle Gypsies." Why did the lady run away? Could she have been a gypsy herself? This is exciting to speak with one group of voices for the narrative, another group for the frightened servants, and single voices for the lord and the lady.

THE CRAFTY FARMER

(Ballad)

The song that I'm going to sing,
    I hope it will give you content,
Concerning a silly old man,
    That was going to pay his rent.

As he was riding along,
    Along all on the highway,
A gentleman-thief overtook him,
    And thus to him did say.

"Well overtaken!" said the thief,
    "Well overtaken!" said he;
And "Well overtaken!" said the old man,
    "If thou be good company."

"How far are you going this way?"
    Which made the old man for to smile;
"By my faith," said the old man,
    "I'm just going two mile.

"I am a poor farmer," he said,
    "And I farm a piece of ground,
And my half-year's rent, kind sir,
    Just comes to forty pound.

"And my landlord has not been at home;
    I've not seen him this twelvemonth or more,
Which makes my rent be large;
    I've to pay him just fourscore."

"Thou shouldst not have told any body,
    For thieves there's ganging many;
If any should light on thee,
    They'll rob thee of thy money."

"O never mind," said the old man,
    "Thieves I fear on no side,
For the money is safe in my bags,
    On the saddle on which I ride."

As they were riding along,
    The old man was thinking no ill,
The thief he pulled out a pistol
    And bid the old man stand still.

"The Crafty Farmer." *This lends itself to speaking with
a group of voices for the story and solo voices for farmer,
robber, and wife.*

But the old man provd crafty,
    As in the world there's many;
He threw his saddle oer the hedge,
    Saying, Fetch it, if thou'lt have any.

The thief got off his horse,
    With courage stout and bold,
To search for the old man's bag,
    And gave him his horse to hold.

The old man put's foot i the stirrup
    And he got on astride;
To its side he clapt his spur up,
    You need not bid the old man ride.

"O stay!" said the thief, "O stay!
    And half the share thou shalt have;"
"Nay, by my faith," said the old man,
    "For once I have bitten a knave."

The thief he was not content,
    But he thought there must be bags;
He out with his rusty old sword
    And chopt the old saddle in rags.

When he came to the landlord's house,
    This old man he was almost spent;
Saying, "Come, show me a private room
    And I'll pay you a whole year's rent.

"I've met a fond fool by the way,
    I swapt horses and gave him no boot;
But never mind," said the old man,
    "For I got the fond fool by the foot."

He opend this rogue's portmantle,
    It was glorious to behold;
There were three hundred pounds in silver,
    And three hundred pounds in gold.

And as he was riding home,
    And down a narrow lane,
He espied his mare tied to a hedge,
    Saying, "Prithee, Tib, wilt thou gang hame?"

When he got home to his wife
    And told her what he had done,
Up she rose and put on her clothes,
    And about the house did run.

She sung, and she sung, and she sung,
    She sung with a merry devotion,
Saying, If ever our daughter gets wed,
    It will help to enlarge her portion.

GET UP AND BAR THE DOOR

(Ballad)

It fell about the Martinmas time,
    And a gay time it was then,
When our goodwife got puddings to make,
    And she's boild them in the pan.

The wind sae cauld blew south and north,
    And blew into the floor;
Quoth our goodman to our goodwife,
    "Gae out and bar the door."

"My hand is in my hussyfskap,
    Goodman, as ye may see:
An it shoud nae be barrd this hundred year,
    It's no be barrd for me."

They made a paction tween them twa,
    They made it firm and sure,
That the first word whaeer shoud speak,
    Shoud rise and bar the door.

Then by there came two gentlemen,
    At twelve o clock at night,
And they could neither see house nor hall,
    Nor coal nor candle-light.

"Now whether is this a rich man's house,
    Or whether is it a poor?"
But neer a word wad ane o them speak,
    For barring of the door.

And first they ate the white puddings,
    And then they ate the black;
Tho muckle thought the goodwife to hersel,
    Yet neer a word she spake.

Then said the one unto the other,
    "Here, man, tak ye my knife;
Do ye tak aff the auld man's beard,
    And I'll kiss the goodwife."

"But there's nae water in the house,
    And what shall we do than?"
"What ails ye at the pudding-broo,
    That boils into the pan?"

O up then started our goodman,
    An angry man was he:
"Will ye kiss my wife before my een,
    And scad me wi pudding-bree?"

Then up and started our goodwife,
    Gied three skips on the floor:
"Goodman, you've spoken the foremost word,
    Get up and bar the door."

ROBIN HOOD RESCUING THE WIDOW'S THREE SONS

(Ballad)

There are twelve months in all the year,
    As I hear many say,
But the merriest month in all the year
    Is the merry month of May.

Now Robin Hood is to Nottingham gone,
    With a link and a down, and a day,
And there he met a silly old woman,
    Was weeping on the way.

"What news? what news? thou silly old woman,
    What news hast thou for me?"
Said she, "There's my three sons in Nottingham
        town
    Today condemned to die."

"O, have they parishes burnt?" he said,
    "Or have they ministers slain?
Or have they robbèd any virgin?
    Or other men's wives have ta'en?"

"Get Up and Bar the Door." *Hussyfscap means house-wifery, kitchen chores, perhaps. It is such a funny word, it's too bad it's gone. Puddingbree is the hot water in which the pudding is cooking. This poem suggests crude dramatization with lots of exaggeration and fun. Let a* group *speak the story, and solo voices speak and act the absurd roles of husband, wife, and two robbers.*

"Robin Hood Rescuing the Widow's Three Sons." *The old English words of this ballad have been translated into modern English.*

"They have no parishes burnt, good sir,
    Nor yet have ministers slain,
Nor have they robbèd any virgin,
    Nor other men's wives have ta'en."

"O, what have they done?" said Robin Hood,
    "I pray thee tell to me."
"It's for slaying of the king's fallow deer,
    Bearing their long bows with thee."

"Dost thou not mind, old woman," he said,
    "How thou madest me sup and dine?
By the truth of my body," quoth Robin Hood,
    "You could not tell it in better time."

Now Robin Hood is to Nottingham gone,
    With a link and a down, and a day,
And there he met with a silly old palmer,
    Was walking along the highway.

"What news? what news? thou silly old man,
    What news, I do thee pray?"
Said he, "Three squires in Nottingham town
    Are condemned to die this day."

"Come change thy apparel with me, old man,
    Come change thy apparel for mine;
Here is ten shillings in good silver,
    Go drink it in beer or wine."

"O, thine apparel is good," he said,
    "And mine is ragged and torn;
Wherever you go, wherever you ride,
    Laugh not an old man to scorn."

"Come change thy apparel with me, old churl,
    Come change thy apparel with mine;
Here is a piece of good broad gold,
    Go feast thy brethren with wine."

Then he put on the old man's hat,
    It stood full high in the crown:
"The first good bargain that I come at,
    It shall make thee come down."

Then he put on the old man's cloak,
    Was patch'd black, blue and red;
He thought it no shame all the day long,
    To wear the bags of bread.

Then he put on the old man's breeks,
    Was patch'd from leg to side;
"By the truth of my body," bold Robin gan say,
    "This man loved little pride."

Then he put on the old man's hose,
    Were patched from knee to wrist;
"By the truth of my body," said bold Robin Hood,
    "I'd laugh if I had any list."

Then he put on the old man's shoes,
    Were patch'd both beneath and aboon;
Then Robin Hood swore a solemn oath,
    "It's good habit that makes a man."

Now Robin Hood is to Nottingham gone,
    With a link a down, and a down,
And there he met with the proud sheriff,
    Was walking along the town.

"Save you, save you, sheriff!" he said,
    "Now heaven you save and see!
And what will you give to a silly old man
    Today will your hangman be?"

"Some suits, some suits," the sheriff he said,
    "Some suits I'll give to thee;
Some suits, some suits, and pence thirteen,
    Today's a hangman's fee."

Then Robin he turns him round about,
    And jumps from stock to stone;
"By the truth of my body," the sheriff he said,
    "That's well jumpt, thou nimble old man."

"I was ne'er a hangman in all my life,
    Nor yet intends to trade;
But curst be he," said bold Robin,
    "That first a hangman was made."

"I've a bag for meal, and a bag for malt,
    And a bag for barley and corn;
A bag for bread, and a bag for beef,
    And a bag for my little small horn."

"I have a horn in my pocket,
    I got it from Robin Hood,
And still when I set it to my mouth,
    For thee it blows little good."

"O, wind thy horn, thou proud fellow!
  Of thee I have no doubt.
I wish that thou give such a blast,
  Till both thy eyes fall out."

The first loud blast that he did blow,
  He blew both loud and shrill;
A hundred and fifty of Robin Hood's men
  Came riding over the hill.

The next loud blast that he did give,
  He blew both loud and amain,
And quickly sixty of Robin Hood's men
  Came shining over the plain.

"O, who are those," the sheriff he said,
  "Come tripping over the lee?"
"They're my attendants," brave Robin did say;
  "They'll pay a visit to thee."

They took the gallows from the slack,
  They set it in the glen,
They hangèd the proud sheriff on that,
  Released their own three men.

SIR PATRICK SPENCE

(Ballad)

The king sits in Dumferling town,
  Drinking the blood-red wine:
"O where will I get a good sailor,
  To sail this ship of mine?"

*"Sir Patrick Spence." This is a close translation of old
English words into modern. Even so, like all the traditional
ballads, it leaves much unsaid. It is possible that this ballad refers to the shipwreck and drowning of a number of
Scottish nobles who in 1281 were returning from accompanying Margaret, daughter of the king of Scotland, to
Norway, where she was to be married to King Eric.*

Up and spoke an elderly knight,
  (Sat at the king's right knee),
"Sir Patrick Spence is the best sailor
  That sails upon the sea."

The king has written a broad letter,
  And signed it with his hand,
And sent it to Sir Patrick Spence,
  Was walking on the sand.

The first line that Sir Patrick read,
  A loud laugh laughed he;
The next line that Sir Patrick read,
  A tear blinded his eye.

"O who is this has done this deed,
  This ill deed done to me,
To send me out this time of year,
  To sail upon the sea!

"Make haste, make haste, my merry men all,
  Our good ship sails the morn:"
"O say not so, my master dear,
  For I fear a deadly storm.

"Late late yestereven I saw the new moon
  With the old moon in her arm,
And I fear, I fear, my master dear,
  That we will come to harm."

O our Scotch nobles were right loathe
  To wet their cork-heeled shoes;
But long after the play was played
  Their hats floated into view.

O long, long may their ladies sit,
  With their fans within their hand,
Or ever they see Sir Patrick Spence
  Come sailing to the land.

O long, long may their ladies stand,
  With their gold combs in their hair,
Waiting for their own dear lords,
  For they'll see them never more.

Half o'er, half o'er to Aberdour,
  It's fifty fathoms deep,
And there lies good Sir Patrick Spence,
  With the Scotch lords at his feet.

THE WIFE OF USHER'S WELL

(Ballad)

There lived a wife at Usher's well,
  And a wealthy wife was she;
She had three stout and stalwart sons,
  And sent them o'er the sea.

They had not been a week from her,
  A week but barely one,
When word came to the carline wife
  That her three sons were gone.

They had not been a week from her,
  A week but barely three,
When word came to the carline wife
  That her sons she'd never see.

"I wish the wind may never cease,
  Nor fishes in the flood,
Till my three sons come home to me
  In earthly flesh and blood!"

It fell about the Martinmas,
  When nights are long and dark,
The carline wife's three sons came home,
  And their hats were of birch bark.

It neither grew in trench nor ditch,
  Nor yet in any furrow;
But at the gates of Paradise
  That birch grew fair enough.

"Blow up the fire, my maidens!
  Bring water from the well!
For all my house shall feast this night,
  Since my three sons are well."

And she has made for them a bed,
  She's made it large and wide;
And she's put her mantle about her,
  And sat at their bedside.

Up then crowed the red, red cock,
  And up and crowed the gray;

The eldest son to the youngest said,
  " 'Tis time we were away."

The cock he had not crowed but once,
  And clapped his wings at all,
When the youngest to the eldest said,
  "Brother, we must awa'."

"The cock doth crow, the day doth dawn,
  The fretting worm doth chide;
When we are out of our place,
  A sore pain we must bide."

"Lie still, lie still but a little wee while,
  Lie still but if we may;
When my mother misses us when she wakes
  She'll go mad before it's day."

"Fare ye well, my mother dear!
  Farewell to barn and byre!
And fare ye well, the bonny lass
  That kindles my mother's fire."

A SONG OF SHERWOOD

Alfred Noyes

Sherwood in the twilight, is Robin Hood awake?
Grey and ghostly shadows are gliding through
  the brake,
Shadows of the dappled deer, dreaming of the
  morn,
Dreaming of a shadowy man that winds a shadowy horn.

Robin Hood is here again: all his merry thieves
Hear a ghostly bugle-note shivering through the
  leaves,
Calling as he used to call, faint and far away,
In Sherwood, in Sherwood, about the break of
  day.

"The Wife of Usher's Well." *The old English words of this ballad have been translated into modern English. This is a ghost story that is unusually moving. When this wealthy woman (carline wife) learns that her sons have been lost at sea, she curses the sea and wishes her sons home. They appear, and after she has feasted them, she evidently falls asleep at their bedside. As ghosts must al-* ways leave before dawn, these three depart reluctantly shortly after cock's crow. The last two lines suggest that one of them leaves a sweetheart behind him.

"A Song of Sherwood." From *Collected Poems*, Volume I. Copyright 1913, 1941 by Alfred Noyes. Published by J. B. Lippincott Co., Philadelphia and William Blackwood & Sons, London.

Merry, merry England has kissed the lips of
    June:
All the wings of fairyland were here beneath the
    moon,
Like a flight of rose-leaves fluttering in a mist
Of opal and ruby and pearl and amethyst.

Merry, merry England is waking as of old,
With eyes of blither hazel and hair of brighter
    gold:
For Robin Hood is here again beneath the burst-
    ing spray
In Sherwood, in Sherwood, about the break of
    day.

Love is in the greenwood building him a house
Of wild rose and hawthorn and honeysuckle
    boughs:
Love is in the greenwood, dawn is in the skies,
And Marian is waiting with a glory in her eyes.

Hark! The dazzled laverock climbs the golden
    steep!
Marian is waiting: is Robin Hood asleep?
Round the fairy grass-rings frolic elf and fay,
In Sherwood, in Sherwood, about the break of
    day.

Oberon, Oberon, rake away the gold,
Rake away the red leaves, roll away the mould,
Rake away the gold leaves, roll away the red,
And wake Will Scarlett from his leafy forest bed.

Friar Tuck and Little John are riding down to-
    gether
With quarter-staff and drinking-can and grey
    goose-feather.
The dead are coming back again, the years are
    rolled away
In Sherwood, in Sherwood, about the break of
    day.

Softly over Sherwood the south wind blows.
All the heart of England hid in every rose

Hears across the greenwood the sunny whisper
    leap,
Sherwood in the red dawn, is Robin Hood
    asleep?

Hark, the voice of England wakes him as of old
And, shattering the silence with a cry of brighter
    gold,

Bugles in the greenwood echo from the steep,
*Sherwood in the red dawn, is Robin Hood
    asleep?*

Where the deer are gliding down the shadowy
    glen
All across the glades of fern he calls his merry
    men—
Doublets of the Lincoln green glancing through
    the May
In Sherwood, in Sherwood, about the break of
    day—

Calls them and they answer: from aisles of oak
    and ash
Rings the *Follow! Follow!* and the boughs begin
    to crash,
The ferns begin to flutter and the flowers begin
    to fly,
And through the crimson dawning the robber
    band goes by.

Robin! Robin! Robin! All his merry thieves
Answer as the bugle-note shivers through the
    leaves,
Calling as he used to call, faint and far away,
In Sherwood, in Sherwood, about the break of
    day.

THE ADMIRAL'S GHOST

Alfred Noyes

I tell you a tale to-night
  Which a seaman told to me,
With eyes that gleamed in the lanthorn light
  And a voice as low as the sea.

You could almost hear the stars
  Twinkling up in the sky,
And the old wind woke and moaned in the
    spars
And the same old waves went by,

Singing the same old song
  As ages and ages ago,
While he froze my blood in that deep-sea night
  With the things that he seemed to know.

A bare foot pattered on deck;
  Ropes creaked; then—all grew still,
And he pointed his finger straight in my face
  And growled, as a sea-dog will.

"Do 'ee know who Nelson was?
  That pore little shrivelled form
With the patch on his eye and the pinned-up
    sleeve
And a soul like a North Sea storm?

"Ask of the Devonshire men!
  They know, and they'll tell you true;
He wasn't the pore little chawed-up chap
  That Hardy thought he knew.

"He wasn't the man you think!
  His patch was a dern disguise!
For he knew that they'd find him out, d'you
    see,
  If they looked him in both his eyes.

"He was twice as big as he seemed;
  But his clothes were cunningly made.
He'd both of his hairy arms all right!
  The sleeve was a trick of the trade.

"You've heard of sperrits, no doubt;
  Well, there's more in the matter than that!
But he wasn't the patch and he wasn't the
    sleeve,
  And he wasn't the laced cocked-hat.

"Nelson was just—a Ghost!
  You may laugh! But the Devonshire men
They knew that he'd come when England
    called,
  And they know that he'll come again.

"I'll tell you the way it was
  (For none of the landsmen know),
And to tell it you right, you must go a-starn
  Two hundred years or so.

. . . .

"The waves were lapping and slapping
  The same as they are to-day;
And Drake lay dying aboard his ship
  In Nombre Dios Bay.

"The scent of the foreign flowers
  Came floating all around;
'But I'd give my soul for the smell o' the pitch,'
  Says he, 'in Plymouth sound.

" 'What shall I do,' he says,
  'When the guns begin to roar,
An' England wants me, and me not there
  To shatter 'er fores once more?'

"(You've heard what he said, maybe,
  But I'll mark you the p'ints again;
For I want you to box your compass right
  And get my story plain.)

"The Admiral's Ghost." Here is a hero tale, a ghost story, and a famous English legend. But it is difficult to understand in one reading, unless you know something of the background of the story.

England, a small island, has pulled through war after war because of the strength of her navy and her naval heroes. Of all of these, the two who are probably most honored are Sir Francis Drake and Lord Nelson.

In this poem, a story within a story, an old sailor tells

a strange tale. He begins by assuring the listener that there was more to Nelson than met the eye. Nelson may have looked small and "chawed up," with an eye patch and an empty sleeve, but he was far more than he looked. These merely disguised the real man, and the old sailor proposes to explain why the real Nelson was so mighty.

So, he goes back 200 years before Nelson to that other sea hero, Drake, who saved England from the Spanish Armada. The old sailor describes Drake dying on ship-

" 'You must take my drum,' he says,
  'To the old sea-wall at home;
And if ever you strike that drum,' he says,
  'Why, strike me blind, I'll come!

" 'If England needs me, dead
  Or living, I'll rise that day!
I'll rise from the darkness under the sea
  Ten thousand miles away.'

"That's what he said; and he died;
  An' his pirates, listenin' roun'
With their crimson doublets and jewelled
    swords
  That flashed as the sun went down.

"They sewed him up in his shroud
  With a round-shot top and toe,
To sink him under the salt sharp sea
  Where all good seamen go.

"They lowered him down in the deep,
  And there in the sunset light
They boomed a broadside over his grave,
  As meanin' to say 'Good-night.'

"They sailed away in the dark
  To the dear little isle they knew;
And they hung his drum by the old sea-wall
  The same as he told them to.

. . . .

"Two hundred years went by,
  And the guns began to roar,
And England was fighting hard for her life,
  As ever she fought of yore.

" 'It's only my dead that count,'
  She said, as she says to-day;
'It isn't the ships and it isn't the guns
  'Ull sweep Trafalgar's Bay.'

"D'you guess who Nelson was?
  You may laugh, but it's true as true!
There was more in that pore little chawed-up
    chap
  Than ever his best friend knew.

"The foe was creepin' close,
  In the dark, to our white-cliffed isle;
They were ready to leap at England's throat,
  When—O, you may smile, you may smile;

"But—ask of the Devonshire men;
  For they heard in the dead of night
The roll of a drum, and they saw him pass
  On a ship all shining white.

"He stretched out his dead cold face
  And he sailed in the grand old way!
The fishes had taken an eye and his arm,
  But he swept Trafalgar's Bay.

"Nelson—was Francis Drake!
  O, what matters the uniform,
Or the patch on your eye or your pinned-up
    sleeve,
  If your soul's like a North Sea storm?"

board and worrying about what will happen to England when he is gone. He gives his men, from Devonshire like himself, a drum and promises that if Devon men ever strike that drum in time of peril, he will return and fight again for England.

Then, two hundred years later, in Nelson's day the moment of peril came with the foe "creepin' close." In the night the Devonshire men heard Drake's drum and saw a ship pass by with Drake's cold dead face aboard. And Nelson won the battle because, the old sailor thinks, he was more than Nelson, he was Francis Drake too. No patch over the eye, no pinned-up sleeve could disguise his greatness. Drake lived again in Nelson and England was saved.

THE PIED PIPER OF HAMELIN

Robert Browning

Hamelin Town's in Brunswick
By famous Hanover city;
   The river Weser, deep and wide,
Washes its wall on the southern side;
   A pleasanter spot you never spied;
But, when begins my ditty,
   Almost five hundred years ago,
   To see the townsfolk suffer so
     From vermin was a pity.

                      Rats!
They fought the dogs, and killed the cats,
   And bit the babies in the cradles,
And ate the cheeses out of the vats,
   And licked the soup from the cook's own
     ladles,
Split open the kegs of salted sprats,
Made nests inside men's Sunday hats,
And even spoiled the women's chats,
   By drowning their speaking
   With shrieking and squeaking
In fifty different sharps and flats.

   At last the people in a body
   To the Town Hall came flocking:
   " 'Tis clear," cried they, "our Mayor's a noddy;
   And as for our Corporation—shocking
   To think that we buy gowns lined with ermine
   For dolts that can't or won't determine
   What's best to rid us of our vermin!
   You hope, because you're old and obese,
   To find in the furry civic robe ease?
   Rouse up, sirs! Give your brain a racking
   To find the remedy we're lacking,
   Or, sure as fate, we'll send you packing!"
At this the Mayor and Corporation
Quaked with a mighty consternation.

An hour they sat in council,
   At length the Mayor broke silence:
"For a guilder I'd my ermine gown sell;
   I wish I were a mile hence!
It's easy to bid one rack one's brain—
I'm sure my poor head aches again
I've scratched it so, and all in vain,
Oh for a trap, a trap, a trap!"
Just as he said this, what should hap
At the chamber door but a gentle tap?
   "Bless us," cried the Mayor, "what's that?"
(With the Corporation as he sat,
Looking little though wondrous fat;
Nor brighter was his eye, nor moister,
Than a too-long-opened oyster,
Save when at noon his paunch grew mutinous
For a plate of turtle green and glutinous),
"Only a scraping of shoes on the mat?
Anything like the sound of a rat
Makes my heart go pit-a-pat!"

"Come in!"—the Mayor cried, looking bigger:
And in did come the strangest figure.
His queer long coat from heel to head
Was half of yellow and half of red;
And he himself was tall and thin,
With sharp blue eyes, each like a pin,
And light loose hair, yet swarthy skin,
No tuft on cheek nor beard on chin,
But lips where smiles went out and in—
There was no guessing his kith and kin!
And nobody could enough admire
The tall man and his quaint attire.
Quoth one: "It's as my great grandsire,
Starting up at the Trump of Doom's tone,
Had walked this way from his painted tomb-
   stone."

He advanced to the council-table:
And, "Please, your honours," said he, "I'm able,

By means of a secret charm, to draw
All creatures living beneath the sun,
That creep, or swim, or fly, or run,
After me so as you never saw!
And I chiefly use my charm
On creatures that do people harm,
The mole, and toad, and newt, and viper;
And people call me the Pied Piper."
(And here they noticed round his neck
A scarf of red and yellow stripe,
To match with his coat of the selfsame cheque;
And at the scarf's end hung a pipe;
And his fingers, they noticed, were ever straying
As if impatient to be playing
Upon this pipe, as low it dangled
Over his vesture so old-fangled.)
"Yet," said he, "poor piper as I am,
In Tartary I freed the Cham,
Last June, from his huge swarms of gnats;
I eased in Asia the Nizam
Of a monstrous brood of vampire bats:
And, as for what your brain bewilders,
If I can rid your town of rats
Will you give me a thousand guilders?"
"One? fifty thousand!"—was the exclamation
Of the astonished Mayor and Corporation.

Into the street the Piper stept,
    Smiling first a little smile,
As if he knew what magic slept
    In his quiet pipe the while;
Then, like a musical adept,
To blow the pipe his lips he wrinkled,
And green and blue his sharp eyes twinkled
Like a candle-flame where salt is sprinkled;
And ere three shrill notes the pipe uttered,
You heard as if an army muttered;
And the muttering grew to a grumbling;
And the grumbling grew to a mighty rum-
    bling;
And out of the house the rats came tumbling.
Great rats, small rats, lean rats, brawny rats,
Brown rats, black rats, gray rats, tawny rats,
Grave old plodders, gay young friskers,
    Fathers, mothers, uncles, cousins,
Cocking tails and pricking whiskers,
    Families by tens and dozens,
Brothers, sisters, husbands, wives—
Followed the Piper for their lives.
From street to street he piped advancing,

And step by step they followed dancing,
Until they came to the river Weser
Wherein all plunged and perished
—Save one, who, stout as Julius Caesar,
Swam across and lived to carry
(As he the manuscript he cherished)
To Rat-land home his commentary,
Which was, "At the first shrill notes of the
    pipe,
I heard a sound as of scraping tripe,
And putting apples, wondrous ripe,
Into a cider press's gripe;
And a moving away of pickle-tub boards,
And a drawing the corks of train-oil flasks,
And a breaking the hoops of butter casks;
And it seemed as if a voice
(Sweeter far than by harp or by psaltery
Is breathed) called out, Oh, rats! rejoice!
The world is grown to one vast drysaltery!
To munch on, crunch on, take your nuncheon,
Breakfast, supper, dinner, luncheon!
And just as a bulky sugar puncheon,
All ready staved, like a great sun shone
Glorious scarce an inch before me,
Just as methought it said, come, bore me!
—I found the Weser rolling o'er me."

You should have heard the Hamelin people
Ringing the bells till they rocked the steeple.
    "Go," cried the Mayor, "and get long poles!
    Poke out the nests and block up the holes!
    Consult with carpenters and builders,
    And leave in our town not even a trace
    Of the rats!"—when suddenly up the face
    Of the Piper perked in the market-place,
With a, "First, if you please, my thousand
    guilders!"

A thousand guilders! The Mayor looked blue;
So did the Corporation too.
For council dinners made rare havoc
With Claret, Moselle, Vin-de-Grave, Hock;
And half the money would replenish
Their cellar's biggest butt with Rhenish.
To pay this sum to a wandering fellow
With a gipsy coat of red and yellow!
    "Beside," quoth the Mayor, with a knowing
        wink,
    "Our business was done at the river's brink;

We saw with our eyes the vermin sink,
And what's dead can't come to life, I think.
So, friend, we're not the folks to shrink
From the duty of giving you something to
    drink,
And a matter of money to put in your poke,
But, as for the guilders, what we spoke
Of them, as you very well know, was in joke.
Besides, our losses have made us thrifty;
A thousand guilders! Come, take fifty!"

The piper's face fell, and he cried,
"No trifling! I can't wait, beside!
I've promised to visit by dinnertime
Bagdad, and accepted the prime
Of the Head Cook's pottage, all he's rich in,
For having left the Caliph's kitchen,
Of a nest of scorpions no survivor—
With him I proved no bargain-driver,
With you, don't think I'll bate a stiver!
And folks who put me in a passion
May find me pipe to another fashion."

"How?" cried the Mayor, "d'ye think I'll brook
Being worse treated than a Cook?
Insulted by a lazy ribald
With idle pipe and vesture piebald?
You threaten us, fellow? Do your worst,
Blow your pipe there till you burst!"

Once more he stept into the street;
   And to his lips again
Laid his long pipe of smooth straight cane;
   And ere he blew three notes (such sweet
Soft notes as yet musicians cunning
   Never gave the enraptured air),
There was a rustling, that seemed like a bustling
Of merry crowds justling, at pitching and hus-
   tling,
Small feet were pattering, wooden shoes clatter-
   ing,
Little hands clapping, and little tongues chatter-
   ing,
And, like fowls in a farmyard when barley is
   scattering,
Out came the children running.
All the little boys and girls,
With rosy cheeks and flaxen curls,
And sparkling eyes and teeth like pearls,

Tripping and skipping, ran merrily after
The wonderful music with shouting and laughter.

The Mayor was dumb, and the Council stood
As if they were changed into blocks of wood,
Unable to move a step, or cry
To the children merrily skipping by—
And could only follow with the eye
That joyous crowd at the Piper's back.
But how the Mayor was on the rack,
And the wretched Council's bosoms beat,
As the piper turned from the High Street
To where the Weser rolled its waters
Right in the way of their sons and daughters!
However, he turned from South to West,
And to Koppelberg Hill his steps addressed,
And after him the children pressed;
Great was the joy in every breast.
  "He never can cross that mighty top!
   He's forced to let the piping drop
   And we shall see our children stop!"
When lo! As they reached the mountain's side,
A wondrous portal opened wide,
As if a cavern was suddenly hollowed;
And the Piper advanced and the children fol-
   lowed,
And when all were in to the very last,
The door in the mountain-side shut fast.
Did I say all? No! one was lame,
And could not dance the whole of the way;
And in after years, if you would blame
His sadness, he was used to say:
  "It's dull in our town since my playmates left;
   I can't forget that I'm bereft
   Of all the pleasant sights they see,
   Which the Piper also promised me;
   For he led us, he said, to a joyous land,
   Joining the town and just at hand,
Where waters gushed and fruit trees grew,
And flowers put forth a fairer hue,
And everything was strange and new.
The sparrows were brighter than peacocks here,
And their dogs outran our fallow deer,
And honey-bees had lost their stings;
And horses were born with eagle's wings;
And just as I became assured
My lame foot would be speedily cured,
The music stopped, and I stood still,

And found myself outside the Hill,
Left alone against my will,
To go now limping as before,
And never hear of that country more!"

Alas, alas for Hamelin!
 There came into many a burger's pate
 A text which says, that Heaven's Gate
Opes to the Rich at as easy rate
As the needle's eye takes a camel in!
The Mayor sent East, West, North and South,
To offer the Piper by word of mouth,
 Wherever it was men's lot to find him,
Silver and gold to his heart's content,
If he'd only return the way he went,
 And bring the children all behind him.
But when they saw 'twas a lost endeavour,
And Piper and dancers were gone forever
They made a decree that lawyers never
 Should think their records dated duly
If, after the day of the month and year,
These words did not as well appear,
 "And so long after what happened here
 On the twenty-second of July,
 Thirteen hundred and seventy-six:"
And the better in memory to fix
The place of the Children's last retreat,
They called it, the Pied Piper's street—
Where anyone playing on pipe or tabor,
Was sure for the future to lose his labour.
Nor suffered they hostelry or tavern
To shock with mirth a street so solemn;
But opposite the place of the cavern
 They wrote the story on a column,
And on the great church window painted
The same, to make the world acquainted
How their children were stolen away;
And there it stands to this very day.
And I must not omit to say
That in Transylvania there's a tribe
Of alien people that ascribe
The outlandish ways and dress,
On which their neighbours lay such stress,
To their fathers and mothers having risen
Out of some subterraneous prison,
Into which they were trepanned
Long time ago in a mighty band
Out of Hamelin town in Brunswick land,
But how or why they don't understand.

Robert Browning

I sprang to the stirrup, and Joris, and he;
I galloped, Dirck galloped, we galloped all three;
"Good speed!" cried the watch, as the gatebolts
 undrew;
"Speed!" echoed the wall to us galloping
 through;
Behind shut the postern, the lights sank to rest,
And into the midnight we galloped abreast.

Not a word to each other; we kept the great pace
Neck by neck, stride by stride, never changing
 our place;
I turned in my saddle and made its girths tight,
Then shortened each stirrup, and set the pique
 right,
Rebuckled the cheek-strap, chained slacker the
 bit,
Nor galloped less steadily Roland a whit.

'Twas moonset at starting; but while we drew
 near
Lokeren, the cocks crew and twilight dawned
 clear;
At Boom, a great yellow star came out to see;
At Düffeld, 'twas morning as plain as could be;
And from Mecheln church-steeple we heard the
 half-chime,
So Joris broke silence with, "Yet there is time!"

At Aershot, up leaped of a sudden the sun,
And against him the cattle stood black every one,
To stare through the mist at us galloping past,
And I saw my stout galloper Roland at last,
With resolute shoulders, each butting away
The haze, as some bluff river headland its spray;

And his low head and crest, just one sharp ear
 bent back
For my voice, and the other pricked out on his
 track;

"How They Brought the Good News from Ghent to
Aix." *A good rider, a great horse, and an exciting story
told with a galloping rhythm that sets the reader galloping
too—inside himself!*

And one eye's black intelligence—ever that
    glance
O'er its white edge at me, his own master,
    askance!
And the thick heavy spume-flakes which aye and
    anon
His fierce lips shook upwards in galloping on.

By Hasselt, Dirck groaned; and cried Joris, "Stay
    spur!
Your Roos galloped bravely, the fault's not in
    her,
We'll remember at Aix"—for one heard the
    quick wheeze
Of her chest, saw the stretched neck and stagger-
    ing knees,
And sunk tail, and horrible heave of the flank,
As down on her haunches she shuddered and
    sank.

So we were left galloping, Joris and I,
Past Looz and past Tongres, no cloud in the sky;
The broad sun above laughed a pitiless laugh,
'Neath our feet broke the brittle bright stubble
    like chaff;
Till over by Dalhem a dome-spire sprang white,
And "Gallop," gasped Joris, "for Aix is in sight!"

"How they'll greet us!"—and all in a moment his
    roan
Rolled neck and croup over, lay dead as a stone;
And there was my Roland to bear the whole
    weight
Of the news which alone could save Aix from her
    fate,
With his nostrils like pits full of blood to the
    brim,
And with circles of red for his eye-sockets' rim.

Then I cast loose my buffcoat, each holster let
    fall,
Shook off both my jack-boots, let go belt and all,
Stood up in the stirrup, leaned, patted his ear,
Called my Roland his pet-name, my horse with-
    out peer;
Clapped my hands, laughed and sang, any noise,
    bad or good,
Till at length into Aix Roland galloped and
    stood.

And all I remember is—friends flocking round
As I sat with his head 'twixt my knees on the
    ground;
And no voice but was praising this Roland of
    mine,
As I poured down his throat our last measure of
    wine,
Which (the burgesses voted by common consent)
Was no more than his due who brought good
    news from Ghent.

A LADY COMES TO AN INN
Elizabeth Coatsworth

Three strange men came to the Inn.
One was a black man, pocked and thin,
one was brown with a silver knife,
and one brought with him a beautiful wife.

That lovely woman had hair as pale
as French champagne or finest ale,
that lovely woman was long and slim
as a young white birch or a maple limb.

Her face was like cream, her mouth was a rose,
what language she spoke nobody knows,
but sometimes she'd scream like a cockatoo
and swear wonderful oaths that nobody knew.

Her great silk skirts like a silver bell
down to her little bronze slippers fell,
and her low-cut gown showed a dove on its nest
in blue tattooing across her breast.

Nobody learned the lady's name,
nor the marvelous land from which they came,
but still they tell through the countryside
the tale of those men and that beautiful bride.

THE GOATHERD
Grace Hazard Conkling

One day there reached me from the street
The sound of little trampling feet:
And through the dust and sunlight, I
Saw 'most a thousand goats go by.

The goatherd followed close behind:
He looked quite undisturbed and kind,
And Pablo said he knew him well,
And called him Señor Manuel.

His jacket was a shaggy skin,
And scarlet figures woven in
His blue zarape, made it gay
As though for a fiesta day.

His black eyes twinkled in the shade
That his broad-brimmed sombrero made:
And all his teeth were shiny bright
Like Mother's porcelain, and as white.

Before he went he took a drink
Of something very good, I think,
For he held up the gourd he wore
To Pablo's lips—then drank some more.

I told him there had seemed to be
At least a thousand goats, and he
Just laughed and said—to make a guess—
There *were* a thousand, more or less!

NEW MEXICO

Polly Chase Boyden

Out West is windy
And Out West is wide.
I pass villages of prairie dogs
On every horseback ride.

    I pass jack rabbits and sunsets
    And pueblo Indians,
    And Mexicans in great big hats,
    And they are all my friends.

But when the moon comes sliding
And sagebrush turns to foam,
Then outdoors is Out West,
But indoors is Home.

NOONDAY SUN

Kathryn and Byron Jackson

Oh, I've ridden plenty of horses
    And I've broken a score in my time,
But there never was one
    Like the colt Noonday Sun—
Now there was a horse that was prime!
    Oh, yippi ippi ai—Oh, yippi ippi ay,
Now there was a horse that was prime!

She'd run up the side of a mountain
    Or she'd tackle a wildcat alone.
Oh, she stood twelve hands high
    And her proud shining eye
Would soften the heart of a stone.
    Oh, yippi ippi ai—Oh, yippi ippi ay,
Would soften the heart of a stone.

She'd splash through a treach'rous river,
    Or she'd tease for an apple or sweet,
She'd buck and she'd prance,
    Or she'd do a square dance
On her four little white little feet.
    Oh, yippi ippi ai—Oh, yippi ippi ay,
On her four little white little feet.

But one night the rustlers stole her,
    They stole her and took her away.
Now the sun never shines,
    And the wind in the pines
Says, "You've lost your colt, lack-a-day!"
    Oh, yippi ippi ai—Oh, yippi ippi ay,
Says, "You've lost your colt, lack-a-day!"

Someday I'll ride through the prairie.
    Someday I'll pull out my gun,
And I'll plug him—bang-bang!—
    And I may even hang—
The outlaw who stole Noonday Sun.
    Oh, yippi ippi ai—Oh, yippi ippi ay,
The outlaw that stole Noonday Sun.

Oh, I still have her bridle and saddle,
   And I still have her bare empty stall
But there'll never be one
   Like the colt Noonday Sun,
And she'll never more come to my call!
   Oh, yippi ippi ai—Oh, yippi ippi ay,
And she'll never more come to my call!

WHOOPEE TI YI YO, GIT ALONG LITTLE DOGIES

(Unknown)

As I walked out one morning for pleasure,
I spied a cow-puncher all riding alone;
His hat was throwed back and his spurs was a-
   jingling,
And he approached me a-singin' this song,

   Whoopee ti yi yo, git along little dogies,
   It's your misfortune, and none of my own.
   Whoopee ti yi yo, git along little dogies,
   For you know Wyoming will be your new
      home.

Early in the spring we round up the dogies,
Mark and brand and bob off their tails;
Round up our horses, load up the chuck-wagon,
Then throw the dogies upon the trail.

It's whooping and yelling and driving the dogies;
Oh how I wish you would go on;
It's whooping and punching and go on little
   dogies,
For you know Wyoming will be your new home.

Some boys goes up the trail for pleasure,
But that's where you get it most awfully wrong:
For you haven't any idea the trouble they give us
While we go driving them along.

When the night comes on and we hold them on
   the bedground,
These little dogies that roll on so slow;
Roll up the herd and cut out the strays,
And roll the little dogies that never rolled before.

Your mother she was raised way down in Texas,
Where the jimson weed and sand-burrs grow;
Now we'll fill you up on prickly pear and cholla
Till you are ready for the trail to Idaho.

Oh, you'll be soup for Uncle Sam's Injuns;
"It's beef, heap beef," I hear them cry.
Git along, git along, git along little dogies,
You're going to be beef steers by and by.

OPEN RANGE

Kathryn and Byron Jackson

   Prairie goes to the mountain,
      Mountain goes to the sky.
   The sky sweeps across to the distant hills
   And here, in the middle,
      Am I.

   Hills crowd down to the river,
      River runs by the tree.
   Tree throws its shadow on sunburnt grass
   And here, in the shadow,
      Is me.

   Shadows creep up the mountain,
      Mountain goes black on the sky,
   The sky bursts out with a million stars
   And here, by the campfire,
      Am I.

THE COWBOY'S LIFE

Attributed to James Barton Adams

The bawl of a steer,
To a cowboy's ear,
Is music of sweetest strain;
And the yelping notes
Of the gay coyotes
To him are a glad refrain.

For a kingly crown
In the noisy town
His saddle he wouldn't change;
No life so free
As the life we see
Way out on the Yaso range.

The rapid beat
Of his broncho's feet
On the sod as he speeds along,
Keeps living time
To the ringing rhyme
Of his rollicking cowboy song.

The winds may blow
And the thunder growl
Or the breezes may safely moan;—
A cowboy's life
Is a royal life,
His saddle his kingly throne.

A SONG OF GREATNESS

Mary Austin

When I hear the old men
Telling of heroes,
Telling of great deeds
Of ancient days,

When I hear that telling
Then I think within me
I too am one of these.

When I hear the people
Praising great ones,
Then I know that I too
Shall be esteemed,
I too when my time comes
Shall do mightily.

INDIAN CHILDREN

Annette Wynne

Where we walk to school each day
Indian children used to play—
All about our native land,
Where the shops and houses stand.

And the trees were very tall,
And there were no streets at all,
Not a church and not a steeple—
Only woods and Indian people.

Only wigwams on the ground,
And at night bears prowling round—
What a different place to-day
Where we live and work and play!

COTTONWOOD LEAVES

Badger Clark

Red firelight on the Sioux tepees,
  (Oh, the camp-smoke down the wind!)
Red firelight on the cottonwood trees
That clap, clap, clap in the dry night breeze.
  (Oh, the camp-smoke down the wind!)

Red-skinned braves in the circling dance;
  (Oh, the bright sparks toward the stars!)
The moccasined feet that stamp and prance
And the brandished knife and the lifted lance.
  (Oh, the bright sparks toward the stars!)

Eagle plumes in the swirling troop,
　(Oh, the wild flame leaping high!)
And the painted bodies ramp and stoop
To the drum's hot thump and the vaunting
　　whoop.
　(Oh, the wild flame leaping high!)

Back where the darkness drops its veil
　(Oh, the sad smoke drifting low!)
The far wolves howl and the widows wail
For the graveless dead on the grim war trail.
　(Oh, the sad smoke drifting low!)

Night on the plains, and the dreams it weaves,
　(Oh, the embers black and cold!)
Where painted ghosts with the step of thieves
Dance to the clap of the cottonwood leaves.
　(Oh, the embers black and cold!)

HIAWATHA'S CHILDHOOD

Henry Wadsworth Longfellow

By the shores of Gitche Gumee,
By the shining Big-Sea-Water,
Stood the wigwam of Nokomis,
Daughter of the Moon, Nokomis.
Dark behind it rose the forest,
Rose the black and gloomy pine-trees,
Rose the firs with cones upon them;
Bright before it beat the water,
Beat the clear and sunny water,
Beat the shining Big-Sea-Water.
　There the wrinkled, old Nokomis
Nursed the little Hiawatha,
Rocked him in his linden cradle,
Bedded soft in moss and rushes,
Safely bound with reindeer sinews;
Stilled his fretful wail by saying,
"Hush! the Naked Bear will hear thee!"
Lulled him into slumber, singing,
"Ewa-yea! my little owlet!
Who is this, that lights the wigwam?
With his great eyes lights the wigwam?
Ewa-yea! my little owlet!"
　Many things Nokomis taught him
Of the stars that shine in heaven;
Showed him Ishkoodah, the comet,
Ishkoodah, with fiery tresses;

Showed the Death-Dance of the spirits,
Warriors with their plumes and war-clubs,
Flaring far away to northward
In the frosty nights of Winter;
Showed the broad, white road in heaven,
Pathway of the ghosts, the shadows,
Running straight across the heavens,
Crowded with the ghosts, the shadows.
　At the door on summer evenings
Sat the little Hiawatha;
Heard the whispering of the pine-trees,
Heard the lapping of the water,
Sounds of music, words of wonder;
"Minne-wawa!" said the pine-trees,
"Mudway-aushka!" said the water.
　Saw the fire-fly, Wah-wah-taysee,
Flitting through the dusk of evening,
With the twinkle of its candle
Lighting up the brakes and bushes,
And he sang the song of children,
Sang the song Nokomis taught him:
"Wah-wah-taysee, little fire-fly,
Little, flitting, white-fire insect,
Little, dancing, white-fire creature,
Light me with your little candle,
Ere upon my bed I lay me,
Ere in sleep I close my eyelids!"
　Saw the moon rise from the water,
Rippling, rounding from the water,
Saw the flecks and shadows on it,
Whispered, "What is that, Nokomis?"
And the good Nokomis answered:
　"Once a warrior, very angry,
Seized his grandmother, and threw her
Up into the sky at midnight;
Right against the moon he threw her;
'T is her body that you see there."
　Saw the rainbow in the heaven,
In the eastern sky, the rainbow,
Whispered, "What is that, Nokomis?"
And the good Nokomis answered:
　" 'T is the heaven of flowers you see there;
All the wild flowers of the forest,
All the lilies of the prairie,
When on earth they fade and perish,
Blossom in that heaven above us."
　When he heard the owls at midnight,
Hooting, laughing in the forest,
"What is that?" he cried in terror;
"What is that?" he said, "Nokomis?"

And the good Nokomis answered:
"That is but the owl and owlet,
Talking in their native language,
Talking, scolding at each other."
    Then the little Hiawatha
Learned of every bird its language,
Learned their names and all their secrets,
How they built their nests in Summer,
Where they hid themselves in Winter,
Talked with them whene'er he met them,
Called them "Hiawatha's Chickens."
    Of all beasts he learned the language,
Learned their names and all their secrets,
How the beavers built their lodges,
Where the squirrels hid their acorns,
How the reindeer ran so swiftly,
Why the rabbit was so timid,
Talked with them whene'er he met them,
Called them "Hiawatha's Brothers."

THE PIONEER

Arthur Guiterman

Long years ago I blazed a trail
    Through lovely woods unknown till then
And marked with cairns of splintered shale
    A mountain way for other men;

For other men who came and came:
    They trod the path more plain to see,
They gave my trail another's name
    And no one speaks or knows of me.

The trail runs high, the trail runs low
    Where windflowers dance or columbine;
The scars are healed that long ago
    My ax cut deep on birch and pine.

Another's name my trail may bear,
    But still I keep, in waste and wood,
My joy because the trail is there,
    My peace because the trail is good.

BUFFALO DUSK

Carl Sandburg

The buffaloes are gone.
And those who saw the buffaloes are gone.
Those who saw the buffaloes by thousands and
    how they pawed the prairie sod into dust
    with their hoofs, their great heads down
    pawing on in a great pageant of dusk,
Those who saw the buffaloes are gone.
And the buffaloes are gone.

THE GOOD JOAN

Lizette Woodworth Reese

Along the thousand roads of France,
Now there, now here, swift as a glance,
A cloud, a mist blown down the sky,
Good Joan of Arc goes riding by.

In Domremy at candlelight,
The orchards blowing rose and white
About the shadowy houses lie;
And Joan of Arc goes riding by.

On Avignon there falls a hush,
Brief as the singing of a thrush
Across old gardens April-high;
And Joan of Arc goes riding by.

The women bring the apples in,
Round Arles when the long gusts begin,

"The Pioneer," Taken from *I Sing the Pioneer*, by Arthur Guiterman, published and copyright, 1926, by E. P. Dutton & Co., Inc., New York

"Buffalo Dusk." *A great period in American history passed with the passing of the buffalo. The West was no longer frontier but settlements.* From *Early Moon* by Carl Sandburg, copyright, 1930, by Harcourt, Brace and Company, Inc.

"The Good Joan." From *Spicewood* by Lizette Woodworth Reese. The Norman, Remington Co., Baltimore, 1920

Then sit them down to sob and cry;
And Joan of Arc goes riding by.

Dim fall the hoofs down old Calais;
In Tours a flash of silver-gray,
Like flaw of rain in a clear sky;
And Joan of Arc goes riding by.

Who saith that ancient France shall fail,
A rotting leaf driv'n down the gale?
Then her sons knew not how to die;
Then good God dwells no more on high,

Tours, Arles, and Domremy reply!
For Joan of Arc goes riding by.

COLUMBUS
Annette Wynne

An Italian boy that liked to play
In Genoa about the ships all day,
With curly head and dark, dark eyes,
That gazed at earth in child surprise;
And dreamed of distant stranger skies.

He watched the ships that came crowding in
With cargo of riches; he loved the din
Of the glad rush out and the spreading sails
And the echo of far-off windy gales.

He studied the books of the olden day;
He studied but knew far more than they;
He talked to the learned men of the school—
So wise he was they thought him a fool,
A fool with the dark, dark, dreamful eyes,
A child he was—grown wonder-wise.

Youth and dreams are over past
And out, far out he is sailing fast
Toward the seas he dreamed;—strange lands
    arise—
The world is made rich by his great emprise—
And the wisest know he was more than wise.

COLUMBUS
Joaquin Miller

Behind him lay the gray Azores,
    Behind the Gates of Hercules;
Before him not the ghost of shores,
    Before him only shoreless seas.
The good mate said: "Now must we pray,
    For lo! the very stars are gone.
Brave Admiral, speak, what shall I say?"
    "Why, say 'Sail on! sail on! and on!' "

"My men grow mutinous day by day;
    My men grow ghastly wan and weak."
The stout mate thought of home; a spray
    Of salt wave washed his swarthy cheek.
"What shall I say, brave Admiral, say,
    If we sight naught but seas at dawn?"
"Why, you shall say at break of day,
    'Sail on! sail on! sail on! and on!' "

They sailed and sailed, as winds might blow,
    Until at last the blanched mate said,
"Why, now not even God would know
    Should I and all my men fall dead.
These very winds forget their way,
    For God from these dread seas is gone.
Now speak, brave Admiral, speak and say"—
    He said: "Sail on! sail on! and on!"

They sailed. They sailed. Then spake the
    mate:
    "This mad sea shows his teeth tonight.
He curls his lip, he lies in wait,
    With lifted teeth, as if to bite!
Brave Admiral, say but one good word:
    What shall we do when hope is gone?"
The words leapt like a leaping sword:
    "Sail on! sail on! sail on! and on!"

Then, pale and worn, he kept his deck,
    And peered through darkness. Ah, that
    night
Of all dark nights! And then a speck—
    A light! a light! a light! a light!

It grew, a starlit flag unfurled!
  It grew to be Time's burst of dawn.
He gained a world; he gave that world
  Its grandest lesson: "On! sail on!"

ATLANTIC CHARTER, A.D. 1620–1942

Francis Brett Young

What are you carrying Pilgrims, Pilgrims?
What did you carry beyond the sea?
  We carried the Book, we carried the Sword,
  A steadfast heart in the fear of the Lord,
  And a living faith in His plighted word
  That all men should be free.

What were your memories, Pilgrims, Pilgrims?
What of the dreams you bore away?
  We carried the songs our fathers sung
  By the hearths of home when they were young,
  And the comely words of the mother-tongue
  In which they learnt to pray.

What did you find there, Pilgrims, Pilgrims?
What did you find beyond the waves?
  A stubborn land and a barren shore,
  Hunger and want and sickness sore:
  All these we found and gladly bore
  Rather than be slaves.

How did you fare there, Pilgrims, Pilgrims?
What did you build in that stubborn land?
  We felled the forest and tilled the sod
  Of a continent no man had trod
  And we established there, in the Grace of God,
  The rights whereby we stand.

What are you bringing us, Pilgrims, Pilgrims?
Bringing us back in this bitter day?
  The selfsame things we carried away:
  The Book, the Sword,
  The fear of the Lord,
  And the boons our fathers dearly bought:
  Freedom of Worship, Speech and Thought,
  Freedom from Want, Freedom from Fear,
  The liberties we hold most dear,
  And who shall say us Nay?

"Atlantic Charter, A.D. 1620–1942." From *The Island.*
Copyright 1946 by Francis Brett Young

THE LANDING OF THE PILGRIM FATHERS

(NOVEMBER 19, 1620)

Felicia Dorothea Hemans

The breaking waves dashed high
  On a stern and rock-bound coast,
And the woods, against a stormy sky,
  Their giant branches tossed;

And the heavy night hung dark
  The hills and waters o'er,
When a band of exiles moored their bark
  On the wild New England shore.

Not as the conquerer comes,
  They, the true-hearted came:
Not with the roll of the stirring drums,
  And the trumpet that sings of fame;

Not as the flying come,
  In silence and in fear,—
They shook the depths of the desert's gloom
  With their hymns of lofty cheer.

Amidst the storm they sang,
  And the stars heard, and the sea;
And the sounding aisles of the dim woods rang
  To the anthem of the free!

The ocean-eagle soared
  From his nest by the white waves' foam,
And the rocking pines of the forest roared;
  This was their welcome home!

There were men with hoary hair
  Amidst that pilgrim-band;
Why had they come to wither there,
  Away from their childhood's land?

There was woman's fearless eye,
  Lit by her deep love's truth;
There was manhood's brow, serenely high,
  And the fiery heart of youth.

What sought they thus afar?
  Bright jewels of the mine?
The wealth of seas, the spoils of war?—
  They sought a faith's pure shrine!

Aye, call it holy ground,
  The soil where first they trod!
They have left unstained what there they
    found—
  Freedom to worship God!

PAUL REVERE'S RIDE

Henry Wadsworth Longfellow

Listen, my children, and you shall hear
Of the midnight ride of Paul Revere,
On the eighteenth of April, in seventy-five;
Hardly a man is now alive
Who remembers that famous day and year.
He said to his friend, "If the British march
By land or sea from the town tonight,
Hang a lantern aloft in the belfry arch
Of the North Church tower as a signal light,—
One, if by land, and two, if by sea;
And I on the opposite shore will be,
Ready to ride and spread the alarm
Through every Middlesex village and farm,
For the country folk to be up and to arm."

Then he said, "Good Night!" and with muffled
    oar
Silently rowed to the Charleston shore,
Just as the moon rose over the bay,
Where swinging wide at her moorings lay
The *Somerset,* British man-of-war;
A phantom ship, with each mast and spar
Across the moon like a prison bar,
And a huge black hulk, that was magnified
By its own reflection in the tide.

Meanwhile, his friend, through alley and street,
Wanders and watches with eager ears,
Till in the silence around him he hears
The muster of men at the barrack door,
The sound of arms, and the tramp of feet,
And the measured tread of the grenadiers,
Marching down to their boats on the shore.

Then he climbed the tower of the Old North
    Church
By the wooden stairs, with stealthy tread,
To the belfry-chamber overhead,
And startled the pigeons from their perch
On the somber rafters, that round him made
Masses and moving shapes of shade,—
By the trembling ladder, steep and tall,
To the highest window in the wall,
Where he paused to listen and look down
A moment on the roofs of the town,
And the moonlight flowing over all.

Beneath in the churchyard, lay the dead,
In their night-encampment on the hill,
Wrapped in silence so deep and still
That he could hear, like a sentinel's tread,
The watchful night-wind, as it went
Creeping along from tent to tent,
And seeming to whisper, "All is Well!"
A moment only he feels the spell
Of the place and the hour, and the secret dread
Of the lonely belfry and the dead;
For suddenly all his thoughts are bent
On a shadowy something far away,
Where the river widens to meet the bay,—
A line of black that bends and floats
On the rising tide, like a bridge of boats.

Meanwhile, impatient to mount and ride,
Booted and spurred, with a heavy stride
On the opposite shore walked Paul Revere.
Now he patted his horse's side,
Now gazed at the landscape far and near,
Then, impetuous, stamped the earth,
And turned and tightened his saddle-girth;
But mostly he watched with eager search
The belfry-tower of the Old North Church,
As it rose above the graves on the hill,
Lonely and spectral and somber and still.
And lo! as he looks, on the belfry's height
A glimmer, and then a gleam of light!
He springs to the saddle, the bridle he turns,
But lingers and gazes, till full on his sight
A second lamp in the belfry burns!

A hurry of hoofs in a village street,
A shape in the moonlight, a bulk in the dark,
And beneath, from the pebbles, in passing, a
    spark
Struck out by a steed flying fearless and fleet:
That was all! And yet, through the gloom and
    the light,
The fate of a nation was riding that night;
And the spark struck out by that steed, in his
    flight
Kindled the land into flame with its heat.
He has left the village and mounted the steep,
And beneath him, tranquil and broad and deep,
Is the Mystic, meeting the ocean tides;
And under the alders that skirt its edge,
Now soft on the sand, now loud on the ledge,
Is heard the tramp of his steed as he rides.

It was twelve by the village clock,
When he crossed the bridge into Medford town.
He heard the crowing of the cock,
And the barking of the farmer's dog,
And felt the damp of the river fog,
That rises after the sun goes down.
It was one by the village clock,
When he galloped into Lexington.
He saw the gilded weathercock
Swim in the moonlight as he passed.
And the meeting-house windows, blank and bare,
Gaze at him with a spectral glare,
As if they already stood aghast
At the bloody work they would look upon.

It was two by the village clock,
When he came to the bridge in Concord town.
He heard the bleating of the flock,
And the twitter of birds among the trees,
And felt the breath of the morning breeze
Blowing over the meadows brown.
And one was safe and asleep in his bed
Who at the bridge would be first to fall,
Who that day would be lying dead,
Pierced by a British musket-ball.

You know the rest. In the books you have read,
How the British Regulars fired and fled,—
How the farmers gave them ball for ball,
From behind each fence and farmyard wall,
Chasing the red-coats down the lane,
Then crossing the fields to emerge again
Under the trees at the turn of the road,
And only pausing to fire and load.

So through the night rode Paul Revere;
And so through the night went his cry of alarm
To every Middlesex village and farm,—
A cry of defiance and not of fear,
A voice in the darkness, a knock at the door,
And a word that shall echo forevermore!
For, borne on the night-wind of the Past,
Through all our history, to the last,
In the hour of darkness and peril and need,
The people will waken and listen to hear
The hurrying hoof-beats of that steed,
And the midnight message of Paul Revere.

"A Ballad of Johnny Appleseed." Helmer O. Oleson. In *Story Parade*, November 1952. Copyright 1952 by Story Parade, Inc. Reprinted by permission

BALLAD OF JOHNNY APPLESEED
Helmer O. Oleson

Through the Appalachian valleys, with his kit
    a buckskin bag,
Johnny Appleseed went plodding past high peak
    and mountain crag.
Oh, his stockings were of leather, and his moc-
    casins were tough;
He was set upon a journey where the going
    would be rough.
        See him coming in the springtime,
        Passing violets in the glade.
        Many apple trees are needed,
        And the pioneers want shade.
Johnny carried many orchards in the bag upon
    his back,
And the scent of apple blossoms always lingered
    in his track.
Over half a fertile continent he planted shiny
    seed;
He would toss them in the clearings where the
    fawn and yearling feed.
        In the summer see him tramping
        Through the windings of the wood.
        Big red apples in the oven
        Make the venison taste good.
He would wander over mountain; he would
    brave a raging stream,
For his eyes were filled with visions like an an-
    cient prophet's dream.
He would travel after nightfall, start again at
    early morn;
He was planting seeds of apples for the children
    yet unborn.
    Where the autumn leaves turned crimson,
    He was eager to explore.
    Apple dumplings never blossomed
    On a shady sycamore.
Johnny traveled where the war whoop of the
    painted tribes rang loud;
And he walked among grim chieftains and their
    hot-eyed warrior crowd.
He told them of his vision, of his dream that
    would not die,
So he never was molested, and the settlers had
    their pie.
        Bitter winter found him trudging,
        Not for glory or applause,
        Only happy for the winesaps
        In tomorrow's applesauce!

WASHINGTON

Nancy Byrd Turner

He played by the river when he was young,
He raced with rabbits along the hills,
He fished for minnows, and climbed and swung,
And hooted back at the whippoorwills.
Strong and slender and tall he grew—
And then, one morning, the bugles blew.

Over the hills the summons came,
Over the river's shining rim.
He said that the bugles called his name,
He knew that his country needed him,
And he answered, "Coming!" and marched away
For many a night and many a day.

Perhaps when the marches were hot and long
He'd think of the river flowing by
Or, camping under the winter sky,
Would hear the whippoorwill's far-off song.
Working or playing, in peace or strife,
He loved America all his life!

THOMAS JEFFERSON
1743–1826

Rosemary Carr and
Stephen Vincent Benét

Thomas Jefferson,
What do you say
Under the gravestone
Hidden away?

"I was a giver,
I was a molder,
I was a builder
With a strong shoulder."

Six feet and over,
Large-boned and ruddy,
The eyes grey-hazel
But bright with study.

The big hands clever
With pen and fiddle
And ready, ever,
For any riddle.

From buying empires
To planting 'taters,
From Declarations
To trick dumb-waiters.

"I liked the people,
The sweat and crowd of them,
Trusted them always
And spoke aloud of them.

"I liked all learning
And wished to share it
Abroad like pollen
For all who merit.

"I liked fine houses
With Greek pilasters,
And built them surely,
My touch a master's.

"I liked queer gadgets
And secret shelves,
And helping nations
To rule themselves.

"Jealous of others?
Not always candid?

"Washington." From *Child Life*, February 1930. Child Life, Inc., Boston. Used by permission of the author
"Thomas Jefferson 1743–1826." *The four poems by the Benéts are remarkable bits of portraiture. You actually catch more of the real man (or woman) from these verses than you do from many a page of history. Turn to the whole Book of Americans for others equally good.* From *A Book of Americans*, published by Rinehart & Company, Inc. Copyright, 1933, by Rosemary Carr and Stephen Vincent Benét

But huge of vision
And open-handed.

"A wild-goose-chaser?
Now and again,
Build Monticello,
You little men!

"Design my plow, sirs,
They use it still,
Or found my college
At Charlottesville.

"And still go questing
New things and thinkers,
And keep as busy
As twenty tinkers.

"While always guarding
The people's freedom—
You need more hands, sir?
I didn't need 'em.

"They call you rascal?
They called me worse,
You'd do grand things, sir,
But lack the purse?

"I got no riches.
I died a debtor.
I died free-hearted
And that was better.

"For life was freakish
But life was fervent,
And I was always
Life's willing servant.

"Life, life's too weighty?
Too long a haul, sir?
I lived past eighty.
I liked it all, sir."

"Benjamin Franklin 1706–1790." From *A Book of Americans*, published by Rinehart & Company, Inc. Copyright, 1933, by Rosemary Carr and Stephen Vincent Benét

BENJAMIN FRANKLIN
1706–1790

Rosemary Carr and
Stephen Vincent Benét

Ben Franklin munched a loaf of bread while walking down the street
And all the Philadelphia girls tee-heed to see him eat,
A country boy come up to town with eyes as big as saucers
At the ladies in their furbelows, the gempmum on their horses.

Ben Franklin wrote an almanac, a smile upon his lip,
It told you when to plant your corn and how to cure the pip,
But he salted it and seasoned it with proverbs sly and sage,
And people read "Poor Richard" till Poor Richard was the rage.

Ben Franklin made a pretty kite and flew it in the air
To call upon a thunderstorm that happened to be there,
—And all our humming dynamos and our electric light
Go back to what Ben Franklin found the day he flew his kite.

Ben Franklin was the sort of man that people like to see,
For he was very clever but as human as could be.
He had an eye for pretty girls, a palate for good wine,
And all the court of France were glad to ask him in to dine.

But it didn't make him stuffy and he wasn't spoiled by fame
But stayed Ben Franklin to the end, as Yankee as his name.

"Nancy Hanks 1784–1818." From *A Book of Americans*, published by Rinehart & Company, Inc. Copyright, 1933, by Rosemary Carr and Stephen Vincent Benét

"He wrenched their might from tyrants and its
   lightning from the sky."
And oh, when he saw pretty girls, he had a taking eye!

NANCY HANKS
1784–1818

*Rosemary Carr and
Stephen Vincent Benét*

If Nancy Hanks
Came back as a ghost,
Seeking news
Of what she loved most,
She'd ask first
"Where's my son?
What's happened to Abe?
What's he done?"

"Poor little Abe,
Left all alone
Except for Tom,
Who's a rolling stone;
He was only nine
The year I died.
I remember still
How hard he cried.

"Scraping along
In a little shack,
With hardly a shirt
To cover his back,
And a prairie wind
To blow him down,
Or pinching times
If he went to town.

"You wouldn't know
About my son?
Did he grow tall?
Did he have fun?
Did he learn to read?
Did he get to town?
Do you know his name?
Did he get on?"

"A Reply to Nancy Hanks." From *Children and Books*.
Scott, Foresman and Company, Chicago, 1957
   "I Saw a Ghost." From *Children and Books*. Scott,

A REPLY TO NANCY HANKS
Julius Silberger

Yes, Nancy Hanks,
The news we will tell
Of your Abe
Whom you loved so well.
You asked first,
"Where's my son?"
He lives in the heart
Of everyone.

I SAW A GHOST
Joan Boilleau

As twilight fell
O'er the river's banks,
I saw the ghost
Of Nancy Hanks
Floating in mist
O'er the river's banks.

I told the ghost
Of Nancy Hanks
Floating in mist
O'er the river's banks,
How Abe saved our nation
And kept it one,
How slaves were made free
By a great man; her son.

As moonlight fell
O'er the river's banks,
The smiling ghost
Of Nancy Hanks
Faded in mist
O'er the river's banks.

LINCOLN
Nancy Byrd Turner

There was a boy of other days,
A quiet, awkward, earnest lad,
Who trudged long weary miles to get
A book on which his heart was set—
And then no candle had!

Foresman and Company, Chicago, 1957
   "Lincoln." From *Child Life*, February 1929. Child Life,
Inc., Boston. Used by permission of the author

He was too poor to buy a lamp
But very wise in woodmen's ways.
He gathered seasoned bough and stem,
And crisping leaf, and kindled them
Into a ruddy blaze.

Then as he lay full length and read,
The firelight flickered on his face,
And etched his shadow on the gloom.
And made a picture in the room,
In that most humble place.

The hard years came, the hard years went,
But, gentle, brave, and strong of will,
He met them all. And when to-day
We see his pictured face, we say,
"There's light upon it still."

ABRAHAM LINCOLN

Mildred Plew Meigs

Remember he was poor and country-bred;
  His face was lined; he walked with awkward
    gait.
Smart people laughed at him sometimes and
    said,
  "How can so very plain a man be great?"

Remember he was humble, used to toil.
  Strong arms he had to build a shack, a fence,
Long legs to tramp the woods, to plow the soil,
  A head chuck full of backwoods common
    sense.

Remember all he ever had he earned.
  He walked in time through stately White
    House doors;
But all he knew of men and life he learned
  In little backwoods cabins, country stores.

Remember that his eyes could light with fun;
  That wisdom, courage, set his name apart;
But when the rest is duly said and done,
  Remember that men loved him for his heart.

ABRAHAM LINCOLN
1809–1865

Rosemary Carr and
Stephen Vincent Benét

Lincoln was a long man.
He liked out of doors.
He liked the wind blowing
And the talk in country stores.

He liked telling stories,
He liked telling jokes.
"Abe's quite a character,"
Said quite a lot of folks.

Lots of folks in Springfield
Saw him every day,
Walking down the street
In his gaunt, long way.

Shawl around his shoulders,
Letters in his hat.
"That's Abe Lincoln."
They thought no more than that.

Knew that he was honest,
Guessed that he was odd,

Knew he had a cross wife
Though she was a Todd.

Knew he had three little boys
Who liked to shout and play,
Knew he had a lot of debts
It took him years to pay.

Knew his clothes and knew his house.
"That's his office, here.
Blame good lawyer, on the whole,
Though he's sort of queer.

"Sure, he went to Congress, once,
But he didn't stay.
Can't expect us all to be
Smart as Henry Clay.

"Need a man for troubled times?
Well, I guess we do.
Wonder who we'll ever find?
Yes—I wonder who."

That is how they met and talked,
Knowing and unknowing.
Lincoln was the green pine.
Lincoln kept on growing.

AND YET FOOLS SAY
George S. Holmes

He captured light and caged it in a glass,
Then harnessed it forever to a wire;
He gave men robots with no backs to tire
In bearing burdens for the toiling mass.

He freed the tongue in wood and wax and brass,
Imbued dull images with motions' fire,
Transmuted metal into human choir—
These man-made miracles he brought to pass.

Bulbs banish night along the Great White Way,
Thin threads of copper throb with might unseen;
On silver curtains shadow-actors play
That walk and talk from magic-mouthed machine,

While continents converse through skies o'erhead—
And yet fools say that Edison is dead!

ALEXANDER GRAHAM BELL DID NOT INVENT THE TELEPHONE
Robert P. Tristram Coffin

Alexander Graham Bell
Did not invent the telephone,
No good thing was ever yet
The work of any man alone.

My old Grandmother Sarah Bates,
Halfway out from coast to sky,
On Bates's Island, had a fine
Hand in that electric pie.

Grandma Bates with a small child
On her lap with quick hot breath

Willed the telephone to be
As she sat and stood off death.

Another grandmother I had,
Her head all over gimlet curls,
Ran that road of whispers to
Three other merry little girls.

Your Grandmother Fisher with her man
Down with fever of the lung
Willed that wiry line of life
Through the woodlands to be hung.

Your other Grandma Mary Snow,
Miles from your tall father's sire,
Sent out her love so stout, so straight,
It turned into a singing wire.

Little lonely barefoot boys
Aching for their freckled kind,
Old farmers through long nights of snow
Unrolled that wire from their mind.

Alexander Graham Bell
Had lots of help at his strange labor,
Maybe an arm down through the clouds
Helped him make the whole world neighbor.

"I Hear America Singing." *You may wish to end this poem with the line, "Each sings what belongs to him or her and to none else." Its emphasis on the importance of*

I HEAR AMERICA SINGING

Walt Whitman

I hear America singing, the varied carols I hear,
Those of the mechanics, each singing his as it
should be blithe and strong,
The carpenter singing his as he measures his
plank or beam,
The mason singing his as he makes ready for
work or leaves off work,
The boatman singing what belongs to him in his
boat, the deck hand singing on the steamboat deck,
The shoemaker singing as he sits on his bench,
the hatter singing as he stands,
The wood-cutter's song, the ploughboy's on his
way in the morning, or at noon intermission
or at sundown,
The delicious singing of the mother, or the
young wife at work, or the girl sewing or
washing,
Each sings what belongs to him or her and to
none else,
The day what belongs to the day—at night the
party of young fellows, robust, friendly,
Singing with open mouths their strong melodious songs.

each person's unique contribution is a thought worth discussing.

(*Mother Goose*)

Bow, wow, wow!
Whose dog art thou?
Little Tommy Tinker's dog.
Bow, wow, wow!

Christina Georgina Rossetti

Pussy has a whiskered face,
Kitty has such pretty ways;
Doggie scampers when I call,
And has a heart to love us all.

THE ANIMAL FAIR

THE EXTRAORDINARY DOG

Nancy Byrd Turner

When Mother takes me calling
I say, "Oh, please and please
Let's visit with the folks who own
The funny Pekinese!"

I walk around him softly
Upon my tipsy-toes;
He sits so queer and solemn there,
So scornful in the nose.

I wonder very often:
Suppose I gave a sneeze,
A loud "Kerchoo!"—what would he do,
The pompous Pekinese?

THE ORDINARY DOG

Nancy Byrd Turner

When Brother takes me walking
I cry, "Oh, hip, hooray!
We're sure to see the jolly pup
That joins us every day!"

His ears are raggy-shaggy;
His coat's a dusty brown;
He meets me like a cannon ball
And nearly knocks me down.

He tells me all his secrets,
With joyful jumpings-up.
I wish the pompous Pekinese
Could know the Jolly Pup!

JIPPY AND JIMMY

Laura E. Richards

Jippy and Jimmy were two little dogs.
They went to sail on some floating logs;
The logs rolled over, the dogs rolled in,
And they got very wet, for their clothes were
    thin.

Jippy and Jimmy crept out again.
They said, "The river is full of rain!"
They said, "The water is far from dry!
Ki-hi! ki-hi! ki-*hi*-yi! ki-hi!"

Jippy and Jimmy went shivering home.
They said, "On the river no more we'll roam;
And we won't go to sail until we learn how,
Bow-wow! bow-wow! bow-*wow*-wow! bow-wow!"

"Bow, wow, wow." *See record album* Poetry Time
"Pussy has a whiskered face." From *Sing-Song* by Christina Georgina Rossetti
"The Extraordinary Dog" and "The Ordinary Dog." From *Magpie Lane* by Nancy Byrd Turner, copyright 1927 by Harcourt, Brace and Company, Inc.; renewed 1955 by Nancy Byrd Turner. Reprinted by permission of the publishers.
"Jippy and Jimmy." From *Tirra Lirra* by Laura E. Richards. Little, Brown & Company, Boston, 1932

PUPPY AND I

A. A. Milne

I met a man as I went walking;
We got talking,
Man and I.
"Where are you going to, Man?" I said
    (I said to the Man as he went by).
"Down to the village, to get some bread.
    Will you come with me?" "No, not I."

I met a Horse as I went walking;
We got talking,
Horse and I.
"Where are you going to, Horse, to-day?"
    (I said to the Horse as he went by).
"Down to the village to get some hay.
    Will you come with me?" "No, not I."

I met a Woman as I went walking;
We got talking,
Woman and I.
"Where are you going to, Woman, so early?"
    (I said to the Woman as she went by).
"Down to the village to get some barley.
    Will you come with me?" "No, not I."

I met some Rabbits as I went walking;
We got talking,
Rabbits and I.
"Where are you going in your brown fur coats?"
    (I said to the Rabbits as they went by).
"Down to the village to get some oats.
    Will you come with us?" "No, not I."

I met a Puppy as I went walking;
We got talking,
Puppy and I.
"Where are you going this nice fine day?"
    (I said to the Puppy as he went by).
"Up in the hills to roll and play."
    "*I'll* come with you, Puppy," said I.

"Puppy and I." *Whenever you find a poem with a repetitional refrain it is apt to be monotonous unless you can get a little variety into your speaking of the refrain. Listen when you say the "We got talking" part and if you sing-song it, stop and experiment. And you see Milne uses italics in the last line to make sure you notice the change from the other verses.* Taken from *When We Were Very Young,* by A. A. Milne, published and copyright, 1924, by E. P. Dutton & Co., Inc., New York

VERN

Gwendolyn Brooks

When walking in a tiny rain
Across the vacant lot,
A pup's a good companion—
If a pup you've got.

And when you've had a scold,
And no one loves you very,
And you cannot be merry,
A pup will let you look at him,
And even let you hold
His little wiggly warmness—

And let you snuggle down beside.
Nor mock the tears you have to hide.

A MALTESE DOG

(*Greek,* second century B.C.)

Trans. by Edmund Blunden

He came from Malta; and Eumêlus says
He had no better dog in all his days.
We called him Bull; he went into the dark.
Along those roads we cannot hear him bark.

THE BUCCANEER

Nancy Byrd Turner

Danny was a rascal,
    Danny was a scamp;
He carried off a lady doll
    And left her in the damp.

He took her off on Monday;
    On Wednesday in he came
And dumped her gayly on the floor
    Without a bit of shame.

He was not sad or humble,
    He begged nobody's pardon;
He merely barked: "A lady doll
    I found out in the garden!"

MY DOG

Marchette Chute

His nose is short and scrubby;
    His ears hang rather low;
And he always brings the stick back,
    No matter how far you throw.

He gets spanked rather often
    For things he shouldn't do,
Like lying-on-beds, and barking,
    And eating up shoes when they're new.

He always wants to be going
    Where he isn't supposed to go.
He tracks up the house when it's snowing—
    Oh, puppy, I love you so.

TOM'S LITTLE DOG

Walter de la Mare

Tom told his dog called Tim to beg,
    And up at once he sat,
His two clear amber eyes fixed fast,
    His haunches on his mat.

Tom poised a lump of sugar on
    His nose; then, "Trust!" says he;
Stiff as a guardsman sat his Tim;
    Never a hair stirred he.

"Paid for!" says Tom; and in a trice
    Up jerked that moist black nose;
A snap of teeth, a crunch, a munch,
    And down the sugar goes!

THE HAIRY DOG

Herbert Asquith

My dog's so furry I've not seen
His face for years and years:
His eyes are buried out of sight,
I only guess his ears.

When people ask me for his breed,
I do not know or care:
He has the beauty of them all
Hidden beneath his hair.

SUNNING

James S. Tippett

Old Dog lay in the summer sun
Much too lazy to rise and run.
He flapped an ear
At a buzzing fly.
He winked a half opened
Sleepy eye.
He scratched himself
On an itching spot,
As he dozed on the porch
Where the sun was hot.
He whimpered a bit
From force of habit
While he lazily dreamed
Of chasing a rabbit.
But Old Dog happily lay in the sun
Much too lazy to rise and run.

THE BANDOG

Walter de la Mare

Has anybody seen my Mopser?—
    A comely dog is he,
With hair of the colour of a Charles the Fifth.
    And teeth like ships at sea,

His tail it curls straight upwards,
    His ears stand two abreast,
And he answers to the simple name of **Mopser,**
    When civilly addressed.

DOGS AND WEATHER

Winifred Welles

I'd like a different dog
    For every kind of weather—
A narrow greyhound for a fog,
    A wolfhound strange and white,
    With a tail like a silver feather
        To run with in the night,
        When snow is still, and winter stars **are**
        bright.

In the fall I'd like to see
    In answer to my whistle,
A golden spaniel look at me.
    But best of all for rain
    A terrier, hairy as a thistle,
        To trot with fine disdain
        Beside me down the soaked, sweet-smelling
        lane.

LONE DOG

Irene Rutherford McLeod

I'm a lean dog, a keen dog, a wild dog, and lone;
I'm a rough dog, a tough dog, hunting on my
    own;
I'm a bad dog, a mad dog, teasing silly sheep;
I love to sit and bay the moon, to keep fat souls
    from sleep.

I'll never be a lap dog, licking dirty feet,
A sleek dog, a meek dog, cringing for my meat,
Not for me the fireside, the well-filled plate,
But shut door, and sharp stone, and cuff, and
    kick, and hate.

Company. By permission also of William Heinemann, Ltd.
    "Sunning." From *A World to Know* by James S. Tippett.
Copyright, 1933, Harper & Brothers
    "The Bandog." *A bandog is a dog that is kept on a
chain or rope. A Charles the Fifth is a small black and tan
spaniel.* From *Collected Poems, 1901–1918,* by Walter de
la Mare. Copyright, 1920, by Henry Holt and Company,
Inc. Copyright, 1948, by Walter de la Mare. Reprinted by

permission of the publishers
    "Dogs and Weather." *The wire-haired terrier doesn't
mind how wet it is because his coat sheds rain as well as
any raincoat.* From *Skipping Along Alone* by Winifred
Welles. The Macmillan Company, New York, 1931. Used
by permission of James Welles Shearer
    "Lone Dog." From *Songs to Save a Soul* by Irene Ruther-
ford McLeod. Chatto & Windus, London, 1915

Not for me the other dogs, running by my side,
Some have run a short while, but none of them
    would bide.
O mine is still the lone trail, the hard trail, the
    best,
Wide wind, and wild stars, and hunger of the
    quest!

THE ANIMAL STORE
Rachel Field

If I had a hundred dollars to spend,
  Or maybe a little more,
I'd hurry as fast as my legs would go
  Straight to the animal store.

I wouldn't say, "How much for this or that?"—
  "What kind of a dog is he?"
I'd buy as many as rolled an eye,
  Or wagged a tail at me!

I'd take the hound with the drooping ears
  That sits by himself alone;
Cockers and Cairns and wobbly pups
  For to be my very own.

I might buy a parrot all red and green,
  And the monkey I saw before,
If I had a hundred dollars to spend,
  Or maybe a little more.

I LOVE LITTLE PUSSY
Jane Taylor

I love little Pussy,
  Her coat is so warm,
And if I don't hurt her,
  She'll do me no harm;
So I'll not pull her tail,
  Nor drive her away,
But Pussy and I
  Very gently will play.

(*Mother Goose*)

"Pussy-cat, pussy-cat,
  Where have you been?"
"I've been to London
  To visit the Queen."
"Pussy-cat, pussy-cat,
  What did you there?"
"I frightened a little mouse
  Under the chair."

A KITTEN
Eleanor Farjeon

He's nothing much but fur
And two round eyes of blue,
He has a giant purr
And a midget mew.

He darts and pats the air,
He starts and cocks his ear,
When there is nothing there
For him to see and hear.

He runs around in rings,
But why we cannot tell;
With sideways leaps he springs
At things invisible—

Then half-way through a leap
His startled eyeballs close,
And he drops off to sleep
With one paw on his nose.

TIGER-CAT TIM
Edith H. Newlin

Timothy Tim was a very small cat
Who looked like a tiger the size of a rat.
There were little black stripes running all over
  him,
With just enough white on his feet for a trim
On Tiger-Cat Tim.

Timothy Tim had a little pink tongue
That was spoon, comb and washcloth all made
  into one.
He lapped up his milk, washed and combed all
  his fur,
And then he sat down in the sunshine to purr,
Full little Tim.

Timothy Tim had a queer little way
Of always pretending at things in his play.
He caught pretend mice in the grass and the
  sand,
And fought pretend cats when he played with
  your hand,
Fierce little Tim!

He drank all his milk, and he grew and he grew.
He ate all his meat and his vegetables, too.
He grew very big and he grew very fat,
And now he's a lazy old, sleepy old cat,
Timothy Tim!

CAT

Dorothy Baruch

My cat
Is quiet.
She moves without a sound.
Sometimes she stretches herself curving
On tiptoe.
Sometimes she crouches low
And creeping.

Sometimes she rubs herself against a chair,
And there
 With a *miew* and a *miew*
 And a purrrr purrrr purrrr
 She curls up
 And goes to sleep.

My cat
Lives through a black hole
Under the house.

So one day I
Crawled in after her.
And it was dark
And I sat
And didn't know
Where to go.
And then—

Two yellow-white
Round little lights
Came moving . . . moving . . . toward me.
And there
With a *miew* and a *miew*
 And a purrrr purrrr purrrr
My cat
Rubbed, soft, against me.

 And I knew
 The lights
 Were MY CAT'S EYES
 In the dark.

IN HONOUR OF TAFFY TOPAZ

Christopher Morley

Taffy, the topaz-coloured cat,
Thinks now of this and now of that,
But chiefly of his meals.
Asparagus, and cream, and fish,
Are objects of his Freudian wish;
What you don't give, he steals.

His gallant heart is strongly stirred
By clink of plate or flight of bird,
He has a plumy tail;
At night he treads on stealthy pad
As merry as Sir Galahad
A-seeking of the Grail.

His amiable amber eyes
Are very friendly, very wise;
Like Buddha, grave and fat,
He sits, regardless of applause,
And thinking, as he kneads his paws,
What fun to be a cat!

THE MYSTERIOUS CAT

Vachel Lindsay

I saw a proud, mysterious cat,
I saw a proud, mysterious cat
Too proud to catch a mouse or rat—
Mew, mew, mew.

But catnip she would eat, and purr,
But catnip she would eat, and purr.
And goldfish she did much prefer—
Mew, mew, mew.

I saw a cat—'twas but a dream,
I saw a cat—'twas but a dream,
Who scorned the slave that brought her cream—
Mew, mew, mew.

Unless the slave were dressed in style,
Unless the slave were dressed in style
And knelt before her all the while—
Mew, mew, mew.

Did you ever hear of a thing like that?
Did you ever hear of a thing like that?
Did you ever hear of a thing like that?
Oh, what a proud mysterious cat.
Oh, what a proud mysterious cat.
Oh, what a proud mysterious cat.
Mew . . . Mew . . . Mew.

CAT

Mary Britton Miller

The black cat yawns,
Opens her jaws,
Stretches her legs,
And shows her claws.

Then she gets up
And stands on four
Long stiff legs
And yawns some more.

She shows her sharp teeth,
She stretches her lip,
Her slice of a tongue
Turns up at the tip.

Lifting herself
On her delicate toes,
She arches her back
As high as it goes.

She lets herself down
With particular care,
And pads away
With her tail in the air.

Elizabeth Coatsworth

"Who are *you?*" asked the cat of the bear.
"I am a child of the wood,
I am strong with rain-shedding hair,
I hunt without fear for my food,
The others behold me and quail."
Said the cat, "You are lacking a tail."

"What can you *do?*" asked the cat.
"I can climb for the honey I crave.
In the fall when I'm merry and fat
I seek out a suitable cave
And sleep till I feel the spring light."
Said the cat, "Can you see in the night?"

Said the cat, "*I* sit by man's fire,
But I am much wilder than you.
I do the thing I desire
And do nothing I don't want to do.
I am small, but then, what is that?
My spirit is great," said the cat.

LITTLE LADY WREN

Tom Robinson

Little Lady Wren,
Hopping from bough to bough,
Bob your tail for me,
Bob it now!

You carry it so straight
Up in the air and when
You hop from bough to bough
You bob it now and then.

Why do you bob your tail,
Hopping from bough to bough,
And will not bob it when I say,
"Bob it now!"?

Christina Georgina Rossetti

Wrens and robins in the hedge,
    Wrens and robins here and there;
Building, perching, pecking, fluttering,
    Everywhere!

THE SECRET

(*Unknown*)

We have a secret, just we three,
The robin, and I, and the sweet cherry-tree;
The bird told the tree, and the tree told me,
And nobody knows it but just us three.

But of course the robin knows it best,
Because he built the—I shan't tell the rest;
And laid the four little—something in it—
I'm afraid I shall tell it every minute.

But if the tree and the robin don't peep,
I'll try my best the secret to keep;
Though I know when the little birds fly about
Then the whole secret will be out.

"Little Lady Wren." From *In and Out* by Tom Robinson. Copyright, 1943, by Tom Robinson. Reprinted by permission of The Viking Press, Inc., New York
"Wrens and robins in the hedge." From *Sing-Song* by

WHAT ROBIN TOLD
George Cooper

How do robins build their nests?
    Robin Redbreast told me—
First a wisp of yellow hay
In a pretty round they lay;

Then some shreds of downy floss,
Feathers, too, and bits of moss,
Woven with a sweet, sweet song,
This way, that way, and across;
    That's what Robin told me.

Where do robins hide their nests?
    Robin Redbreast told me—
Up among the leaves so deep,
Where the sunbeams rarely creep,
Long before the winds are cold,
Long before the leaves are gold,
Bright-eyed stars will peep and see
Baby robins—one, two, three;
    That's what Robin told me.

"TALENTS DIFFER"
Laura E. Richards

"What are you doing there, Robin a Bobbin,
    Under my window, out in the blue?"
"Building my nest, O Little One, Pretty One,
    Doing the thing that you cannot do!"

"What are you doing now, Robin a Bobbin,
    Under my window, out in the blue?"
"Brooding my eggs, O Little One, Pretty One,
    Doing the thing that you cannot do!"

Christina Georgina Rossetti
"Talents Differ." From *Tirra Lirra* by Laura E. Richards, by permission of Little, Brown & Co. Copyright 1918, 1930, 1932 by Laura E. Richards

"What are you doing there, Robin a Bobbin,
   Under my window, out in the blue?"
"Feeding my nestlings, Little One, Pretty One,
   Doing the thing that you cannot do.

"And what are *you* doing, pray, Little One,
   Pretty One,
What are you doing, tell me now true?"
"Sewing my patchwork, Robin a Bobbin,
   Doing the thing that *you* cannot do!"

CROWS
David McCord

I like to walk
And hear the black crows talk.

I like to lie
And watch crows sail the sky.

I like the crow
That wants the wind to blow:

I like the one
That thinks the wind is fun.

I like to see
Crows spilling from a tree,

And try to find
The top crow left behind.

I like to hear
Crows caw that spring is near.

I like the great
Wild clamor of crow hate

Three farms away
When owls are out by day.

I like the slow
Tired homeward-flying crow;

I like the sight
Of crows for my good night.

"Crows." From *Far and Few* by David McCord. Copyright 1929, 1931, 1952 by David McCord. By permission of Little, Brown & Company, Boston

"Mrs. Peck-Pigeon." *When you read this aloud you will discover that the words and lines suggest the bobbing, teetering gait of the pigeon "picking for bread."* From *Over the Garden Wall*. Copyright 1933 by Eleanor Farjeon. Reprinted by permission of J. B. Lippincott Company

MRS. PECK-PIGEON
Eleanor Farjeon

Mrs. Peck-Pigeon
Is picking for bread,
Bob-bob-bob
Goes her little round head.
Tame as a pussy-cat
In the street,
Step-step-step
Go her little red feet.
With her little red feet
And her little round head,
Mrs. Peck-Pigeon
Goes picking for bread.

CHICKADEE
Hilda Conkling

The chickadee in the appletree
Talks all the time very gently.
He makes me sleepy.
I rock away to the sea-lights.
Far off I hear him talking
The way smooth bright pebbles
Drop into water . . .
Chick-a-*dee-dee-dee* . . .

THE WOODPECKER
Elizabeth Madox Roberts

The woodpecker pecked out a little round hole
And made him a house in the telephone pole.

One day when I watched he poked out his head,
And he had on a hood and a collar of red.

When the streams of rain pour out of the sky,
And the sparkles of lightning go flashing by,

And the big, big wheels of thunder roll,
He can snuggle back in the telephone pole.

"Chickadee." From *Poems by a Little Girl* by Hilda Conkling. Copyright 1920 by J. B. Lippincott Company

"The Woodpecker." From *Under the Tree* by Elizabeth Madox Roberts. Copyright 1922 by B. W. Huebsch, Inc., 1950 by Ivor S. Roberts. Reprinted by permission of The Viking Press, Inc., New York

"The Blackbird." From *Kensington Gardens* by Humbert Wolfe. Reprinted by permission of Doubleday & Com-

THE SNOW-BIRD

Frank Dempster Sherman

When all the ground with snow is white,
  The merry snow-bird comes,
And hops about with great delight
  To find the scattered crumbs.

How glad he seems to get to eat
  A piece of cake or bread!
He wears no shoes upon his feet,
  Nor hat upon his head.

But happiest is he, I know,
  Because no cage with bars
Keeps him from walking on the snow
  And printing it with stars.

WILD GEESE

Elinor Chipp

  I heard the wild geese flying
    In the dead of the night,
  With beat of wings and crying
  I heard the wild geese flying,
  And dreams in my heart sighing
    Followed their northward flight.
  I heard the wild geese flying
    In the dead of the night.

THE SANDHILL CRANE

Mary Austin

Whenever the days are cool and clear
The sandhill crane goes walking
Across the field by the flashing weir
Slowly, solemnly stalking.
The little frogs in the tules hear
And jump for their lives when he comes near,
The minnows scuttle away in fear,
When the sandhill crane goes walking.

THE BLACKBIRD

Humbert Wolfe

In the far corner
close by the swings,
every morning
a blackbird sings.

His bill's so yellow,
his coat's so black,
that he makes a fellow
whistle back.

Ann, my daughter,
thinks that he
sings for us two
especially.

Emily Dickinson

A bird came down the walk:
He did not know I saw;
He bit an angle-worm in halves
And ate the fellow, raw.

And then he drank a dew
From a convenient grass,
And then hopped sidewise to the wall
To let a beetle pass.

pany, Inc. By permission also of Miss Ann Wolfe
  "A bird came down the walk." From *The Poems of Emily Dickinson*. Little, Brown & Company, Boston, 1939
  "Wild Geese." From *The City and Other Poems* by Elinor Chipp. Copyright, 1923, by The Four Seas Co. Reprinted by permission of Bruce Humphries, Inc.
  "The Sandhill Crane." *There is a significant contrast in the movement of these lines. The first four lines of each verse have the slow movement of the crane's long legs, "solemnly stalking." The next three lines in each verse are full of hurry and fear. And then the concluding line of each resumes the slow, nonchalant rhythm of the walking crane.* From *The Children Sing in the Far West* by Mary Austin. Reprinted by permission of and arrangement with Houghton Mifflin Company, the authorized publishers

The field folk know if he comes that way,
Slowly, solemnly stalking,
There is danger and death in the least delay
When the sandhill crane goes walking.
The chipmunks stop in the midst of their play,
The gophers hide in their holes away
And hush, oh, hush! the field mice say,
When the sandhill crane goes walking.

THE PHEASANT
Robert P. Tristram Coffin

A pheasant cock sprang into view,
A living jewel, up he flew.

His wings laid hold on empty space,
Scorn bulged his eyeballs out with grace.

He was a hymn from tail to beak
With not a tender note or meek.

Then the gun let out its thunder,
The bird descended struck with wonder.

He ran a little, then, amazed,
Settled with his head upraised.

The fierceness flowed out of his eyes
And left them meek and large and wise.

Gentleness relaxed his head,
He lay in jewelled feathers, dead.

GULL
William Jay Smith

Life is seldom if ever dull
For the lazy long-winged white Sea Gull.
    It is as interesting as can be;
He lies on the wind, a slender reed,
And wheels and dips for hours to feed
On scruffy fish and pickleweed
    And to smell the smell of the sea.

He wheels and dips: beneath his wings
The pirate grins, the sailor sings,
    As they ply the China Sea.
While cold winds grip a schooner's sail
And water spouts from a great White Whale,
Perched on a mast, he rides the gale—
    What a wonderful life has he!

Elizabeth Coatsworth

    The sea gull curves his wings,
    The sea gull turns his eyes.
    Get down into the water, fish!
    (If you are wise.)

    The sea gull slants his wings,
    The sea gull turns his head.
    Get down into the water, fish!
    (Or you'll be dead.)

THE EAGLE
Alfred, Lord Tennyson

    He clasps the crag with crooked hands;
    Close to the sun in lonely lands,
    Ringed with the azure world, he stands.

    The wrinkled sea beneath him crawls;
    He watches from his mountain walls,
    And like a thunderbolt he falls.

MOUSE
Hilda Conkling

    Little Mouse in gray velvet,
    Have you had a cheese-breakfast?
    There are no crumbs on your coat,
    Did you use a napkin?
    I wonder what you had to eat,
    And who dresses you in gray velvet?

    "The Pheasant." From *Strange Holiness* by Robert P. Tristram Coffin. Copyright 1935 by The Macmillan Company and used with their permission
    "Gull." From *Boy Blue's Book of Beasts.* Copyright © 1956, 1957 by William Jay Smith. By permission of the author and publisher, Little, Brown & Company, Boston
    "The sea gull curves his wings." *This is a wonderful example of the music of words and rhythm actually suggesting the idea the poem is presenting. The first couplet of each verse has the smooth, flowing rhythm of the gulls'*

MICE

Rose Fyleman

I think mice
Are rather nice.

Their tails are long,
Their faces small,
They haven't any
Chins at all.
Their ears are pink,
Their teeth are white,
They run about
The house at night.
They nibble things
They shouldn't touch
And no one seems
To like them much.

But *I* think mice
Are nice.

THE HOUSE OF THE MOUSE

Lucy Sprague Mitchell

The house of the mouse
is a wee little house,
a green little house in the grass,
which big clumsy folk
may hunt and may poke
and still never see as they pass
this sweet little, neat little,
wee little, green little,
cuddle-down hide-away
house in the grass.

Christina Georgina Rossetti

The city mouse lives in a house;—
The garden mouse lives in a bower,

He's friendly with the frogs and toads,
And sees the pretty plants in flower.

The city mouse eats bread and cheese;—
The garden mouse eats what he can;
We will not grudge him seeds and stalks,
Poor little timid furry man.

THE MOUSE

Elizabeth Coatsworth

I heard a mouse
Bitterly complaining
In a crack of moonlight
Aslant on the floor—

"Little I ask
And that little is not granted.
There are few crumbs
In this world any more.

"The bread-box is tin
And I cannot get in.

"The jam's in a jar
My teeth cannot mar.

"The cheese sits by itself
On the pantry shelf—

"All night I run
Searching and seeking,
All night I run
About on the floor,

"Moonlight is there
And a bare place for dancing,
But no little feast
Is spread any more."

soaring flight. They are all beauty and grace. The concluding couplets are in startling contrast. They come like a cry of warning, which, of course, they are. From *Plum Daffy Adventure* by Elizabeth Coatsworth. Copyright 1947 by The Macmillan Company and used with their permission

"Mouse." From *Poems by a Little Girl* by Hilda Conkling. Copyright 1920 by J. B. Lippincott Company

"Mice." From *Fifty-One New Nursery Rhymes* by Rose Fyleman. Copyright 1931, 1932 by Doubleday & Company,

Inc. By permission also of Miss Rose Fyleman, The Society of Authors, and Messrs. Methuen & Co.

"The House of the Mouse." Taken from *Another Here and Now Story Book*, edited by Lucy Sprague Mitchell, published and copyright, 1937, by E. P. Dutton & Co., Inc., New York

"The city mouse lives in a house." From *Sing-Song* by Christina Georgina Rossetti

"The Mouse." From *Compass Rose* by Elizabeth Coatsworth. Copyright, 1929, by Coward-McCann

A LITTLE SQUIRREL

Child in Winnetka Nursery

I saw a little squirrel,
Sitting in a tree;
He was eating a nut
And wouldn't look at me.

THE STORY
OF THE BABY SQUIRREL

Dorothy Aldis

He ran right out of the woods to me,
Little and furry and panting with fright;
I offered a finger just to see—
And both of his paws held on to it tight.

Was it dogs that had scared him? A crashing
    limb?
I waited a while but there wasn't a sign
Of his mother coming to rescue him.
So then I decided he was mine.

I lifted him up and he wasn't afraid
To ride along in the crook of my arm.
"A very fine place," he thought, "just made
For keeping me comfortable, safe and warm."

At home he seemed happy to guzzle his milk
Out of an eye dropper six times a day.
We gave him a pillow of damask silk
On which he very royally lay.

He frisked on the carpets, he whisked up the
    stairs
(Where he played with some soap till it made
    him sneeze).
He loved it exploring the tables and chairs,
And he climbed up the curtains exactly like
    trees.

He watched his fuzzy gray stomach swell.
He grew until he could leave a dent
In the pillow on which he'd slept so well—
And then . . . Oh, then one morning he went.

Perhaps a squirrel around the place
Adopted him: oh, we're certain it's true
For once a little looking down face
Seemed to be saying: "How do you do?"

THE SQUIRREL

(Unknown)

Whisky, frisky,
Hippity hop.
Up he goes
To the tree top!

Whirly, twirly,
Round and round,
Down he scampers
To the ground.

Furly, curly,
What a tail!
Tall as a feather,
Broad as a sail!

Where's his supper?
In the shell,
Snappity, crackity,
Out it fell!

JOE

David McCord

We feed the birds in winter,
And outside in the snow
We have a tray of many seeds
For many birds of many breeds
And one gray squirrel named Joe.
    But Joe comes early,
    Joe comes late,
    And all the birds
    Must stand and wait.
And waiting there for Joe to go
Is pretty cold work in the snow.

"A Little Squirrel." Reprinted from *Very Young Verses* published by Houghton Mifflin Company. The editors of this book searched diligently to find the source and to obtain permission to use this poem, but without success
"The Story of the Baby Squirrel." From *Before Things Happen* by Dorothy Aldis. G. P. Putnam's Sons, New York,

1939. Copyright 1939 by Dorothy Aldis
"Joe" and "Fred." From *Far and Few* by David McCord. Copyright 1929, 1931, 1952 by David McCord. By permission of Little, Brown & Company, Boston
"Little Charlie Chipmunk." From *Animal Etiquette Book* by Helen Cowles LeCron. Frederick A. Stokes Co.,

FRED

David McCord

Speaking of Joe, I should have said
Our flying squirrel's name is Fred.

Fred is no flyer, but a glider.
His skin is loose and soft as eider.

But Fred himself is no softy:
He likes tough trees, and likes them lofty.

Fred is not around much at noon;
But at night, and under a bright full moon,

He sails from tree to tree like a circus performer;
And once last summer he sailed right into the
  dormer

Window of the empty house next door.
But that's Fred all over. Need I say more?

LITTLE CHARLIE CHIPMUNK

Helen Cowles LeCron

Little Charlie Chipmunk was a *talker*. Mercy me!
He chattered after breakfast and he chattered
  after tea!
He chattered to his father and he chattered to
  his mother!
He chattered to his sister and he chattered to his
  brother!
He chattered till his family was almost driven
  wild!
Oh, little Charlie Chipmunk was a *very* tiresome
  child!

RABBITS

Dorothy Baruch

My two white rabbits
Chase each other
With humping, bumping backs.
  They go hopping, hopping,
  And their long ears
    Go flopping, flopping.

1926. Used by permission of the author
  "Rabbits." From *I Like Animals* by Dorothy Baruch.
Harper & Brothers, New York, 1933. Used by permission
of the author

And they
Make faces
With their noses
Up and down.

Today
I went inside their fence
To play rabbit with them.
And in one corner
Under a loose bush
I saw something shivering the leaves.
  And I pushed
  And I looked.
  And I found—
  There
  In a hole
  In the ground—
  Three baby rabbits
  Hidden away.
    And *they*
    Made faces
    with their noses
    Up and down.

THE RABBIT

Elizabeth Madox Roberts

When they said the time to hide was mine,
I hid back under a thick grapevine.

And while I was still for the time to pass,
A little gray thing came out of the grass.

He hopped his way through the melon bed
And sat down close by a cabbage head.

He sat down close where I could see,
And his big still eyes looked hard at me,

His big eyes bursting out of the rim,
And I looked back very hard at him.

"The Rabbit." From *Under the Tree* by Elizabeth
Madox Roberts. Copyright 1922 by B. W. Huebsch, Inc.,
1950 by Ivor S. Roberts. Reprinted by permission of The
Viking Press, Inc., New York

WHITE SEASON

Frances M. Frost

In the winter the rabbits match their pelts to the
    earth.
With ears laid back, they go
Blown through the silver hollow, the silver
    thicket,
Like puffs of snow.

A STORY IN THE SNOW

Pearl Riggs Crouch

This morning, as I walked to school
    Across the fluffy snow,
I came upon a bunny's tracks—
    A jumping, zigzag row.

He must have hurried very fast,
    For here and there I saw
Along his jerky, winding trail
    The print of Rover's paw!

I set my lunch pail on the snow
    And stood there very still,
For only Rover's clumsy tracks
    Led down the little hill.

Then suddenly I thought I heard
    A rustling sound close by;
And there within a grassy clump
    Shone Bunny's twinkling eye!

THE HARE

Walter de la Mare

In the black furrow of a field
I saw an old witch-hare this night;
And she cocked a lissome ear,
And she eyed the moon so bright,

And she nibbled of the green;
And I whispered "Whsst! witch-hare,"
Away like a ghostie o'er the field
She fled, and left the moonlight there.

THE SNARE

James Stephens

I hear a sudden cry of pain!
There is a rabbit in a snare:
Now I hear the cry again,
But I cannot tell from where.

But I cannot tell from where
He is calling out for aid!
Crying on the frightened air,
Making everything afraid!

Making everything afraid!
Wrinkling up his little face!
As he cries again for aid;
—And I cannot find the place!

And I cannot find the place
Where his paw is in the snare!
Little One! Oh, Little One!
I am searching everywhere!

THE RABBITS' SONG OUTSIDE THE TAVERN

Elizabeth Coatsworth

We, who play under the pines,
We, who dance in the snow
That shines blue in the light of the moon,
Sometimes halt as we go—
Stand with our ears erect,
Our noses testing the air,
To gaze at the golden world
Behind the windows there.

Suns they have in a cave,
Stars, each on a tall white stem,
And the thought of a fox or an owl
Seems never to trouble them.
They laugh and eat and are warm,
Their food is ready at hand,
While hungry out in the cold
We little rabbits stand.

But they never dance as we dance!
They haven't the speed nor the grace.
We scorn both the dog and the cat
Who lie by their fireplace.
We scorn them licking their paws,
Their eyes on an upraised spoon—
We who dance hungry and wild
Under a winter's moon.

THE SKUNK
Robert P. Tristram Coffin

When the sun has slipped away
And the dew is on the day,
Then the creature comes to call
Men malign the most of all.

The little skunk is very neat,
With his sensitive, plush feet
And a dainty, slim head set
With diamonds on bands of jet.

He walks upon his evening's duty
Of declaring how that beauty
With her patterns is not done
At the setting of the sun.

He undulates across the lawn,
He asks nobody to fawn
On his graces. All that he
Asks is that men let him be.

He knows that he is very fine
In every clean and rippling line,
He is a conscious black and white
Little symphony of night.

THE JOLLY WOODCHUCK
Marion Edey and Dorothy Grider

The woodchuck's very very fat
But doesn't care a pin for that.

When nights are long and the snow is deep,
Down in his hole he lies asleep.

Under the earth is a warm little room
The drowsy woodchuck calls his home.

Rolls of fat and fur surround him,
With all his children curled around him,

Snout to snout and tail to tail.
He never awakes in the wildest gale;

When icicles snap and the north wind blows
He snores in his sleep and rubs his nose.

PRAIRIE-DOG TOWN
Mary Austin

Old Peter Prairie-Dog
Builds him a house
In Prairie-Dog Town,
With a door that goes down
And down and down,
And a hall that goes under
And under and under,
Where you can't see the lightning,
You can't hear the thunder,
For they don't *like* thunder
In Prairie-Dog Town.

Old Peter Prairie-Dog
Digs him a cellar
In Prairie-Dog Town,
With a ceiling that is arched
And a wall that is round,
And the earth he takes out he makes into a
    mound.
And the hall and the cellar
Are dark as dark,
And you can't see a spark,
Not a single spark;
And the way to them cannot be found.

Old Peter Prairie-Dog
Knows a very clever trick
Of behaving like a stick
When he hears a sudden sound,
Like an old dead stick;
And when you turn your head
He'll jump quick, quick,
And be another stick
When you look around.
It *is* a clever trick,
And it keeps him safe and sound
In the cellar and the halls
That are under the mound
In Prairie-Dog Town.

THE LITTLE FOX

Marion Edey and Dorothy Grider

Who came in the quiet night,
Trotting so lightly?
It was the russet fox who came
And with his shadow played a game;
Where the snow lay whitely
And the moon shone brightly
There he wrote his name.

Who spoke in the winter night,
A cold sound and lonely?
The clock-faced owl, so round and hunchy,
The yellow-eyed owl, in a voice so crunchy:

"Who-oo-oo-oo, are you?
I *like* to be only
Squat and bunchy—
Do you-oo-oo-oo, too?"

NIGHT OF WIND
Frances M. Frost

How lost is the little fox at the borders of night,
Poised in the forest of fern, in the trample of
    wind!
Caught by the blowing cold of the mountain
    darkness,
He shivers and runs under tall trees, whimper-
    ing,
Brushing the tangles of dew. Pausing and run-
    ning,
He searches the warm and shadowy hollow, the
    deep
Home on the mountain's side where the nuz-
    zling, soft
Bodies of little foxes may hide and sleep.

FOUR LITTLE FOXES
Lew Sarett

Speak gently, Spring, and make no sudden sound;
For in my windy valley, yesterday I found
New-born foxes squirming on the ground—
        Speak gently.

Walk softly, March, forbear the bitter blow;
Her feet within a trap, her blood upon the snow,
The four little foxes saw their mother go—
        Walk softly.

Go lightly, Spring, oh, give them no alarm;
When I covered them with boughs to shelter
    them from harm,
The thin blue foxes suckled at my arm—
        Go lightly.

Step softly, March, with your rampant hurricane;
Nuzzling one another, and whimpering with
    pain,
The new little foxes are shivering in the rain—
        Step softly.

"The Little Fox." Reprinted from *Open the Door* by Marion Edey and Dorothy Grider. Copyright 1949 by Marion Edey and Dorothy Grider. Used by permission of the publishers, Charles Scribner's Sons

"Night of Wind." From *Pool in the Meadow* by Frances M. Frost. Reprinted by permission of and arrangement with Houghton Mifflin Company, the authorized publishers

"Four Little Foxes." From *Covenant with Earth*, by Lew Sarett. Edited and copyrighted, 1956, by Alma Johnson Sarett. Gainesville: University of Florida Press, 1956. Reprinted by permission of Mrs. Sarett

THE WOLF

Georgia R. Durston

When the pale moon hides and the wild wind
    wails,
And over the treetops the nighthawk sails,
The gray wolf sits on the world's far rim,
And howls: and it seems to comfort him.

The wolf is a lonely soul, you see,
No beast in the wood, nor bird in the tree,
But shuns his path; in the windy gloom
They give him plenty, and plenty of room.

So he sits with his long, lean face to the sky
Watching the ragged clouds go by.
There in the night, alone, apart,
Singing the song of his lone, wild heart.

Far away, on the world's dark rim
He howls, and it seems to comfort him.

LITTLE THINGS

James Stephens

Little things, that run, and quail,
And die, in silence and despair!

Little things, that fight, and fail,
And fall, on sea, and earth, and air!

All trapped and frightened little things,
The mouse, the coney, hear our prayer!

As we forgive those done to us,
—The lamb, the linnet, and the hare—

Forgive us all our trespasses,
Little creatures, everywhere!

FEATHER OR FUR

John Becker

When you watch for
Feather or fur
Feather or fur
Do not stir
Do not stir.

Feather or fur
Come crawling
Creeping
Some come peeping
Some by night
And some by day.
Most come gently
All come softly
Do not scare
A friend away.

When you watch for
Feather or fur
Feather or fur
Do not stir
Do not stir.

FIREFLY

Elizabeth Madox Roberts

A little light is going by,
Is going up to see the sky,
A little light with wings.

I never could have thought of it,
To have a little bug all lit
And made to go on wings.

Lillian Schulz Vanada

Fuzzy wuzzy, creepy crawly
Caterpillar funny,
You will be a butterfly
When the days are sunny.

Winging, flinging, dancing, springing
  Butterfly so yellow,
You were once a caterpillar,
  Wriggly, wiggly fellow.

BUTTERFLY

Hilda Conkling

As I walked through my garden
I saw a butterfly light on a flower.
His wings were pink and purple:
He spoke a small word . . .
It was *Follow!*
"I cannot follow"
I told him,
"I have to go the opposite way."

BUTTERFLY

William Jay Smith

Of living creatures most I prize
Black-spotted yellow Butterflies
Sailing softly through the skies,

Whisking light from each sunbeam,
Gliding over field and stream—
Like fans unfolding in a dream,

Like fans of gold lace flickering
Before a drowsy elfin king
For whom the thrush and linnet sing—

Soft and beautiful and bright
As hands that move to touch the light
When Mother leans to say good night.

GREEN MOTH

Winifred Welles

The night the green moth came for me,
  A creamy moon poured down the hill,

The meadow seemed a silver sea,
Small pearls were hung in every tree,
  And all so still, so still—

He floated in on my white bed,
  A strange and soundless fellow.
I saw the horns wave on his head,
  He stepped across my pillow
In tiny ermine boots, and spread
  His cape of green and yellow.

He came so close that I could see
  His golden eyes, and sweet and chill,
His faint breath wavered over me.
"Come Child, my Beautiful," said he,
  And all so still, so still—

LITTLE SNAIL

Hilda Conkling

I saw a little snail
Come down the garden walk.
He wagged his head this way . . . that
    way . . .
Like a clown in a circus.
He looked from side to side
As though he were from a different country.
I have always said he carries his house on his
    back . . .
To-day in the rain
I saw that it was his umbrella!

SNAIL

Langston Hughes

Little snail,
Dreaming you go.
Weather and rose
Is all you know.

Weather and rose
Is all you see,
Drinking
The dewdrop's
Mystery.

THE LITTLE TURTLE

Vachel Lindsay

There was a little turtle.
He lived in a box.
He swam in a puddle.
He climbed on the rocks.

He snapped at a mosquito.
He snapped at a flea.
He snapped at a minnow.
And he snapped at me.

He caught the mosquito.
He caught the flea.
He caught the minnow.
But he didn't catch me.

GRANDFATHER FROG

Louise Seaman Bechtel

Fat green frog sits by the pond,
Big frog, bull frog, grandfather frog.
Croak—croak—croak.
Shuts his eye, opens his eye,
Rolls his eye, winks his eye,
Waiting for
A little fat fly.

Croak, croak.
I go walking down by the pond,
I want to see the big green frog,
I want to stare right into his eye,
Rolling, winking, funny old eye.
But oh! he hears me coming by.
Croak—croak—
SPLASH!

OUR MR. TOAD

David McCord

Our Mr. Toad
Has a nice abode
Under the first front step.
When it rains he's cool
In a secret pool
Where the water goes
     drip
     drop
     drep.

Our Mr. Toad
Will avoid the road:
He's a private-cellar man.
And it's not much fun
In the broiling sun
When you *have* a good
     ten
     tone
     tan.

Our Mr. Toad
Has a kind of code
That tells him the coast is clear.
Then away he'll hop
With a stop, stop, stop
When the dusk draws
     nigh
     no
     near.

THE NEWT

David McCord

The little newt
Is not a brute,
A fish or fowl,
A kind of owl:
He doesn't prowl
Or run or dig
Or grow too big.
He doesn't fly
Or laugh or cry—
He doesn't try.

The little newt
Is mostly mute,
And grave and wise,
And has two eyes.
He lives inside,
Or likes to hide;
But after rain
He's out again
And rather red,
I should have said.

The little newt
Of great repute
Has legs, a tail,
A spotted veil.
He walks alone
From stone to stone,
From log to log,
From bog to bog,
From tree to tree,
From you to me.

The little newt
By grass or root
Is very kind
But hard to find.
His hands and feet
Are always neat:
They move across
The mildest moss.
He's very shy,
He's never spry—
Don't ask me why.

SNAKE

D. H. Lawrence

A snake came to my water-trough
On a hot, hot day, and I in pyjamas for the
    heat,
To drink there.

In the deep, strange-scented shade of the great
    dark carob-tree
I came down the steps with my pitcher
And must wait, must stand and wait, for there
    he was at the trough before me.

He reached down from a fissure in the earth-wall
    in the gloom
And trailed his yellow-brown slackness soft-
    bellied down, over the edge of the stone
    trough
And rested his throat upon the stone bottom,
And where the water had dripped from the tap,
    in a small clearness,
He sipped with his straight mouth,
Softly drank through his straight gums, into his
    slack long body,
Silently.

Someone was before me at my water-trough,
And I, like a second comer, waiting.

He lifted his head from this drinking, as cattle do,
And looked at me vaguely, as drinking cattle do,
And flickered his two-forked tongue from his lips,
    and mused a moment,
And stooped and drank a little more,
Being earth brown, earth golden from the burn-
    ing burning bowels of the earth
On the day of Sicilian July, with Etna smoking.

The voice of my education said to me
He must be killed,
For in Sicily the black, black snakes are innocent,
    the gold are venomous.

And voices in me said, If you were a man
You would take a stick and break him now, and
    finish him off.

But I must confess how I liked him,
How glad I was he had come like a guest in
    quiet, to drink at my water-trough
And depart peaceful, pacified, and thankless,
Into the burning bowels of this earth.

Was it cowardice, that I dared not kill him?
Was it perversity, that I longed to talk to him?
Was it humility, to feel so honoured?
I felt so honoured.

And yet those voices:
If you were not afraid, you would kill him!

And truly I was afraid, I was most afraid,
But even so, honoured still more
That he should seek my hospitality
From out the dark door of the secret earth.

He drank enough
And lifted his head, dreamily, as one who has
    drunken,
And flickered his tongue like a forked night on
    the air, so black,
Seeming to lick his lips,
And looked around like a god, unseeing, into
    the air,
And slowly turned his head,
And slowly, very slowly, as if thrice adream,
Proceeded to draw his slow length curving round
And climb again the broken bank of my wall-
    face.

And as he put his head into that dreadful hole,
And as he slowly drew up, snake-easing his
    shoulders, and entered farther,

A sort of horror, a sort of protest against his
    withdrawing into that horrid black hole,
Deliberately going into the blackness, and slowly
    drawing himself after,
Overcame me now his back was turned.

I looked round, I put down my pitcher,
I picked up a clumsy log
And threw it at the water-trough with a clatter.

I think it did not hit him,
But suddenly that part of him that was left be-
    hind convulsed in undignified haste,
Writhed like lightning, and was gone
Into the black hole, the earth-lipped fissure in
    the wall-front,
At which, in the intense still noon, I stared with
    fascination.

And immediately I regretted it.
I thought how paltry, how vulgar, what a mean
    act!
I despised myself and the voices of my accursed
    human education.

And I thought of the albatross,
And I wished he would come back, my snake.

For he seemed to me again like a king,
Like a king in exile, uncrowned in the under-
    world,
Now due to be crowned again.
And so, I missed my chance with one of the
    lords
Of life.
And I have something to expiate;
A pettiness.

THE ANT VILLAGE

Marion Edey and Dorothy Grider

Somebody up in the rocky pasture
  Heaved the stone over.
Here are the cells and a network of furrows
  In the roots of the clover.

Hundreds of eggs lie fitted in patterns,
  Waxy and yellow.
Hundreds of ants are racing and struggling.
  One little fellow

Shoulders an egg as big as his body,
  Ready for hatching.
Darkness is best, so everyone's rushing,
  Hastily snatching

Egg after egg to the lowest tunnels.
  And suddenly, where
Confusion had been, there now is nothing.
  Ants gone. Cells bare.

Mary Britton Miller

A son just born
To a duck is a drake,
And the child of a goose
Is called gosling,
And the moment when
The little chick steps
From the egg of a hen
A chicken is born.
But who knows the name
Of the new-born son
Of the beautiful swan?

(Cygnet)

GOOD MORNING

Muriel Sipe (Mrs. David Ross)

One day I saw a downy duck,
With feathers on his back;
I said, "Good morning, downy duck,"
And he said, "Quack, quack, quack."

One day I saw a timid mouse,
He was so shy and meek;
I said, "Good morning, timid mouse,"
And he said, "Squeak, squeak, squeak."

One day I saw a curly dog,
I met him with a bow;
I said, "Good morning, curly dog,"
And he said, "Bow-wow-wow."

One day I saw a scarlet bird,
He woke me from my sleep;
I said, "Good morning, scarlet bird,"
And he said, "Cheep, cheep, cheep."

THE BARNYARD

Maude Burnham

When the Farmer's day is done,
In the barnyard, ev'ry one,
Beast and bird politely say,
"Thank you for my food to-day."
The cow says, "Moo!"
The pigeon, "Coo!"
The sheep says, "Baa!"
The lamb says, "Maa!"
The hen, "Cluck! Cluck!"

"The Ant Village." Reprinted from *Open the Door* by Marion Edey and Dorothy Grider. Copyright 1949 by Marion Edey and Dorothy Grider. Used by permission of the publishers, Charles Scribner's Sons
  "A son just born to a duck." From *Give a Guess* by

Mary Britton Miller. New York: Pantheon Books, Inc., 1957
  "Good Morning." From *Sung under the Silver Umbrella*. The Macmillan Company, New York, 1935. Used by permission of the author

"Quack!" says the duck;
The dog, "Bow Wow!"
The cat, "Meow!"
The horse says, "Neigh!
I love sweet hay!"
The pig near by,
Grunts in his sty.

When the barn is locked up tight,
Then the Farmer says, "Good night!";
Thanks his animals, ev'ry one,
For the work that has been done.

Christina Georgina Rossetti

Minnie and Mattie
    And fat little May,
Out in the country,
    Spending a day.

Such a bright day,
    With the sun glowing,
And the trees half in leaf,
    And the grass growing.

Pinky white pigling
    Squeals through his snout,
Woolly white lambkin
    Frisks all about.

Cluck! cluck! the nursing hen
    Summons her folk,—
Ducklings all downy soft,
    Yellow as yolk.

Cluck! cluck! the mother hen
    Summons her chickens
To peck the dainty bits
    Found in her pickings.

Minnie and Mattie
    And May carry posies,
Half of sweet violets,
    Half of primroses.

"Minnie and Mattie." *Did you discover that of the two hens mentioned in this barnyard poem, one has a brood of chicks, but the other has a flock of ducklings? See analysis on the record album,* Poetry Time. From *Sing-Song by* Christina Georgina Rossetti

THE CHICKENS

(*German*)
Rose Fyleman

What a fearful battle,
What a dreadful storm!
Five little chickens
Fighting for a worm.

When the worm had vanished
They all said—Peep—and then
The five little chickens
Were all good friends again.

THE EGG

Laura E. Richards

Oh! how shall I get it, how shall I get it,—
A nice little new-laid egg?
My grandmamma told me to run to the barn-
    yard,
And see if just one I could beg.

"Moolly-cow, Moolly-cow, down in the meadow,
Have you any eggs, I pray?"
The Moolly-cow stares as if I were crazy,
And solemnly stalks away.

"Oh! Doggie, Doggie, perhaps you may have it,
That nice little egg for me."
But Doggie just wags his tail and capers,
And never an egg has he.

"Now, Dobbin, Dobbin, I'm sure you must have
    one,
Hid down in your manger there."
But Dobbin lays back his ears and whinnies,
With "Come and look, if you dare!"

"Piggywig, Piggywig, grunting and squealing,
Are you crying 'Fresh eggs for sale'?"
No! Piggy, you're very cold and unfeeling,
With that impudent quirk in your tail.

"The Chickens." From *Picture Rhymes from Foreign Lands.* Copyright 1935 by Rose Fyleman. Reprinted by permission of J. B. Lippincott Company

"The Egg." From *Tirra Lirra* by Laura E. Richards. Little, Brown & Company, Boston, 1932

"You wise old Gobbler, you look so knowing,
I'm sure you can find me an egg.
You stupid old thing! just to say 'Gobble-gobble!'
And balance yourself on one leg."

Oh! how shall I get it, how shall I get it,—
That little white egg so small?
I've asked every animal here in the barn-yard,
And they won't give me any at all.

But after I'd hunted until I was tired,
I found—not one egg, but ten!
And you *never* could guess where they all were
    hidden,—
Right under our old speckled hen!

CHICKEN

Walter de la Mare

Clapping her platter stood plump Bess,
    And all across the green
Came scampering in, on wing and claw,
    Chicken fat and lean:—
Dorking, Spaniard, Cochin China,
    Bantams sleek and small,
Like feathers blown in a great wind,
    They came at Bessie's call.

CHANTICLEER

John Farrar

High and proud on the barnyard fence
Walks rooster in the morning.
He shakes his comb, he shakes his tail
And gives his daily warning.

"Get up, you lazy boys and girls,
It's time you should be dressing!"
I wonder if he keeps a clock,
Or if he's only guessing.

CHANTICLEER

Katherine Tynan

Of all the birds from East to West
    That tuneful are and dear,
I love that farmyard bird the best,
    They call him Chanticleer.

*Gold plume and copper plume,
    Comb of scarlet gay;
'Tis he that scatters night and gloom,
    And summons back the day!*

He is the sun's brave herald
    Who, ringing his blithe horn,
Calls round a world dew-pearled
    The heavenly airs of morn.

Oh, clear gold, shrill and bold,
    He calls through creeping mist
The mountains from the night and cold
    To rose and amethyst.

He sets the birds to singing,
    And calls the flowers to rise;
The morning cometh, bringing
    Sweet sleep to heavy eyes.

*Gold plume and silver plume,
    Comb of coral gay;
'Tis he packs off the night and gloom,
    And summons home the day.*

Black fear he sends it flying,
    Black care he drives afar;
And creeping shadows sighing
    Before the morning star.

The birds of all the forest
    Have dear and pleasant cheer,

"Chicken." *See record album* Poetry Time. *From Collected Poems, 1901–1918,* by Walter de la Mare. Copyright, 1920, by Henry Holt and Company, Inc. Copyright, 1948, by Walter de la Mare. Reprinted by permission of the publishers
"Chanticleer." From *Songs for Parents* by John Farrar.

Yale University Press, New Haven, 1921
"Chanticleer." From *Collected Poems* by Katherine Tynan. Used with the permission of The Macmillan Company. By permission also of Miss Pamela Hinkson and The Society of Authors
"The Hens." From *Under the Tree* by Elizabeth Madox

But yet I hold the rarest
  The farmyard Chanticleer.

Red cock and black cock,
  Gold cock or white,
The flower of all the feathered flock,
  He summons back the light!

THE HENS

Elizabeth Madox Roberts

The night was coming very fast;
It reached the gate as I ran past.

The pigeons had gone to the tower of the church
And all the hens were on their perch,

Up in the barn, and I thought I heard
A piece of a little purring word.

I stopped inside, waiting and staying,
To try to hear what the hens were saying.

They were asking something, that was plain,
Asking it over and over again.

One of them moved and turned around,
Her feathers made a ruffled sound,

A ruffled sound, like a bushful of birds,
And she said her little asking words.

She pushed her head close into her wing,
But nothing answered anything.

THE DUCKS

Alice Wilkins

When our ducks waddle to the pond,
They're awkward as awkward can be—
But when they get in the water and swim,
They glide most gracefully.

DUCKS AT DAWN

James S. Tippett

"Quack! Quack!"
Said seven ducks at dawn
While night dew
Glimmered on the lawn.

"Quack! Quack!" they said.
"It's time to eat.
We'll go hunt mushrooms
For a treat."

And in the light
Of early dawn
I saw them chasing
On the lawn.

They sought their treat
With hungry quacks
And marked the dew
With criss-cross tracks.

They ate the mushrooms
One by one
And quacked to greet
The rising sun.

But in my bed
I settled back
And slept to tunes
Of "Quack! Quack! Quack!"

DUCKS' DITTY

Kenneth Grahame

All along the backwater,
Through the rushes tall,
Ducks are a-dabbling,
Up tails all!

Ducks' tails, drakes' tails,
Yellow feet a-quiver,

Yellow bills all out of sight
Busy in the river!

Slushy green undergrowth
Where the roach swim—
Here we keep our larder,
Cool and full and dim.

Everyone for what he likes!
We like to be
Heads down, tails up,
Dabbling free!

High in the blue above
Swifts whirl and call—
We are down a-dabbling
Up tails all!

QUACK!
Walter de la Mare

The duck is whiter than whey is,
His tail tips up over his back,
The eye in his head is as round as a button,
And he says, *Quack! Quack!*

He swims on his bright blue mill-pond,
By the willow tree under the shack,
Then stands on his head to see down to the bottom,
And says, *Quack! Quack!*

When Mollie steps out of the kitchen,
For apron—pinned round with a sack;
He squints at her round face, her dish, and
what's in it,
And says, *Quack! Quack!*

He preens the pure snow of his feathers
In the sun by the wheat-straw stack;
At dusk waddles home with his brothers and sisters,
And says, *Quack! Quack!*

"Quack!" From *Bells and Grass* by Walter de la Mare.
Copyright 1942 by Walter de la Mare. Reprinted by permission of The Viking Press, Inc., New York. By permission of the author and by Faber and Faber Limited
"The Cow." From *A Child's Garden of Verses* by Robert

(*Mother Goose*)

Baa, baa, black sheep,
    Have you any wool?
Yes, marry, have I,
    Three bags full;

One for my master,
    One for my dame,
But none for the little boy
    Who cries in the lane.

THE COW
Robert Louis Stevenson

The friendly cow all red and white,
    I love with all my heart:
She gives me cream, with all her might,
    To eat with apple-tart.

She wanders lowing here and there,
    And yet she cannot stray,
All in the pleasant open air,
    The pleasant light of day;

And blown by all the winds that pass
    And wet with all the showers,
She walks among the meadow grass
    And eats the meadow flowers.

GREEN GRASS AND WHITE MILK
Winifred Welles

Teeney and Weeney together are going
    Down to the dairy to fetch the milk,
    Down through the meadow as shiny as silk,
Where grass bends over and daisies are blowing.

With never a word yet somehow hobnobbing,
    Teeney and Weeney, like tots in a dream,
    Trudge solemnly down to bring back the
        cream,
Their bright yellow heads like buttercups bobbing.

Louis Stevenson
"Green Grass and White Milk." From *Skipping Along Alone* by Winifred Welles. The Macmillan Company, New York, 1931. Used by permission of James Welles Shearer
"Buttercup Cow." Elizabeth Rendall from "Here We

Up through the field that the sun makes glossy,
   Tossing their tails and taking their time,
   Tinkling their bells in a rusty chime,
Cropping and crunching, come Bossy and Bossy.

They stoop to the ground or they stand unblink-
      ing,
   Munching and munching, making green grass
   Into white milk to pour into a glass
For Teeney and Weeney to have for drinking.

BUTTERCUP COW

Elizabeth Rendall

Buttercup Cow has milk for me
I drink in my silver cup at tea.
Buttercup Cow is speckled and white,
She lives in the meadow from morning till night.

Buttercup Cow hasn't got any bed,
But the moon and the stars look in at her shed.
Buttercup Cow, I'm glad to be me,
Drinking your pretty white milk for my tea.

THE NEW BABY CALF

Edith H. Newlin

Buttercup, the cow, had a new baby calf,
      a fine baby calf,
         a strong baby calf,

Not strong like his mother
But strong for a calf,
For *this* baby calf was so *new!*

Buttercup licked him with her strong warm
      tongue,
Buttercup washed him with her strong warm
      tongue,
Buttercup brushed him with her strong warm
      tongue,
   And the new baby calf *liked that!*

Come A' Piping," Book I (by Rose Fyleman). By permission of Basil Blackwell & Mott, Ltd., Oxford
   "The New Baby Calf." From *Very Young Verses.* Houghton Mifflin Company, Boston, 1945. Used by permission of the author

The new baby calf took a very little walk,
         a tiny little walk,
            a teeny little walk,

But his long legs wobbled
When he took a little walk,
   And the new baby calf fell down.

Buttercup told him with a low soft "Moo-oo!"
That he was doing very well for one so very new
And she talked very gently, as mother cows do,
   And the new baby calf *liked that!*

The new baby calf took another little walk,
         a little longer walk,
            a little stronger walk,
He walked around his mother and he found the
      place to drink.
   And the new baby calf liked *that!*

Buttercup told him with another low moo
That drinking milk from mother was a fine thing
      to do,
That she had lots of milk for him and for the
      farmer too,
   And the new baby calf liked *that!*

The new baby calf drank milk every day,
His legs grew so strong that he could run and
      play,
He learned to eat grass and then grain and hay,
   And the big baby calf grew fat!

THE PASTURE

Robert Frost

I'm going out to clean the pasture spring;
I'll only stop to rake the leaves away
(And wait to watch the water clear, I may):
I sha'n't be gone long.—You come too.

I'm going out to fetch the little calf
That's standing by the mother. It's so young
It totters when she licks it with her tongue.
I sha'n't be gone long.—You come too.

"The Pasture." From *Collected Poems of Robert Frost.* Copyright, 1930, 1939, by Henry Holt and Company, Inc. Copyright, 1939, by Robert Frost. Reprinted by permission of Henry Holt and Company, Inc.

THE YOUNG CALVES

Robert P. Tristram Coffin

A hush had fallen on the birds,
    And it was almost night,
When I came round a turn and saw
    A whole year's loveliest sight.

Two calves that thought their month of life
    Meant June through all the year
Were coming down the grassy road
    As slender as young deer.

They stopped amazed and took me in,
    Putting their ears out far,
And in each of four round eyes
    There was an evening star.

They did not breathe, they stared so hard,
    Brother close to brother,
Then their legs awoke, and they
    Turned flank to flank for mother.

A small boy in torn knickers came
    And caught them as they fled,
He put a slender arm around
    Each slender, startled head.

He never looked at me at all,
    I was not in his mind;
The three of them went down the road
    And never glanced behind.

GREEN AFTERNOON

Frances M. Frost

The mother cow looked up and great surprise
Darkened her soft eyes
To see a spotted fawn come out to play
With her young calf that day.

The young ones both were tan with narrow
    shanks.
The puzzled cow gave thanks

Hers wasn't crazy-spotted like the other:
It must have a careless mother

If she would let it leave the wood's soft shadow
For this wide clover meadow.
Fawn danced on air toward calf, and calf half-
    stumbled,
Bawled as it nearly tumbled.

The mother cow grew nervous and said so—
With a soft commanding low—
And then she saw the tawny doe keen-watching
From a hemlock's thatching.

Both mothers watched their young—the tame,
    the free—
Rub foreheads awkwardly.
The calf pushed fawn, the slender fawn pushed
    calf.
Both mothers had to laugh.

Then suddenly the wind changed: in a breath
The fawn was gone beneath
Green boughs; the cow beside the meadow's rail
Scrubbed her calf from nose to tail.

GREEN HILL NEIGHBORS

Frances M. Frost

When I look at our green hill,
I think of all the wild
Small hearts that live inside it:
The woodchuck's chubby child,

Rabbits with busy whiskered faces
Peering out of rocks,
The big-eared meadow mouse, the dainty
Gold-eyed baby fox.

When I look at our green hill
Beneath the sunny sky,
I'm pleased to have such friends inside—
And glad I live nearby!

(Mother Goose)

This is the way the ladies ride,
  Tri, tre, tre, tree,
  Tri, tre, tre, tree!
This is the way the ladies ride,
  Tri, tre, tre, tre, tri-tre-tre-tree!

This is the way the gentlemen ride,
  Gallop-a-trot,
  Gallop-a-trot!
This is the way the gentlemen ride,
  Gallop-a-gallop-a-trot!

This is the way the farmers ride,
  Hobbledy-hoy,
  Hobbledy-hoy!
This is the way the farmers ride,
  Hobbledy-hobbledy-hoy!

FOAL

Mary Britton Miller

Come trotting up
Beside your mother,
Little skinny.

Lay your neck across
Her back, and whinny,
Little foal.

You think you're a horse
Because you can trot—
But you're not.

Your eyes are so wild,
And each leg is as tall
As a pole;

And you're only a skittish
Child, after all,
Little foal.

TROT ALONG, PONY

Marion Edey and Dorothy Grider

Trot along, pony.
  Late in the day,
Down by the meadow
  Is the loveliest way.

The apples are rosy
  And ready to fall.
The branches hang over
  By Grandfather's wall.

But the red sun is sinking
  Away out of sight.
The chickens are settling
  Themselves for the night.

Your stable is waiting
  And supper will come.
So turn again, pony,
  Turn again home.

THE RUNAWAY

Robert Frost

Once, when the snow of the year was beginning
    to fall,
We stopped by a mountain pasture to say,
    "Whose colt?"
A little Morgan had one forefoot on the wall,
The other curled at his breast. He dipped his
    head
And snorted to us. And then he had to bolt.
We heard the miniature thunder where he fled
And we saw him or thought we saw him dim
    and gray,

"Foal." From *Menagerie* by Mary Britton Miller, published by The Macmillan Company, 1928. By permission of the author

"Trot Along, Pony." Reprinted from *Open the Door* by Marion Edey and Dorothy Grider. Copyright 1949 by

Marion Edey and Dorothy Grider. Used by permission of the publishers, Charles Scribner's Sons

"The Runaway." *Morgan horses are Vermont horses and their story has been well told by Marguerite Henry in* Justin Morgan Had a Horse. *From* New Hampshire *by*

Like a shadow against the curtain of falling
    flakes.
"I think the little fellow's afraid of the snow.
He isn't winter-broken. It isn't play
With the little fellow at all. He's running away.
I doubt if even his mother could tell him, 'Sakes,
It's only weather.' He'd think she didn't know!
Where is his mother? He can't be out alone."
And now he comes again with a clatter of stone,
And mounts the wall again with whited eyes
And all his tail that isn't hair up straight.
He shudders his coat as if to throw off flies.
"Whoever it is that leaves him out so late,
When other creatures have gone to stall and bin,
Ought to be told to come and take him in."

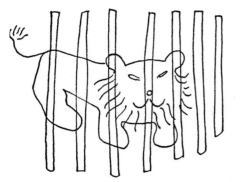

EXCUSE US, ANIMALS IN THE ZOO
Annette Wynne

Excuse us, Animals in the Zoo,
I'm sure we're very rude to you;
Into your private house we stare
And never ask you if you care;
And never ask you if you mind.
Perhaps we really are not kind;
I think it must be hard to stay
And have folks looking in all day,
I wouldn't like my house that way.

Excuse us, Animals in the Zoo,
I'm sure we're very rude to you;
Suppose you all to our house came
And stared at us and called our name.

I hardly think we'd like it at all
In a house that didn't have a wall.
No wonder you pace up and down the floor
And growl a little or even roar—
I'm sure if 'twere we, we'd growl much more.

Excuse us, Animals in the Zoo,
I'm sure we're very rude to you.

THE ELEPHANT'S TRUNK
Alice Wilkins

The elephant always carries his trunk.
I couldn't do that with my own.
His trunk is a part of himself, you see—
It's part of his head—it's grown!

HOLDING HANDS
Lenore M. Link

Elephants walking
Along the trails

Are holding hands
By holding tails.

Trunks and tails
Are handy things

When elephants walk
In Circus rings.

Elephants work
And elephants play

And elephants walk
And feel so gay.

And when they walk—
It never fails

They're holding hands
By holding tails.

THE ELEPHANT
Hilaire Belloc

When people call this beast to mind,
   They marvel more and more
At such a *little* tail behind,
   So LARGE a trunk before.

THE ELEPHANT
Herbert Asquith

Here comes the elephant
Swaying along
With his cargo of children
All singing a song:
To the tinkle of laughter
He goes on his way,
And his cargo of children
Have crowned him with may.
His legs are in leather
And padded his toes:
He can root up an oak
With a whisk of his nose:
With a wave of his trunk
And a turn of his chin
He can pull down a house,
Or pick up a pin.
Beneath his gray forehead
A little eye peers;
Of what is he thinking
Between those wide ears?
Of what does he think?
If he wished to tease,
He could twirl his keeper
Over the trees:
If he were not kind,
He could play cup and ball
With Robert and Helen,
And Uncle Paul:
But that gray forehead,
Those crinkled ears,
Have learned to be kind
In a hundred years:

And so with the children
He goes on his way
To the tinkle of laughter
And crowned with the may.

THE MONKEYS
Edith Osborne Thompson

Sing a song of monkeys,
A jolly bunch of monkeys!
Leaping, swinging in their cages
Looking wise as ancient sages,
Nonchalant and carefree manner,
Nibbling peanut or banana,
Every day is just another
To a monkey or his brother.

Sing a song of monkeys,
Happy, merry monkeys,
If you're ever tired or blue
I can tell you what to do!
Let the monkeys at the Zoo
Make a monkey out of you!

THE HIPPOPOTAMUS
Georgia Roberts Durston

In the squdgy river,
   Down the oozely bank,
Where the ripples shiver,
   And the reeds are rank.

Where the purple Kippo
   Makes an awful fuss,
Lives the hip-hip-hippo
   Hippo-pot-a-mus!

Broad his back and steady;
   Broad and flat his nose;
Sharp and keen and ready
   Little eyes are those.

You would think him dreaming
   Where the mud is deep.

"The Elephant." Reprinted from *Cautionary Verses* by Hilaire Belloc. By permission of Alfred A. Knopf, Inc. Copyright 1931 by Hilaire Belloc

"The Elephant." From *Pillicock Hill* by Herbert Asquith. Used with the permission of The Macmillan Company. By permission also of the author and William Heinemann, Ltd.

"The Monkeys." From *St. Nicholas*, February 1936. Used with the kind permission of Juliet Lit Stern

"The Hippopotamus." From *Junior Home Magazine*. Used by permission of Child Training Association, Incorporated, publishers of *Children's Activities*

It is only seeming—
He is not asleep.

Better not disturb him,
 There'd be an awful fuss
If you touched the Hippo,
 Hippo-pot-a-mus.

THE SEALS
Dorothy Aldis

The seals all flap
Their shining flips
And bounce balls on
Their nosey tips,
And beat a drum,
And catch a bar,
And wriggle with
How pleased they are.

SEAL LULLABY
Rudyard Kipling

Oh! hush thee, my baby, the night is behind us,
 And black are the waters that sparkled so
   green.
The moon, o'er the combers, looks downward
   to find us
 At rest in the hollows that rustle between.
Where billow meets billow, then soft be thy pil-
   low,
 Ah, weary wee flipperling, curl at thy ease!
The storm shall not wake thee, nor shark over-
   take thee,
 Asleep in the arms of the slow-swinging seas!

"The Seals." From *Hop, Skip and Jump* by Dorothy Aldis. Minton, Balch and Company, New York, 1934. Copyright 1934 by Dorothy Aldis
"Seal Lullaby." From *The Jungle Book* by Rudyard Kipling. Reprinted by permission of Mrs. George Bam-

THE KANGAROO
Elizabeth Coatsworth

It is a curious thing that you
don't wish to be a kangaroo,
 to hop hop hop
 and never stop
the whole day long and the whole night, too!

to hop across Australian plains
with tails that sweep behind like trains
 and small front paws
 and pointed jaws
and pale neat coats to shed the rains.

If skies be blue, if skies be gray,
they bound in the same graceful way
 into dim space
 at such a pace
that where they go there's none to say!

HERE SHE IS
Mary Britton Miller

Jungle necklaces are hung
Around her tiger throat
And on her tiger arms are slung
Bracelets black and brown;
She shows off when she lies down
All her tiger strength and grace,
You can see the tiger blaze
In her tiger eyes, her tiger face.

THE TIGER
William Blake

Tiger! Tiger! burning bright
In the forests of the night,
What immortal hand or eye
Could frame thy fearful symmetry?

In what distant deeps or skies
Burnt the fire of thine eyes?
On what wings dare he aspire?
What the hand dare seize the fire?

bridge, The Macmillan Company of Canada, Ltd., and Macmillan & Company, Ltd., London
"The Kangaroo." From *Summer Green* by Elizabeth Coatsworth. Copyright 1948 by The Macmillan Company and used with their permission

And what shoulder, and what art,
Could twist the sinews of thy heart?
And when thy heart began to beat,
What dread hand? and what dread feet?

What the hammer? what the chain?
In what furnace was thy brain?
What the anvil? what dread grasp
Dare its deadly terrors clasp?

When the stars threw down their spears,
And watered heaven with their tears,
Did He smile His work to see?
Did He who made the Lamb make thee?

Tiger! Tiger! burning bright
In the forests of the night,
What immortal hand or eye
Dare frame thy fearful symmetry?

FRANCIS JAMMES: A PRAYER TO GO TO PARADISE WITH THE DONKEYS

Richard Wilbur

When I must come to you, O my God, I pray
It be some dusty-roaded holiday,
And even as in my travels here below,
I beg to choose by what road I shall go
To Paradise, where the clear stars shine by day.
I'll take my walking-stick and go my way,
And to my friends the donkeys I shall say,
"I am Francis Jammes, and I'm going to Paradise,
For there is no hell in the land of the loving God."
And I'll say to them: "Come, sweet friends of the blue skies,
Poor creatures who with a flap of the ears or a nod
Of the head shake off the buffets, the bees, the flies . . ."

Let me come with these donkeys, Lord, into your land,
These beasts who bow their heads so gently, and stand

With their small feet joined together in a fashion
Utterly gentle, asking your compassion.
I shall arrive, followed by their thousands of ears,
Followed by those with baskets at their flanks,
By those who lug the carts of mountebanks
Or loads of feather-dusters and kitchen-wares,
By those with humps of battered water-cans,
By bottle-shaped she-asses who halt and stumble,
By those tricked out in little pantaloons
To cover their wet, blue galls where flies assemble
In whirling swarms, making a drunken hum.
Dear God, let it be with these donkeys that I come,
And let it be that angels lead us in peace
To leafy streams where cherries tremble in air,
Sleek as the laughing flesh of girls; and there
In that haven of souls let it be that, leaning above
Your divine waters, I shall resemble these donkeys,
Whose humble and sweet poverty will appear
Clear in the clearness of your eternal love.

THE FLOWER-FED BUFFALOES

Vachel Lindsay

The flower-fed buffaloes of the spring
In the days of long ago,
Ranged where the locomotives sing
And the prairie flowers lie low:—
The tossing, blooming, perfumed grass
Is swept away by the wheat,
Wheels and wheels and wheels spin by
In the spring that still is sweet.
But the flower-fed buffaloes of the spring
Left us, long ago.
They gore no more, they bellow no more,
They trundle around the hills no more:—
With the Blackfeet, lying low.
With the Pawnees, lying low,
Lying low.

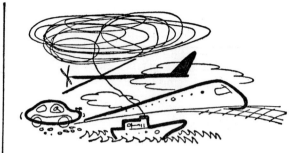

William Shakespeare

> Jog on, jog on, the foot-path way,
>   And merrily hent the stile-a:
> A merry heart goes all the day,
>   Your sad tires in a mile-a.

A MODERN DRAGON

Rowena Bastin Bennett

A train is a dragon that roars through the dark.
He wriggles his tail as he sends up a spark.
He pierces the night with his one yellow eye,
And all the earth trembles when he rushes by.

TRAVELING WE GO

THE BABY GOES TO BOSTON

Laura E. Richards

> What does the train say?
>   Jiggle joggle, jiggle joggle!
> What does the train say?
>   Jiggle joggle jee!
> Will the little baby go
> Riding with the locomo?
> Loky moky poky stoky
>   Smoky choky chee!

Ting! ting! the bells ring,
  Jiggle joggle, jiggle joggle!
Ting! ting! the bells ring,
  Jiggle joggle jee!
Ring for joy because we go
Riding with the locomo,
Loky moky poky stoky
  Smoky choky chee!

Look! how the trees run,
  Jiggle joggle, jiggle joggle!
Each chasing t' other one,
  Jiggle joggle jee!
Are they running for to go
Riding with the locomo?
Loky moky poky stoky
  Smoky choky chee!

Over the hills now,
  Jiggle joggle, jiggle joggle!
Down through the vale below,
  Jiggle joggle jee!
All the cows and horses run,
Crying, "Won't you take us on,
Loky moky poky stoky
  Smoky choky chee?"

So, so, the miles go,
  Jiggle joggle, jiggle joggle!
Now it's fast and now it's slow,
  Jiggle joggle jee!
When we're at our journey's end,
Say good-by to snorting friend,
Loky moky poky stoky
  Smoky choky chee!

TEXAS TRAINS AND TRAILS

Mary Austin

Whenever I ride on the Texas plains
I never hear the couplings cluck,

I never hear the trains
Go chuck-a-luck, chuck-a-luck, chuck-a-luck,
I never hear the engine snort and snuffle,
I never see the smoke plume, I never watch the
  rails,
But I see the moving dust where the beef herds
  shuffle,
And I think I am a cowboy,
A rope and tie 'em cowboy,
Punching Texas longhorns
On the Texas trails.

And the engine goes *Whoop!*
Whoopee, whoopala!
And the cars go *Ki-yi,*
Ki-yi, ki-yi, coma-la ky-yi,
        Whoopala,
Ki-yi!
    Whoop!

No, I never hear the bell, nor the brakeman call
When I ride on the Texas trains;
But I hear the steers bellow and the yearlings
  bawl,
And the lone wolf howl on the wire grass plains.
And I never play I'm fireman, nor anything like
  that,
For I'm playing I'm a cowboy,
A bronco-bustin' cowboy,
Riding Texas longhorns
In a ten-gallon hat.

And the trains go *Youpi-ya,*
Get a-long, dogies,
Get a-long, get a-long
Youpi-yi, youpi-ya,
Youpi-youpi-youpi-ya
Get a-long, get a-long,
Youpi-ya,
    Yo-o-u-u-p!

"Jog on, jog on, the foot-path way." *See May Hill Arbuthnot,* Children and Books, *p. 181.* From *The Winter's Tale,* Act IV, Sc. 3

"A Modern Dragon." From *Around a Toadstool Table* by Rowena Bastin Bennett. Follett Publishing Company, Chicago, 1930

"The Baby Goes to Boston." *This poem jiggles along like the Toonerville Trolley. See record album* Poetry Time. *From* Tirra Lirra *by Laura E. Richards. Little, Brown & Company, Boston, 1932*

"Texas Trains and Trails." *This poem sounds for all the world like a train in motion but it is not easy to read. You will just have to try it aloud repeatedly till you get it. In the first refrain, there seems to be a silent beat after the line, "Whoopee, whoopala!" In each refrain the train seems to start slowly, gain momentum, and end with a grand "whoop" for full speed ahead!* From *The Children Sing in the Far West* by Mary Austin. Reprinted by permission of and arrangement with Houghton Mifflin Company, the authorized publishers

FROM A RAILWAY CARRIAGE

Robert Louis Stevenson

Faster than fairies, faster than witches,
Bridges and houses, hedges and ditches;
And charging along like troops in a battle
All through the meadows the horses and cattle:
All of the sights of the hill and the plain
Fly as thick as driving rain;
And ever again, in the wink of an eye,
Painted stations whistle by.

Here is a child who clambers and scrambles,
All by himself and gathering brambles;
Here is a tramp who stands and gazes;
And there is the green for stringing the daisies!
Here is a cart run away in the road
Lumping along with man and load;
And here is a mill, and there is a river:
Each a glimpse and gone for ever!

TRAINS AT NIGHT

Frances M. Frost

I like the whistle of trains at night,
The fast trains thundering by so proud!
They rush and rumble across the world,
They ring wild bells and they toot so loud!

But I love better the slower trains.
They take their time through the world instead,
And whistle softly and stop to tuck
Each sleepy blinking town in bed!

TRAINS

James S. Tippett

Over the mountains,
Over the plains,
Over the rivers,
Here come the trains.

Carrying passengers,
Carrying mail,
Bringing their precious loads
In without fail.

Thousands of freight cars
All rushing on
Through day and darkness,
Through dusk and dawn.

Over the mountains,
Over the plains,
Over the rivers,
Here come the trains.

THE WAYS OF TRAINS

Elizabeth Coatsworth

I hear the engine pounding
in triumph down the track—
trains take away the ones you love
and then they bring them back!

trains take away the ones you love
to worlds both strange and new
and then, with care and courtesy,
they bring them back to you.

The engine halts and snuffs and snorts,
it breathes forth smoke and fire,
then snatches crowded strangers on—
but leaves what you desire!

TRAVEL

Edna St. Vincent Millay

The railroad track is miles away,
  And the day is loud with voices speaking,
Yet there isn't a train goes by all day
  But I hear its whistle shrieking.

All night there isn't a train goes by,
  Though the night is still for sleep and dream-
    ing
But I see its cinders red on the sky,
  And hear its engine steaming.

My heart is warm with the friends I make,
  And better friends I'll not be knowing,
Yet there isn't a train I wouldn't take,
  No matter where it's going.

TAKING OFF

Unknown

The airplane taxis down the field
And heads into the breeze,
It lifts its wheels above the ground,
It skims above the trees,
It rises high and higher
Away up toward the sun,
It's just a speck against the sky
—And now it's gone!

UP IN THE AIR

James S. Tippett

Zooming across the sky
Like a great bird you fly,
    Airplane,
    Silvery white
    In the light.

Turning and twisting in air,
When shall I ever be there,

Airplane,
Piloting you
Far in the blue?

AEROPLANE

Mary McB. Green

There's a humming in the sky
There's a shining in the sky
Silver wings are flashing by
Silver wings are shining by
Aeroplane
Aeroplane
Flying—high

Silver wings are shining
As it goes gliding by
First it zooms
And it booms
Then it buzzes in the sky
Then its song is just a drumming
A soft little humming
Strumming
Strumming

The wings are very little things
The silver shine is gone
Just a little black speck
Away down the sky
With a soft little strumming
And a far-away humming
Aeroplane
Aeroplane
Gone—by.

SILVER SHIPS

Mildred Plew Meigs

There are trails that a lad may follow
  When the years of his boyhood slip,
But I shall soar like a swallow
  On the wings of a silver ship,

"Taking Off." Reprinted from *Very Young Verses* published by Houghton Mifflin Company. The editors of this
book searched diligently to find the source and to obtain
permission to use this poem, but without success
"Up in the Air." From *I Go A-Traveling* by James S.
Tippett. Copyright, 1929, Harper & Brothers

"Aeroplane." Taken from *Another Here and Now Story
Book,* edited by Lucy Sprague Mitchell, published and
copyright, 1937, by E. P. Dutton & Co., Inc., New York
"Silver Ships." From *Child Life*, May 1930. Child Life,
Inc., Boston. By permission of Marion Plew Ruckel

Guiding my bird of metal,
   One with her throbbing frame,
Floating down like a petal,
   Roaring up like a flame;

Winding the wind that scatters
   Smoke from the chimney's lip,
Tearing the clouds to tatters
   With the wings of a silver ship;

Grazing the broad blue sky light
   Up where the falcons fare,
Riding the realms of twilight,
   Brushed by a comet's hair;

Snug in my coat of leather,
   Watching the skyline swing,
Shedding the world like a feather
   From the tip of a tilted wing.

There are trails that a lad may travel
   When the years of his boyhood wane,
But I'll let a rainbow ravel
   Through the wings of my silver plane.

COCKPIT IN THE CLOUDS
Dick Dorrance

Two thousand feet beneath our wheels
The city sprawls across the land
Like heaps of children's blocks outflung,
In tantrums, by a giant hand.
To east a silver spire soars
And seeks to pierce our lower wing.
Above its grasp we drift along,
A tiny, droning, shiny thing.

The noon crowds pack the narrow streets.
The el trains move so slow, so slow.
Amidst their traffic, chaos, life,
The city's busy millions go.
Up here, aloof, we watch them crawl.
In crystal air we seem to poise
Behind our motor's throaty roar—
Down there, we're just another noise.

NIGHT PLANE
Frances M. Frost

The midnight plane with its riding lights
looks like a footloose star
wandering west through the blue-black night
to where the mountains are,

a star that's journeyed nearer earth
to tell each quiet farm
and little town, "Put out your lights,
children of earth. Sleep warm."

TO BEACHEY, 1912
Carl Sandburg

   Riding against the east,
   A veering, steady shadow
   Purrs the motor-call
   Of the man-bird
   Ready with the death-laughter
   In his throat
   And in his heart always
   The love of the big blue beyond.

   Only a man,
   A far fleck of shadow on the east
   Sitting at ease
   With his hands on a wheel
   And around him the large gray wings.
   Hold him, great soft wings,
   Keep and deal kindly, O wings,
   With the cool, calm shadow at the wheel.

BOATS
Rowena Bastin Bennett

   The steamboat is a slow poke,
      You simply cannot rush him.

"Cockpit in the Clouds." From *The* (New York) *Sun.* Used by permission of the *New York World Telegram* and *The Sun.* By permission also of the author
   "Night Plane." From the *New York Herald Tribune,* May 1956. Reprinted by permission of the author

"To Beachey, 1912." *See the introduction, p. xx.* From *Chicago Poems* by Carl Sandburg. Copyright, 1916, by Henry Holt and Company, Inc. Copyright, 1944, by Carl Sandburg. Used by permission of the publishers
   "Boats." From *Around a Toadstool Table* by Rowena

The sailboat will not move at all
  Without a wind to push him;

But the speed boat, with his sharp red nose,
  Is quite a different kind;
He tosses high the spray and leaves
  The other boats behind.

FERRY-BOATS

James S. Tippett

Over the river,
Over the bay,
Ferry-boats travel
Every day.

Most of the people
Crowd to the side
Just to enjoy
Their ferry-boat ride.

Watching the seagulls,
Laughing with friends,
I'm always sorry
When the ride ends.

WHISTLES

Rachel Field

I never even hear
The boats that pass by day;
By night they seem so near,
A-whistling down the bay,
That I can almost understand
The things their whistles say.

I've waked sometimes all warm
In my bed, when eerily
I have heard them out of the dark
A-whistling cheerily
To tell the sleepy folk on land
All's well at sea.

A WET SHEET AND A FLOWING SEA

Allan Cunningham

A wet sheet and a flowing sea,
  A wind that follows fast
And fills the white and rustling sail,
  And bends the gallant mast!
And bends the gallant mast, my boys,
  While, like the eagle free,
Away the good ship flies, and leaves
  Old England on the lee.

O for a soft and gentle wind!
  I heard a fair one cry;
But give to me the swelling breeze,
  And white waves heaving high:
The white waves heaving high, my lads,
  The good ship tight and free;
The world of waters is our home,
And merry men are we.

There's tempest in yon horned moon,
  And lightning in yon cloud;
And hark the music, mariners!
  The wind is wakening loud.

Bastin Bennett. Follett Publishing Company, Chicago, 1930
  "Ferry-Boats." From *I Go A-Traveling* by James S. Tippett. Copyright, 1929, Harper & Brothers

"Whistles." From *The Pointed People* by Rachel Field. The Macmillan Company, New York, 1930. Used by permission of Arthur S. Pederson, Trustee, Estate of Rachel Field Pederson

The wind is wakening loud, my boys,
  The lightning flashes free—
The hollow oak our palace is,
  Our heritage the sea.

Elizabeth Coatsworth

A horse would tire,
But I, I do not tire.
A stag would turn,
But I still keep my course.
A bird must rest,
And ashes follow fire,
But I excel
Flame, bird, or deer, or horse.

Only the wind
Do I require for ration,
Only the waves
Beneath my forefoot curled.
Eager I run
From nation unto nation
And seek my harbor
Halfway round the world.

SEA-FEVER

John Masefield

I must go down to the seas again, to the lonely
  sea and the sky,
And all I ask is a tall ship and a star to steer
  her by,
And the wheel's kick and the wind's song and the
  white sail's shaking
And a gray mist on the sea's face and a gray dawn
  breaking.

I must go down to the seas again, for the call of
  the running tide
Is a wild call and a clear call that may not be
  denied;

And all I ask is a windy day with the white
  clouds flying,
And the flung spray and the blown spume, and
  the sea-gulls crying.

I must go down to the seas again to the vagrant
  gypsy life,
To the gull's way and the whale's way where the
  wind's like a whetted knife;
And all I ask is a merry yarn from a laughing
  fellow-rover,
And quiet sleep and a sweet dream when the
  long trick's over.

CARGOES

John Masefield

Quinquireme of Nineveh from distant Ophir
Rowing home to haven in sunny Palestine,
With a cargo of ivory,
And apes and peacocks,
Sandalwood, cedarwood, and sweet white wine.

Stately Spanish galleon coming from the Isth-
  mus,
Dipping through the Tropics by the palm-green
  shores,
With a cargo of diamonds,
Emeralds, amethysts,
Topazes, and cinnamon, and gold moidores.

Dirty British coaster with a salt-caked smoke-
  stack
Butting through the Channel in the mad March
  days,
With a cargo of Tyne coal,
Road-rails, pig-lead,
Firewood, iron-ware, and cheap tin trays.

RED IRON ORE

Come all you bold sailors that follow the Lakes
On an iron ore vessel your living to make.
I shipped in Chicago, bid adieu to the shore,
Bound away to Escanaba for red iron ore.
    Derry down, down, down derry down.

The wind from the south'ard sprang up a fresh
    breeze,
And away through Lake Michigan the *Roberts*
    did sneeze.
Down through Lake Michigan the *Roberts* did
    roar,
And on Friday morning we passed through
    death's door.
    Derry down, down, down derry down.

This packet she howled across the mouth of
    Green Bay,
And before her cutwater she dashed the white
    spray.
We rounded the sand point, our anchor let go,
We furled in our canvas and the watch went
    below.
    Derry down, down, down derry down.

Next morning we hove alongside the *Exile*,
And soon was made fast to an iron ore pile,
They lowered their chutes and like thunder did
    roar,
They spouted into us that red iron ore.
    Derry down, down, down derry down.

Some sailors took shovels while others got spades,
And some took wheelbarrows, each man to his
    trade.
We looked like red devils, our fingers got sore,
We cursed Escanaba and damned iron ore.
    Derry down, down, down derry down.

House by John Masefield. Copyright 1912, 1940 by The Macmillan Company and used with their permission. Permission granted also by Dr. John Masefield, O.M., and The Society of Authors

"Red Iron Ore." *Stanzas 2 and 8–12 are omitted. See May Hill Arbuthnot,* Children and Books, *p. 95. From* The American Songbag *compiled by Carl Sandburg. Harcourt,*

The tug *Escanaba* she towed out the *Minch*,
The *Roberts* she thought she had left in a pinch,
And as she passed by us she bid us good-bye,
Saying, "We'll meet you in Cleveland next
    Fourth of July!"
    Derry down, down, down derry down.

STOP—GO
Dorothy Baruch

    Automobiles
    In
      a
        row
    Wait to go
    While the signal says:
                 STOP

    Bells ring
    Tingaling
    Red light's gone!
    Green light's on!
    Horns blow!
    And the row
    Starts
        to
              GO

Brace and Company, Inc., New York, 1927

"Stop—Go." *A study in slow and fast like this one is fun to say with two people or two groups of children, one speaking the first and one the second verse, with slow and fast tempos. From* I Like Automobiles *by Dorothy Baruch. The John Day Company, New York, 1931. Copyright, 1931, by Dorothy Walter Baruch*

MOTOR CARS

Rowena Bastin Bennett

From a city window, 'way up high,
I like to watch the cars go by.
They look like burnished beetles, black,
That leave a little muddy track
Behind them as they slowly crawl.
Sometimes they do not move at all
But huddle close with hum and drone
As though they feared to be alone.
They grope their way through fog and night
With the golden feelers of their light.

SONG FOR A BLUE ROADSTER

Rachel Field

Fly, Roadster, fly!
    The sun is high,
Gold are the fields
    We hurry by,
Green are the woods
    As we slide through,
Past harbor and headland,
    Blue on blue.

Fly, Roadster, fly!
    The hay smells sweet,
And the flowers fringing
    Each village street,
Where carts are blue,
    And barns are red,
And the road unwinds
    Like a twist of thread.

Fly, Roadster, fly!
    Leave Time behind;
Out of sight
    Shall be out of mind.
Shine and shadow,
    Blue sea, green bough,
Nothing is real
    But Here and Now.

from ALL AROUND THE TOWN

Phyllis McGinley

J's the jumping Jay-walker,
    A sort of human jeep.
He crosses where the lights are red.
    Before he looks, he'll leap!
Then many a wheel
Begins to squeal,
    And many a brake to slam.
He turns your knees to jelly
    And the traffic into jam.

TAXIS

Rachel Field

Ho, for taxis green or blue,
    Hi, for taxis red,
They roll along the Avenue
    Like spools of colored thread!

Jack-o'-Lantern yellow,
Orange as the moon,
Greener than the greenest grass
Ever grew in June.
Gayly striped or checked in squares,
Wheels that twinkle bright,
Don't you think that taxis make
A very pleasant sight?
Taxis shiny in the rain,
Scudding through the snow,
Taxis flashing back the sun
Waiting in a row.

Ho, for taxis red and green,
    Hi, for taxis blue,
I wouldn't be a private car
    In sober black, would you?

from ALL AROUND THE TOWN

Phyllis McGinley

B's the Bus,
The bouncing Bus,
    That bears a shopper store-ward.

"Motor Cars." From *Around a Toadstool Table* by Rowena Bastin Bennett. Follett Publishing Company, Chicago, 1930

"Song for a Blue Roadster." From *Poems* by Rachel Field. Copyright © 1957 by The Macmillan Company,

New York, and used with their permission

"J's the jumping Jay-walker," "B's the Bus," "E is the Escalator," and "R is for the Restaurant." From *All Around the Town* by Phyllis McGinley. Copyright © 1948 by Phyllis McGinley. Published by J. B. Lippincott Com-

It's fun to sit
In back of it
   But seats are better forward.
Although it's big as buildings are
   And looks both bold and grand,
It has to stop obligingly
   If you but raise your hand.

from ALL AROUND THE TOWN
Phyllis McGinley

E is the Escalator
   That gives an elegant ride.
You step on the stair
With an easy air
   And up and up you glide.
It's nicer than scaling ladders
   Or scrambling 'round a hill,
For you climb and climb
But all the time
   You're really standing still.

from ALL AROUND THE TOWN
Phyllis McGinley

R is for the Restaurant—
   A really special treat.
(We do respect the relative
   Who takes us there to eat.)
The waiters rush with plates of rolls,
   They run to hold one's chair,
And always seem
To read ice-cream
   Upon the bill-of-fare.

MOVING
Eunice Tietjens

I like to move. There's such a feeling
Of hurrying
   and scurrying,
And such a feeling
Of men with trunks and packing cases,
Of kitchen clocks and mother's laces,
Dusters, dishes, books and vases,
Toys and pans and candles.

I always find things I'd forgotten,
An old brown Teddy stuffed with cotton,
Some croquet mallets without handles,
A marble and my worn-out sandals,
A half an engine and a hat . . .
And I like that.

I like to watch the big vans backing,
And the lumbering
   and the cumbering,
And the hammering and the tacking.
I even like the packing!

And that will prove
I like to move!

COUNTRY TRUCKS
Monica Shannon

Big trucks with apples
   And big trucks with grapes
Thundering through the mountains
   While every wild thing gapes.

Thundering through the valley,
   Like something just let loose,
Big trucks with oranges
   For city children's juice.

Big trucks with peaches,
   And big trucks with pears,
Frightening all the rabbits
   And giving squirrels gray hairs.

Yet, when city children
   Sit down to plum or prune,
They know more trucks are coming
   As surely as the moon.

CITY STREETS AND COUNTRY ROADS
Eleanor Farjeon

The city has streets—
   But the country has roads.

In the country one meets
  Blue carts with their loads
Of sweet-smelling hay,
  And mangolds, and grain:
Oh, take me away
  To the country again!

In the city one sees,
  Big trams rattle by,
And the breath of the chimneys
  That blot out the sky,
And all down the pavements
  Stiff lamp-posts one sees—
But the country has hedgerows,
  The country has trees.

As sweet as the sun
  In the country is rain:
Oh, take me away
  To the country again!

ROADS GO EVER EVER ON

J. R. R. Tolkien

Roads go ever ever on,
  Over rock and under tree,
By caves where never sun has shone,
  By streams that never find the sea;
Over snow by winter sown,
  And through the merry flowers of June,
Over grass and over stone,
  And under mountains in the moon.

T. S. Eliot

And now you live dispersed on ribbon roads,
And no man knows or cares who is his neighbour
Unless his neighbour makes too much disturb-
    ance,
But all dash to and fro in motor cars,
Familiar with the roads and settled nowhere.

"Roads Go Ever Ever On." From *The Hobbitt* by J. R. R. Tolkien. London: George Allen and Unwin, Ltd., 1936, and Boston: Houghton Mifflin Company, 1938

"And now you live dispersed on ribbon roads." From "The Rock" in *Collected Poems 1909–1935* by T. S. Eliot, copyright, 1936, by Harcourt, Brace and Company, Inc. Reprinted by permission of Harcourt, Brace and Com-

Edna St. Vincent Millay

Wonder where this horseshoe went.
Up and down, up and down,
Up and past the monument,
Maybe into town.

Wait a minute. "Horseshoe,
How far have you been?"
*Says it's been to Salem
And halfway to Lynn.*

Wonder who was in the team.
Wonder what they saw.
Wonder if they passed a bridge—
Bridge with a draw.

*Says it went from one bridge
Straight upon another.
Says it took a little girl
Driving with her mother.*

FAREWELL TO THE FARM

Robert Louis Stevenson

The coach is at the door at last;
The eager children, mounting fast
And kissing hands, in chorus sing:
Good-bye, good-bye, to everything!

To house and garden, field and lawn,
The meadow-gates we swung upon,
To pump and stable, tree and swing,
Good-bye, good-bye, to everything!

And fare you well for evermore,
O ladder at the hayloft door,
O hayloft where the cobwebs cling,
Good-bye, good-bye, to everything!

Crack goes the whip, and off we go;
The trees and houses smaller grow;
Last, round the woody turn we swing:
Good-bye, good-bye, to everything!

pany, Inc., and Faber and Faber, Limited

"Wonder where this horseshoe went." From "A Very Little Sphinx" in *Poems Selected for Young People*, published by Harper & Brothers. Copyright, 1923, by Edna St. Vincent Millay

"Farewell to the Farm." From *A Child's Garden of Verses* by Robert Louis Stevenson

JOHNNY FIFE AND JOHNNY'S WIFE

Mildred Plew Meigs

Oh, Johnny Fife and Johnny's wife,
   To save their toes and heels,
They built themselves a little house
   That ran on rolling wheels.

They hung their parrot at the door
   Upon a painted ring,
And round and round the world they went
   And never missed a thing;

And when they wished to eat they ate,
   And after they had fed,
They crawled beneath a crazy quilt
   And gayly went to bed;

And what they cared to keep they kept,
   And what they both did not,
They poked beneath a picket fence
   And quietly forgot.

Oh, Johnny Fife and Johnny's wife,
   They took their brush and comb,
And round and round the world they went
   And also stayed at home.

ADVENTURE

Harry Behn

It's not very far to the edge of town
Where trees look up and hills look down,
We go there almost every day
To climb and swing and paddle and play.

It's not very far to the edge of town,
Just up one little hill and down,
And through one gate, and over two stiles—
But coming home it's miles and miles.

Sir Walter Scott

Hie away, hie away,
Over bank and over brae,
Where the copsewood is the greenest,
Where the fountains glisten sheenest,
Where the lady fern grows strongest,
Where the morning dew lies longest,
Where the black-cock sweetest sips it,
Where the fairy latest trips it.
Hie to haunts right seldom seen,
Lovely, lonesome, cool, and green,
Over bank and over brae,
Hie away, hie away.

RING AROUND THE WORLD

Annette Wynne

Ring around the world
Taking hands together
All across the temperate
And the torrid weather.
Past the royal palm-trees
By the ocean sand
Make a ring around the world
Taking each other's hand;
In the valleys, on the hill,
Over the prairie spaces,
There's a ring around the world
Made of children's friendly faces.

"Johnny Fife and Johnny's Wife." From *Child Life*, May 1929. Child Life, Inc., Boston. By permission of Marion Plew Ruckel

"Adventure." From *The Little Hill* by Harry Behn. Copyright 1949 by Harry Behn. Reprinted by permission of Harcourt, Brace and Company, Inc., New York

"Hie away, hie away." *This is fun to do with verse* choirs. *See May Hill Arbuthnot,* Children and Books, *p. 218*

"Ring Around the World." *A pleasant picture of what the world might be with friendly faces all round it.* From *All Through the Year.* Copyright 1932 by Annette Wynne. Reprinted by permission of J. B. Lippincott Company

TRAVEL

Robert Louis Stevenson

I should like to rise and go
Where the golden apples grow;—
Where below another sky
Parrot islands anchored lie,
And, watched by cockatoos and goats,
Lonely Crusoes building boats;—
Where in sunshine reaching out
Eastern cities, miles about,
Are with mosque and minaret
Among sandy gardens set,
And the rich goods from near and far
Hang for sale in the bazaar;—
Where the Great Wall round China goes,
And on one side the desert blows,
And with bell and voice and drum,
Cities on the other hum;—
Where are forests, hot as fire,
Wide as England, tall as a spire,
Full of apes and cocoa-nuts
And the Negro hunters' huts;—
Where the knotty crocodile
Lies and blinks in the Nile,
And the red flamingo flies
Hunting fish before his eyes;—
Where in jungles, near and far,
Man-devouring tigers are,
Lying close and giving ear
Lest the hunt be drawing near,
Or a comer-by be seen
Swinging in a palanquin;—
Where among the desert sands
Some deserted city stands,
All its children, sweep and prince,
Grown to manhood ages since,
Not a foot in street or house,
Not a stir of child or mouse,
And when kindly falls the night,
In all the town no spark of light.
There I'll come when I'm a man

With a camel caravan;
Light a fire in the gloom
Of some dusty dining-room;
See the pictures on the walls,
Heroes, fights, and festivals;
And in a corner find the toys
Of the old Egyptian boys.

WANDER-THIRST

Gerald Gould

Beyond the East the sunrise, beyond the West the
   sea,
And East and West the wander-thirst that will
   not let me be;
It works in me like madness, dear, to bid me say
   good-bye;
For the seas call and the stars call, and oh! the
   call of the sky!

I know not where the white road runs, nor what
   the blue hills are,
But a man can have the sun for friend, and for
   his guide a star;
And there's no end of voyaging when once the
   voice is heard,
For the rivers call and the roads call, and oh! the
   call of a bird!

Yonder the long horizon lies, and there by night
   and day
The old ships draw to home again, the young
   ships sail away;
And come I may, but go I must, and if men ask
   you why,
You may put the blame on the stars and the sun
   and the white road and the sky.

"Travel." From *A Child's Garden of Verses* by Robert Louis Stevenson
"Wander-Thirst." From *The Collected Poems of Gerald Gould.* Used by permission of Michael Ayrton

Walt Whitman

Afoot and light-hearted, I take to the open road,
Healthy, free, the world before me,
The long brown path before me, leading wher-
    ever I choose.

Henceforth I ask not good-fortune, I myself am
    good-fortune,
Henceforth I whimper no more, postpone no
    more, need nothing,
Done with indoor complaints, libraries, queru-
    lous criticisms,
Strong and content, I travel the open road.

MAPS

Dorothy Brown Thompson

High adventure
    And bright dream—
Maps are mightier
    Than they seem:

Ships that follow
    Leaning stars—
Red and gold of
    Strange bazaars—

Ice floes hid
    Beyond all knowing—
Planes that ride where
    Winds are blowing!

Train maps, maps of
    Wind and weather,
Road maps—taken
    Altogether

Maps are really
    Magic wands
For home-staying
    Vagabonds!

"Maps." From *Bridled with Rainbows* by Dorothy Brown Thompson. The Macmillan Company, New York, 1949. Used by the permission of the author

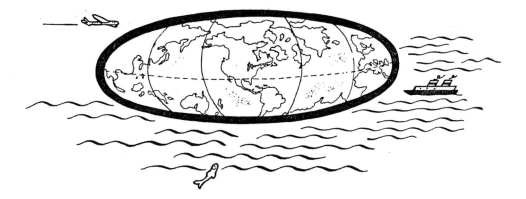

(Mother Goose)

Girls and boys, come out to play,
The moon doth shine as bright as day;
Leave your supper, and leave your sleep,
And come with your playfellows into the street.
Come with a whoop, come with a call,
Come with a good will or not at all.
Up the ladder and down the wall,
A half-penny roll will serve us all.
You find milk, and I'll find flour,
And we'll have a pudding in half an hour.

MY ZIPPER SUIT

Marie Louise Allen

My zipper suit is bunny-brown—
The top zips up, the legs zip down.
I wear it every day.
My daddy brought it out from town.
Zip it up, and zip it down,
And hurry out to play!

LET'S PLAY

Kate Greenaway

School is over,
   Oh, what fun!
Lessons finished,
   Play begun.
Who'll run fastest,
   You or I?
Who'll laugh loudest?
   Let us try.

RIDDLES FROM MOTHER GOOSE

As round as an apple, as deep as a cup,
And all the king's horses can't fill it up.
(*A Well*)

A riddle, a riddle, as I suppose,
A hundred eyes and never a nose!
(*A Sieve*)

Higher than a house,
Higher than a tree,
Oh! whatever can that be?
(*A Star*)

Lives in winter,
Dies in summer,
And grows with its roots upward!
(*An Icicle*)

A hill full, a hole full,
Yet you cannot catch a bowl full.
(*The Mist*)

Thirty white horses upon a red hill,
Now they tramp, now they champ,
Now they stand still.
(*The Teeth and Gums*)

Hick-a-more, Hack-a-more,
On the King's kitchen door;
All the King's horses,
And all the King's men,
Couldn't drive Hick-a-more,
Hack-a-more,
Off the King's kitchen door.
(*Sunshine*)

Old Mother Twitchett had but one eye,
And a long tail which she let fly;
And every time she went through a gap,
A bit of her tail she left in a trap.
(*A Needle and Thread*)

Little Nanny Etticoat
In a white petticoat,
And a red nose;
The longer she stands
The shorter she grows.
(*A Candle*)

Runs all day and never walks,
Often murmurs, never talks.
It has a bed but never sleeps,
It has a mouth, but never eats.
(*A River*)

I have a little sister they call her "Peep-peep,"
She wades in the ocean deep, deep, deep.
She climbs up the mountain high, high, high,
The poor little thing hasn't got but one eye.
(*A Star*)

RHYMING RIDDLES

Mary Austin

I come more softly than a bird,
And lovely as a flower;
I sometimes last from year to year
And sometimes but an hour.

I stop the swiftest railroad train
Or break the stoutest tree.
And yet I am afraid of fire
And children play with me.
(*Snow*)

I have no wings, but yet I fly,
I'm slender as a snake and straight as rain,
Who takes me in must die,
Who lets me quickly go will surest gain.
(*Arrow*)

"My Zipper Suit." From *Sung under the Silver Umbrella*. The Macmillan Company, New York, 1935. Used by permission of the author

"School is over." From *Under the Window* by Kate Greenaway. Frederick Warne and Company, New York and London, 1910

"Riddles from Mother Goose." *These old, old riddles may suggest making rhymed riddles of our own.*

"Runs all day and never walks." From *The American Mother Goose* compiled by Ray Wood. Copyright 1940 by J. B. Lippincott Company

"I have a little sister they call her 'Peep-peep.' " From *The American Mother Goose* compiled by Ray Wood. Copyright 1940 by J. B. Lippincott Company

"Rhyming Riddles." From "Seven Rhyming Riddles" in *The Children Sing in the Far West* by Mary Austin. Reprinted by permission of and arrangement with Houghton Mifflin Company, the authorized publishers

I never speak a word
But when my voice is heard
Even the mountains shake,
No hands I have
And yet great rocks I break.
(*Thunder and Lightning*)

First I am frosted,
Second, I am beaten,
Third, I am roasted,
Fourth, I am eaten.
(*Chestnut*)

(*Mother Goose*)

To market, to market, to buy a fat pig,
Home again, home again, jiggety jig.

To market, to market, to buy a fat hog,
Home again, home again, jiggety jog.

To market, to market, to buy a plum bun,
Home again, home again, market is done.

(*Mother Goose*)

The grand Old Duke of York
  He had ten thousand men,
He marched them up a very high hill
  And he marched them down again.
And when he was up he was up
  And when he was down he was down
And when he was only halfway up
  He was neither up nor down.

(*Mother Goose*)

Hippety hop to the barber shop,
  To get a stick of candy,
One for you and one for me,
  And one for Sister Mandy.

"To market, to market, to buy a fat pig." *This jingle and "The grand Old Duke of York" are as good to march to as music. This one is an everydayish walk to the store and "The Duke" is very martial, military, and snappy.*

"Hippety hop to the barber shop." *See introduction, p. xviii.*

"Hoppity." *The words in this poem go hopping exactly as Christopher hops, ending with a big one, on one foot, perhaps. See record album* Poetry Time. *Taken from*

HOPPITY

A. A. Milne

Christopher Robin goes
Hoppity, hoppity,
Hoppity, hoppity, hop.
Whenever I tell him
Politely to stop it, he
Says he can't possibly stop.

If he stopped hopping, he couldn't go anywhere,
Poor little Christopher
Couldn't go anywhere . . .
That's why he *always* goes
Hoppity, hoppity,
Hoppity,
Hoppity,
Hop.

HIPPITY HOP TO BED

Leroy F. Jackson

O it's hippity hop to bed!
I'd rather sit up instead.
But when father says "must,"
There's nothing but just
Go hippity hop to bed.

(*Mother Goose*)

Dance to your daddie,
  My bonnie laddie;
Dance to your daddie, my bonnie lamb;
  You shall get a fishy,
  On a little dishy;
You shall get a fishy, when the boat comes home.

(*Mother Goose*)

Ride a cock horse
To Banbury Cross
To see a fair lady upon a white horse;

When We Were Very Young, by A. A. Milne, published and copyright, 1924, by E. P. Dutton & Co., Inc., New York

"Hippity Hop to Bed." *See the introduction, p. xx, and record album* Poetry Time. *From* The Peter Patter Book *by Leroy F. Jackson. Rand McNally & Company, Chicago, 1918. Used by permission of the author*

"Dance to your daddie." *You can jounce your baby on your knee to this little jig or you can take hands with*

With rings on her fingers,
And bells on her toes,
She shall have music wherever she goes.

(*Mother Goose*)

Ride away, ride away,
  Johnny shall ride,
And he shall have pussy-cat
  Tied to one side;
And he shall have little dog
  Tied to the other,
And Johnny shall ride
  To see his grandmother.

HUSKY HI

(*Norwegian*)

Rose Fyleman

Husky hi, husky hi,
Here comes Keery galloping by.
She carries her husband tied in a sack,
She carries him home on her horse's back.
Husky hi, husky hi,
Here comes Keery galloping by!

(*Mother Goose*)

Master I have, and I am his man,
  Gallop a dreary dun;
Master I have, and I am his man,
  And I'll get a wife as fast as I can;
With a heighly gaily gamberally,
  Higgledy, piggledy, niggledy, niggledy,
Gallop a dreary dun.

(*Mother Goose*)

Jack be nimble,
  Jack be quick,
Jack jump over
  The candlestick.

Jump it lively,
  Jump it quick,
But don't knock over
  The candlestick.

LITTLE JUMPING JOAN

(*Mother Goose*)

Here am I, little jumping Joan,
  When nobody's with me
  I'm always alone.

Kate Greenaway

Jump—jump—jump—
  Jump away
From this town into
  The next, to-day.

Jump—jump—jump—
  Jump over the moon;
Jump all the morning,
  And all the noon.

Jump—jump—jump—
  Jump all night;
Won't our mothers
  Be in a fright?

Jump—jump—jump—
  Over the sea;
What wonderful wonders
  We shall see.

Jump—jump—jump—
  Jump far away;
And all come home
  Some other day.

your friend and really jig to it while all the other children say it. See record album Poetry Time.
  "Ride a cock horse." *This and the next three jingles are good gallops. Part of the children might say them while the others hold their imaginary reins and cluck to their horses. See record album* Poetry Time.
  "Husky Hi." *See the introduction, p. xviii, and record album* Poetry Time. *From* Picture Rhymes from Foreign

Lands. Copyright 1935 by Rose Fyleman. Reprinted by permission of J. B. Lippincott Company
  "Master I have, and I am his man." *This is the song sung by a lad as he gallops along on his master's errands, riding a dreary old dun colored horse.*
  "Jump—jump—jump." *From* Marigold Garden *by* Kate Greenaway. Frederick Warne and Company, New York and London, 1910

JUMP OR JIGGLE
Evelyn Beyer

Frogs jump
Caterpillars hump

Worms wiggle
Bugs jiggle

Rabbits hop
Horses clop

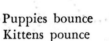

Snakes slide
Sea gulls glide

Mice creep
Deer leap

Puppies bounce
Kittens pounce

Lions stalk—
But—
I walk!

David McCord

Every time I climb a tree
Every time I climb a tree
Every time I climb a tree
I scrape a leg
Or skin a knee
And every time I climb a tree
I find some ants
Or dodge a bee
And get the ants
All over me

And every time I climb a tree
Where have you been?
They say to me
But don't they know that I am free
Every time I climb a tree?
I like it best
To spot a nest
That has an egg
Or maybe three

And then I skin
The other leg
But every time I climb a tree
I see a lot of things to see
Swallows rooftops and TV
And all the fields and farms there be
Every time I climb a tree
Though climbing may be good for ants
It isn't awfully good for pants
But still it's pretty good for me
Every time I climb a tree

(Mother Goose)

Pease porridge hot,
Pease porridge cold,
Pease porridge in the pot,
Nine days old.
Some like it hot,
Some like it cold,
Some like it in the pot,
Nine days old.

(Mother Goose)

Higgledy, piggledy, my black hen,
She lays eggs for gentlemen;
Sometimes nine, and sometimes ten,
Higgledy, piggledy, my black hen.

(Mother Goose)

Intery, mintery, cutery corn,
Apple seed and apple thorn;
Wine, brier, limber lock,
Three geese in a flock,
One flew east, one flew west,
And one flew over the goose's nest.

(Mother Goose)

1, 2, 3, 4, 5!
I caught a hare alive;
6, 7, 8, 9, 10!
I let her go again.

(Mother Goose)

One, two,
Buckle my shoe;
Three, four,
Knock at the door;
Five, six,
Pick up sticks;
Seven, eight,
Lay them straight;
Nine, ten,
A good, fat hen;
Eleven, twelve,
Dig and delve;
Thirteen, fourteen,
Maids a-courting;
Fifteen, sixteen,
Maids in the kitchen;
Seventeen, eighteen,
Maids a-waiting;
Nineteen, twenty,
My plate's empty.

THE A B C BUNNY
Wanda Gág

A for Apple, big and red
B for Bunny snug a-bed
C for Crash!
D for Dash!
E for Elsewhere in a flash
F for Frog—he's fat and funny
"Looks like rain," says he to Bunny
G for Gale!
H for Hail!
Hippy-hop goes Bunny's tail
I for Insects here and there
J for Jay with jaunty air
K for Kitten, catnip-crazy
L for Lizard—look how lazy
M for Mealtime—munch, munch, munch!
M-m-m these greens are good for lunch
N for Napping in a Nook
O for Owl with bookish look
P for prickly Porcupine
Pins and needles on his spine

Q for Quail
R for Rail
S for Squirrel Swishy-tail
T for Tripping back to Town
U for Up and Up-side-down
V for View
Valley too
W—"We welcome you!"
X for eXit—off, away!
That's enough for us today
Y for You, take one last look
Z for Zero—close the book!

Edward Lear

A was once an apple-pie,
    Pidy,
    Widy,
    Tidy,
    Pidy,
  Nice insidy,
  Applie-pie!

B was once a little bear,
    Beary,
    Wary,
    Hairy,
    Beary,
  Taky cary,
  Little bear!

C was once a little cake,
    Caky,
    Baky,
    Maky,
    Caky,
  Taky caky,
  Little cake!

D was once a little doll,
    Dolly,
    Molly,
    Polly,
    Nolly,
  Nursy dolly,
  Little doll!

"Higgledy, piggledy, my black hen." *See record album* Poetry Time.
"The A B C Bunny." *Alphabet books are useful for teaching the names of the letters. The rhymes usually are fun to say and the pictures are amusing to look at.* "The

A B C Bunny" *is an especially good alphabet book and so is Phyllis McGinley's* All Around the Town. From *The A B C Bunny by Wanda Gág. Copyright, 1933, by Wanda Gág. Reprinted by permission of Coward-McCann, Inc.*

E was once a little eel,
    Eely,
    Weely,
    Peely,
    Eely,
Twirly, tweely,
Little eel!

F was once a little fish,
    Fishy,
    Wishy,
    Squishy,
    Fishy,
In a dishy,
Little fish!

G was once a little goose,
    Goosy,
    Moosy,
    Boosey,
    Goosey,
Waddly-woosy,
Little goose!

H was once a little hen,
    Henny,
    Chenny,
    Tenny,
    Henny,
Eggsy-any,
Little hen?

I was once a bottle of ink,
    Inky,
    Dinky,
    Thinky,
    Inky,
Blacky minky,
Bottle of ink!

J was once a jar of jam,
    Jammy,
    Mammy,
    Clammy,
    Jammy,
Sweety, swammy,
Jar of jam!

K was once a little kite,
    Kity,
    Whity,
    Flighty,
    Kity,
Out of sighty,
Little kite!

L was once a little lark,
    Larky,
    Marky,
    Harky,
    Larky,
In the parky,
Little lark!

M was once a little mouse,
    Mousy,
    Bousy,
    Sousy,
    Mousy,
In the housy,
Little mouse!

N was once a little needle,
    Needly,
    Tweedly,
    Threedly,
    Needly,
Wisky, wheedly,
Little needle!

O was once a little owl,
    Owly,
    Prowly,
    Howly,
    Owly,
Browny fowly,
Little owl!

P was once a little pump,
    Pumpy,
    Slumpy,
    Flumpy,
    Pumpy,
Dumpy, thumpy,
Little pump!

Q was once a little quail,
  Quaily,
  Faily,
  Daily,
  Quaily,
  Stumpy-taily,
  Little quail!

R was once a little rose,
  Rosy,
  Posy,
  Nosy,
  Rosy,
  Blows-y, grows-y,
  Little rose!

S was once a little shrimp,
  Shrimpy,
  Nimpy,
  Flimpy,
  Shrimpy,
  Jumpy, jimpy,
  Little shrimp!

T was once a little thrush,
  Thrushy,
  Hushy,
  Bushy,
  Thrushy,
  Flitty, flushy,
  Little thrush!

U was once a little urn,
  Urny,
  Burny,
  Turny,
  Urny,
  Bubbly, burny,
  Little urn!

V was once a little vine,
  Viny,
  Winy,
  Twiny,
  Viny,
  Twisty-twiny,
  Little vine!

W was once a whale,
  Whaly,
  Scaly,
  Shaly,
  Whaly,
  Tumbly-taily,
  Mighty whale!

X was once a great king Xerxes,
  Xerxy,
  Perxy,
  Turxy,
  Xerxy,
  Linxy, lurxy,
  Great King Xerxes!

Y was once a little yew,
  Yewdy,
  Fewdy,
  Crudy,
  Yewdy,
  Growdy, grewdy,
  Little yew!

Z was once a piece of zinc,
  Tinky,
  Winky,
  Blinky,
  Tinky,
  Tinky minky,
  Piece of zinc!

CHOOSING

Eleanor Farjeon

Which will you have, a ball or a cake?
A cake is so nice, yes, that's what I'll take.

Which will you have, a cake or a cat?
A cat is so soft, I think I'll take that.

Which will you have, a cat or a rose?
A rose is so sweet, I'll have that, I suppose.

Which will you have, a rose or a book?
A book full of pictures?—oh, do let me look!

Which will you have, a book or a ball?
Oh, a ball! No, a book! No, a—
    There! have them all!

WHAT THE TOYS ARE THINKING

Ffrida Wolfe

In the jolly, jolly Spring
When we long to leave the shop,
It's the most exciting thing
When any of you stop
And stare and ask the price
Of a Teddy or a top,
Or a baby-doll or Bunny,
Or a little speckled horse.
O, we think it's very nice
When you stand behind the nurses
Counting out what's in your purses;
We are watching you, of course,
Wond'ring what you mean to do,
Hoping, hoping you've the money
And can take us back with you.
But supposing you have not
Quite enough (we cost a lot),
Shake a paw then, stroke a head,
Pat a wistful nose instead,
Whisper in a furry ear,
Comfort us for what we're missing—
Nursery tea and bedtime kissing—
All that never happens here.
You would find it slow yourselves
Sitting still all day on shelves.
Well, next time you're passing through
You'll remember what to do.

TELEGRAM

William Wise

I never got a telegram before;
But I went to the big front door,
And here was a man
Who wanted to see

Master Jonathan Blake!
So I said, "That's me."
And to make things clear,
He said, "Please sign here."
I never got a telegram before,
But I'd like to get at least a million more.

I never got a "wire" in my life;
So I sliced this one open with a knife.
Mother said most men
Prefer to use a cutter,
Since the knife I found
Was designed for butter.
But I never got a "wire" in my life!
So *naturally* I sliced it with a knife.

I never got a telegram before;
And when I went to the big front door,
It said: "Congratulations
On being six today
Every one of us loves you
That's all we can say."
I never got a telegram before,
But I'd like to get at least a *million* more!

US TWO

A. A. Milne

Wherever I am, there's always Pooh,
There's always Pooh and Me.
Whatever I do, he wants to do,
"Where are you going to-day?" says Pooh:
"Well, that's very odd 'cos I was too.
Let's go together," says Pooh, says he.
"Let's go together," says Pooh.

"What's twice eleven?" I said to Pooh.
("Twice what?" said Pooh to Me.)
"I *think* it ought to be twenty-two."
"Just what I think myself," said Pooh.
"It wasn't an easy sum to do,
But that's what it is," said Pooh, said he.
"That's what it is," said Pooh.

"What the Toys Are Thinking." Ffrida Wolfe in *Merry-Go-Round*, December, 1924. By permission of Basil Blackwell & Mott, Ltd., Oxford

"Telegram." From *Jonathan Blake* by William Wise. Copyright © 1956 by William Wise. Reprinted by per-

mission of Alfred A. Knopf, Inc., New York

"Us Two." *Though Pooh was only Christopher Robin's toy teddy bear, this poem gives you the feeling of how alive he seemed to Christopher.* Taken from *Now We Are Six*, by A. A. Milne, published and copyright, 1927,

"Let's look for dragons," I said to Pooh.
"Yes, let's," said Pooh to Me.
We crossed the river and found a few—
"Yes, those are dragons all right," said Pooh.
"As soon as I saw their beaks I knew.
That's what they are," said Pooh, said he.
"That's what they are," said Pooh.

"Let's frighten the dragons," I said to Pooh.
"That's right," said Pooh to Me.
"*I'm* not afraid," I said to Pooh,
And I held his paw and I shouted "Shoo!
Silly old dragons!"—and off they flew.
"I wasn't afraid," said Pooh, said he,
"I'm *never* afraid with you."

So wherever I am, there's always Pooh,
There's always Pooh and Me.
"What would I do?" I said to Pooh,
"If it wasn't for you," and Pooh said: "True,
It isn't much fun for One, but Two
Can stick together," says Pooh, says he.
"That's how it is," says Pooh.

MERRY ARE THE BELLS

Anonymous

Merry are the bells, and merry would they ring,
Merry was myself, and merry could I sing;
With a merry ding-dong, happy, gay, and free,
And a merry sing-song, happy let us be!

Merry have we met, and merry have we been;
Merry let us part, and merry meet again;
With our merry sing-song, happy, gay, and free,
With a merry ding-dong, happy let us be!

Christina Georgina Rossetti

All the bells were ringing
And all the birds were singing,
When Molly sat down crying
    For her broken doll:
    O you silly Moll!

by E. P. Dutton & Co., Inc., New York
    "All the bells were ringing." From *Sing-Song* by Christina Georgina Rossetti
    "Skating." *This is a good example of the rhythm of words suggesting the activity the poet is describing. It*

Sobbing and sighing
    For a broken doll,
When all the bells are ringing,
And all the birds are singing.

THE LITTLE RED SLED
Jocelyn Bush

"Come out with me!" cried the little red sled.
"I'll give you the wings of a bird," it said.
"The ground is all snowy;
The wind is all blowy!
We'll go like a fairy,
So light and so airy!"

SKATING
Herbert Asquith

When I try to skate,
My feet are so wary
They grit and they grate:
And then I watch Mary
Easily gliding,
Like an ice-fairy;
Skimming and curving,
Out and in,
With a turn of her head,
And a lift of her chin,
And a gleam of her eye,
And a twirl and a spin;
Sailing under
The breathless hush
Of the willows, and back
To the frozen rush;
Out to the island
And round the edge,

lends itself to choral speaking. See May Hill Arbuthnot, Children and Books, *p. 219. From* Pillicock Hill *by Herbert Asquith. Used with the permission of The Macmillan Company. By permission also of William Heinemann, Ltd.*

Skirting the rim
Of the crackling sedge,
Swerving close
To the poplar root,
And round the lake
On a single foot,
With a three, and an eight,
And a loop and a ring;
Where Mary glides,
The lake will sing!
Out in the mist
I hear her now
Under the frost
Of the willow-bough
Easily sailing,
Light and fleet,
With the song of the lake
Beneath her feet.

WINGS AND WHEELS

Nancy Byrd Turner

Ahoy and ahoy, birds!
We cannot have wings
And feathers and things,
But dashing on wheels
With the wind at our heels
Is almost like flying—
Such joy, birds!

Oho and oho, birds!
Of course we can't rise
Up and up to the skies;
But skimming and sliding
On rollers, and gliding,
Is almost as jolly,
You know, birds!

DIFFERENT BICYCLES

Dorothy Baruch

When I ride my bicycle
I pedal and pedal
Knees up, knees down.
Knees up, knees down.

But when the boy next door
Rides his,
It's whizz—
A chuck   a chuck—

And away
He's gone
With his
Knees steady-straight
In one place . . .
Because—
His bicycle has
A motor fastened on.

THE SWING

Robert Louis Stevenson

How do you like to go up in a swing,
    Up in the air so blue?
Oh, I do think it the pleasantest thing
    Ever a child can do!

Up in the air and over the wall,
    Till I can see so wide,
Rivers and trees and cattle and all
    Over the countryside—

Till I look down on the garden green,
    Down on the roof so brown—
Up in the air I go flying again,
    Up in the air and down!

PICNIC DAY
Rachel Field

Sing a song of picnics,
    Bread and butter spread,
    Greenery all around about,
    And cherries overhead!

THE PICNIC
Dorothy Aldis

We brought a rug for sitting on,
Our lunch was in a box.
The sand was warm. We didn't wear
Hats or Shoes or Socks.

Waves came curling up the beach.
We waded. It was fun.
Our sandwiches were different kinds.
I dropped my jelly one.

THE HUNTSMEN
Walter de la Mare

Three jolly gentlemen,
    In coats of red,
Rode their horses
    Up to bed.

Three jolly gentlemen
    Snored till morn,
Their horses champing
    The golden corn.

Three jolly gentlemen,
    At break of day,
Came clitter-clatter down the stairs
    And galloped away.

UPON THE BEACH
Ilo Orleans

Upon the beach
    With pail and spade,
My sandy pies and wells I made.

And people passed
    On every hand
And left their footprints on the sand.

Then came a wave
    With the rushing tide—
And everything was washed aside.

AT THE SEA-SIDE
Robert Louis Stevenson

When I was down beside the sea
A wooden spade they gave to me
    To dig the sandy shore.

My holes were empty like a cup.
In every hole the sea came up,
    Till it could come no more.

SKIPPING ALONG ALONE

Winifred Welles

Oh, how I love to skip alone
  Along the beach in moisty weather;
The whole world seems my very own,
Each fluted shell and glistening stone,
  Each wave that twirls a silver feather.

I skip along so brave and big
  Behind the sand-birds gray and tiny,
I love to see their quick feet jig,
Each leaves a mark, neat as a twig,
  Stamped in the sand so clear and shiny.

And fine and faint as drops of spray
  I hear their little voices calling,
"Sweet, sweet! Sweet, sweet!" I hear them say—
I love to skip alone and play
  Along the sand when mist is falling.

SHORE

Mary Britton Miller

Play on the seashore
And gather up shells,
Kneel in the damp sands
Digging wells.

Run on the rocks
Where the seaweed slips,
Watch the waves
And the beautiful ships.

BEACH FIRE

Frances M. Frost

When the picnic was over,
We sat by the tide
And watched the white-winged
Sea gulls slide

Down the evening wind.
The stars came out
Above the sea,
And Dad gave a shout:

"Oh, wish on that little
Brand-new moon!
Let's build up the fire
With wood from the dune!"

We wished on the moon,
We built up the fire,
We sang, while the sparks
Flew higher, higher,

Like stars of our own
Above the foam,
Till, sleepy, we
And the birds went home.

WHERE GO THE BOATS?

Robert Louis Stevenson

Dark brown is the river,
  Golden is the sand.
It flows along forever,
  With trees on either hand.

Green leaves a-floating,
  Castles of the foam,
Boats of mine a-boating—
  Where will all come home?

On goes the river
  And out past the mill,
Away down the valley,
  Away down the hill.

Away down the river,
  A hundred miles or more,
Other little children
  Shall bring my boats ashore.

"Skipping Along Alone." *Say the title over and over and feel its gay skipping rhythm! The whole poem skips.* From *Skipping Along Alone* by Winifred Welles. The Macmillan Company, New York, 1931. Used by permission of James Welles Shearer

"Shore." From *Menagerie* by Mary Britton Miller. Copyright 1928 by The Macmillan Company and used with their permission

"Beach Fire." From *The Little Whistler* by Frances M. Frost. Whittlesey House, McGraw-Hill Book Company, Inc., New York, 1949

"Where Go the Boats?" *These words and lines have the smooth, flowing movement of a quiet river. Notice from the beginning of the third verse, the lines flow on and on and never really come to a rest until the last line.* From *A Child's Garden of Verses* by Robert Louis Stevenson

Zhenya Gay

The world is full of wonderful smells,
And you have a nose that always tells
Of bread in the oven, hot and nice,
Of cake being baked with lots of spice,
Of a barn with fresh-cut hay in the mows,
Of horses and pigs and cats and cows,
Of a dog when he's warm and lies in the sun,
Of applesauce and chocolate and a sugar bun.
Wouldn't it be dreadful if you'd no nose to tell
Of every wonderful, wonderful smell?

THE LITTLE WHISTLER
Frances M. Frost

My mother whistled softly,
My father whistled bravely,
My brother whistled merrily,
And I tried all day long!
I blew my breath inwards,
I blew my breath outwards,
But all you heard was breath blowing
And not a bit of song!

But today I heard a bluebird,
A happy, young, and new bird,
Whistling in the apple tree—
He'd just discovered how!
Then quick I blew my breath in,
And gay I blew my breath out,
And sudden I blew three wild notes—
And I can whistle now!

NEW SHOES
Alice Wilkins

I have new shoes in the Fall-time
And new ones in the Spring.
Whenever I wear my new shoes
I always have to sing!

HAPPINESS
A. A. Milne

John had
Great Big
Waterproof
Boots on;
John had a
Great Big
Waterproof
Hat;
John had a
Great Big
Waterproof
Mackintosh—
And that
(Said John)
Is
That.

CHOOSING SHOES
Ffrida Wolfe

New shoes, new shoes,
    Red and pink and blue shoes.
Tell me, what would *you* choose,
    If they'd let us buy?

Buckle shoes, bow shoes,
    Pretty pointy-toe shoes,
Strappy, cappy low shoes;
    Let's have some to try.

Bright shoes, white shoes,
    Dandy-dance-by-night shoes,
Perhaps-a-little-tight shoes,
    Like some? So would I.

But

Flat shoes, fat shoes,
    Stump-along-like-that shoes,
Wipe-them-on-the-mat shoes,
    That's the sort they'll buy.

MARCHING SONG

Robert Louis Stevenson

Bring the comb and play upon it!
   Marching, here we come!
Willie cocks his highland bonnet,
   Johnnie beats the drum.

Mary Jane commands the party,
   Peter leads the rear;
Feet in time, alert and hearty,
   Each a Grenadier!

All in the most martial manner
   Marching double-quick;
While the napkin, like a banner,
   Waves upon the stick!

Here's enough of fame and pillage,
   Great commander Jane!
Now that we've been round the village,
   Let's go home again.

MY SHADOW

Robert Louis Stevenson

I have a little shadow that goes in and out
   with me,
And what can be the use of him is more than I
   can see.
He is very, very like me from the heels up to the
   head;
And I see him jump before me, when I jump into
   my bed.

The funniest thing about him is the way he likes
   to grow—
Not at all like proper children, which is always
   very slow;
For he sometimes shoots up taller like an India-
   rubber ball,
And he sometimes gets so little that there's none
   of him at all.

He hasn't got a notion of how children ought to
   play,
And can only make a fool of me in every sort of
   way.
He stays so close beside me, he's a coward you
   can see;
I'd think shame to stick to nursie as that shadow
   sticks to me!

One morning, very early, before the sun was up,
I rose and found the shining dew on every buttercup;
But my lazy little shadow, like an arrant sleepyhead,
Had stayed at home behind me and was fast
   asleep in bed.

SHADOW DANCE

Ivy O. Eastwick

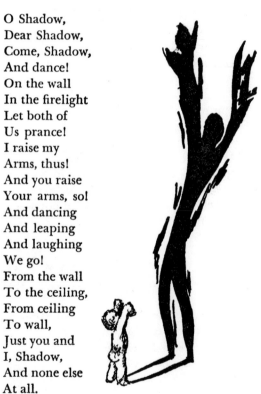

O Shadow,
Dear Shadow,
Come, Shadow,
And dance!
On the wall
In the firelight
Let both of
Us prance!
I raise my
Arms, thus!
And you raise
Your arms, so!
And dancing
And leaping
And laughing
We go!
From the wall
To the ceiling,
From ceiling
To wall,
Just you and
I, Shadow,
And none else
At all.

"Marching Song." From *A Child's Garden of Verses* by
Robert Louis Stevenson

"My Shadow." *It is easy to singsong this poem. Think
of the story it is telling and keep it alive in natural storytelling style.* From *A Child's Garden of Verses* by Robert Louis Stevenson

"Shadow Dance." Taken from *Fairies and Suchlike*, by
Ivy O. Eastwick, published and copyright, 1946, by E. P.
Dutton & Co., Inc., New York

"Sniff." By Frances M. Frost. From *American Junior Red
Cross News*. Copyright 1944 by the American National
Red Cross

SNIFF

Frances M. Frost

When school is out, we love to follow
our noses over hill and hollow,
smelling jewelweed and vetch,
sniffing fern and milkweed patch.

The airy fifth of our five senses
leads us under, over, fences.
We run like rabbits through bright hours
and poke our noses into flowers!

THE TOASTER

William Jay Smith

A silver-scaled Dragon with jaws flaming red
Sits at my elbow and toasts my bread.
I hand him fat slices, and then, one by one,
He hands them back when he sees they are done.

HIDING

Dorothy Aldis

I'm hiding, I'm hiding,
And no one knows where;
For all they can see is my
Toes and my hair.

And I just heard my father
Say to my mother—
"But, darling, he must be
Somewhere or other;

"Have you looked in the ink well?"
And Mother said, "Where?"
"In the INK WELL," said Father. But
I was not there.

Then "Wait!" cried my mother—
"I think that I see
Him under the carpet." But
It was not me.

Reprinted by permission of the author
  "The Toaster." From *Laughing Time* by William Jay Smith, by permission of Little, Brown & Company. Copyright 1955 by William Jay Smith
  "Hiding." From *Everything and Anything* by Dorothy Aldis. Minton, Balch and Company, New York, 1927.

"Inside the mirror's
A pretty good place,"
Said Father and looked, but saw
Only his face.

"We've hunted," sighed Mother,
"As hard as we could
And I AM so afraid that we've
Lost him for good."

Then I laughed out aloud
And I wiggled my toes
And Father said—"Look, dear,
I wonder if those

Toes could be Benny's.
There are ten of them. See?"
And they WERE so surprised to find
Out it was me!

FUN IN A GARRET
Emma C. Dowd

"We're having a lovely time to-day!
We're all of us up in the garret at play!
We have three houses under the eaves—
Not real, you know, but make-believes;
Two we live in, and one is a store,
Where a little old screen makes a truly door.
Warren keeps store, and Joe is his clerk,
And Betty and I stay at home and work.
Joe comes around and knocks or rings,
And we order potatoes and steaks and things;
And sometimes we go to the store and buy,
Or send the children for ribbons or pie.
It's lots of fun—just try it some day
When it rains too hard to go out and play.

A GOOD PLAY
Robert Louis Stevenson

We built a ship upon the stairs
All made of the back-bedroom chairs,
And filled it full of sofa pillows
To go a-sailing on the billows.

Copyright 1925, 1926, 1927 by Dorothy Aldis
  "Fun in a Garret." From *The Owl and the Bobolink* by Emma C. Dowd. Houghton Mifflin Company, Boston, 1914
  "A Good Play." From *A Child's Garden of Verses* by Robert Louis Stevenson

We took a saw and several nails,
And water in the nursery pails;
And Tom said, "Let us also take
An apple and a slice of cake;"—
Which was enough for Tom and me
To go a-sailing on, till tea.

We sailed along for days and days,
And had the very best of plays;
But Tom fell out and hurt his knee,
So there was no one left but me.

PIRATE STORY

Robert Louis Stevenson

Three of us afloat in the meadow by the swing,
   Three of us aboard in the basket on the lea.
Winds are in the air, they are blowing in the
   spring,
   And waves are on the meadow like the waves
   there are at sea.

Where shall we adventure, to-day that we're
   afloat,
   Wary of the weather and steering by a star?
Shall it be to Africa, a-steering of the boat,
   To Providence, or Babylon, or off to Malabar?

Hi! but here's a squadron a-rowing on the sea—
   Cattle on the meadow a-charging with a roar!
Quick, and we'll escape them, they're as mad as
   they can be,
   The wicket is the harbour and the garden is
   the shore.

THE LAND OF STORY-BOOKS

Robert Louis Stevenson

At evening when the lamp is lit,
Around the fire my parents sit;
They sit at home and talk and sing,
And do not play at anything.

Now, with my little gun, I crawl
All in the dark along the wall,
And follow round the forest track
Away behind the sofa back.

There, in the night, where none can spy,
All in my hunter's camp I lie,
And play at books that I have read
Till it is time to go to bed.

These are the hills, these are the woods,
These are my starry solitudes;
And there the river by whose brink
The roaring lions come to drink.

I see the others far away
As if in firelit camp they lay,
And I, like to an Indian scout,
Around their party prowled about.

So, when my nurse comes in for me,
Home I return across the sea,
And go to bed with backward looks
At my dear Land of Story-books.

BEDTIME /

Eleanor Farjeon

Five minutes, five minutes more, please!
   Let me stay five minutes more!
Can't I just finish the castle
   I'm building here on the floor?
Can't I just finish the story
   I'm reading here in my book?
Can't I just finish this bead-chain—
   It *almost* is finished, look!
Can't I just finish this game, please?
   When a game's once begun
It's a pity never to find out
   Whether you've lost or won.
Can't I just stay five minutes?
   Well, can't I stay just four?
Three minutes, then? two minutes?
   Can't I stay *one* minute more?

MRS. BROWN

Rose Fyleman

As soon as I'm in bed at night
And snugly settled down,
The little girl I am by day
Goes very suddenly away,
And then I'm Mrs. Brown.

I have a family of six,
And all of them have names,
The girls are Joyce and Nancy Maud,
The boys are Marmaduke and Claude
And Percival and James.

We have a house with twenty rooms
A mile away from town;
I think it's good for girls and boys
To be allowed to make a noise—
And so does Mr. Brown.

We do the most exciting things,
Enough to make you creep;
And on and on and on we go—
I sometimes wonder if I know
When I have gone to sleep.

MERRY-GO-ROUND

Unison

Dorothy Baruch

I climbed up on the merry-go-round,
And it went round and round.
I climbed up on a big brown horse
And it went up and down.
   Around and round
   And up and down,
   Around and round
   And up and down,
   I sat high up
   On a big brown horse
   And rode around
   On the merry-go-round

And rode around
On the merry-go-round
I rode around
On the merry-go-round
   Around
      And round
   And
      Round.

from ALL AROUND THE TOWN

Phyllis McGinley

C is for the Circus
   Which springtime brings to town.
(The country has its crocus,
   But we much prefer the clown.)
C's for canes and cracker-jack
   And curious camels, too.
I wouldn't trade a Circus
   For some crocuses. Would you?

THE CIRCUS PARADE

Olive Beaupré Miller

O Goody, it's coming, the circus parade
   And all the way up the street,
What crowds of people in gay-colored clothes,
   With popcorn and peanuts to eat!

The children have red, blue, and yellow bal-
      loons,
   As up by the curbing they stand,
And now, in the distance, we suddenly hear
   The circus's big brass band!

Behind the crash-bang! of the music they play,
  Come riders in red velvet gowns,
And after them doing the funniest things,
  A silly procession of clowns.

Then lions and tigers that pace up and down,
  In wagons all painted with gold,
And monkeys a-playing just all kinds of tricks,
  As they grimace and chatter and scold.

O, next there come camels and elephants, too,
  High on their backs men ride;
There are queer little ponies, no bigger than
    dogs,
  With a clown on a donkey, beside!

And then there come chariots rumbling by
  With horses all four in a row;
And the wheezing, old, piping calliope is
  The very tail end of the show!

OUR CIRCUS

Laura Lee Randall

We had a circus in our shed
(Admission, three new pins a head)
And every girl and boy I know
Is talking yet about our show.

They laughed so hard at Fatty Brown
When he came out to be the clown,
That all the neighbors ran to see
Whatever such a noise could be.

Our tin-pan and mouth-organ band
Played tunes that sounded simply grand;
We had a truly sawdust ring,
Pink lemonade, 'n everything.

The big menagerie was nice:
Three cats, one dog, and five white mice,
A parrot that Bill's uncle lent;
All underneath a bedspread tent.

Then Ned and Buster took a sheet
That covered them from head to feet
And made a horse that kicked and pranced
And when it heard the band, it danced.

And Sally Ann was "Bareback Queen"!
No finer rider could be seen;
She stood right up, and looked so proud,
But kissed her hand to all the crowd.

We took some chalk—blue, green, and red—
And made a "Tattooed Man" of Fred;
Jim juggled lighted cigarettes,
And Tom turned double somersets.

We had tall stilts—and flying rings—
And lots and lots of other things—
And every boy and girl I know
Said yes, it was a *dandy* show!

Richard LeGallienne

I meant to do my work to-day—
  But a brown bird sang in the apple-tree,
And a butterfly flitted across the field,
  And all the leaves were calling me.

And the wind went sighing over the land,
  Tossing the grasses to and fro,
And a rainbow held out its shining hand—
  So what could I do but laugh and go?

JILL CAME FROM THE FAIR

Eleanor Farjeon

Jill came from the Fair
With her pennies all spent.
She had had her full share
Of delight and content;

"Our Circus." From *Child Life*, September 1924. Child Life, Inc., Boston. By permission of the author

"I meant to do my work to-day." From *The Lonely Dancer* by Richard LeGallienne. Reprinted by permission of Dodd, Mead & Company

"Jill Came from the Fair." *This poem is as full of hurry and confusion as the fair! And the excitement seems to grow until, like Jill, you reach the end a bit dazed and breathless. See the introduction, p. xx.* From *Over the Garden Wall.* Copyright 1933 by Eleanor Farjeon. Re-

She had ridden the ring
To a wonderful tune,
She had flown in a swing
Half as high as the moon,
In a boat that was drawn
By an ivory swan
Beside a green lawn
On a lake she had gone,
She had bought a gold packet
That held her desire,
She had touched the red jacket
Of one who ate fire,
She had stood at the butt,
And although she was small
She had won a rough nut
With the throw of a ball,
And across the broad back
Of a donkey a-straddle,
She had jolted like Jack-
In-the-Box on a saddle—
Till mid frolic and shout
And tinsel and litter,
The lights started out
Making everything glitter,
And dazed by the noise
And the blare and the flare,
With her toys and her joys
Jill came from the Fair.

AFTER ALL AND AFTER ALL

Mary Carolyn Davies

Dreaming of a prince,
Cinderella sat among the ashes long ago;
Dreaming of a prince,
She scoured the pots and kettles till they shone;
    and so,
After all and after all,
Gaily at the castle ball
Cinderella met her prince long and long ago!

printed by permission of J. B. Lippincott Company
"After All and After All." From *The Century*. The Century Company, New York, June 1917. Used by permission of A. H. Davies

Dreaming of a prince,
Sleeping Beauty lay in happy slumber, white and
    still;
Dreaming of a prince,
She waited for a hundred years, and then his
    bugles shrill,
After all and after all,
Woke the castle, bower, and hall,
And he found her waiting him long and long
    ago!

Dreaming of a prince,
I polish bowl and tea-pot and the spoons, each
    one;
Dreaming of a prince,
I hang the new-washed clothes to wave a-drying
    in the sun;
After all and after all,
Great adventures may befall
Like to those that happened once long and long
    ago!

LAUGHING SONG

William Blake

When the green woods laugh with the voice of
    joy,
And the dimpling stream runs laughing by;
When the air does laugh with our merry wit,
And the green hill laughs with the noise of it;

When the meadows laugh with lively green,
And the grasshopper laughs in the merry scene;
When Mary and Susan and Emily
With their sweet round mouths sing, "Ha ha he!"

When the painted birds laugh in the shade,
When our table with cherries and nuts is spread;
Come live, and be merry, and join with me,
To sing the sweet chorus of "Ha ha he!"

"Laughing Song." *This charming poem about laughter is as gay as a sunny day. You may not visualize all of the pictures because they pass by so quickly. See May Hill Arbuthnot,* Children and Books, *p. 166*

(*Mother Goose*)

Hey, diddle, diddle!
The cat and the fiddle,
The cow jumped over the moon;
The little dog laughed
To see such sport,
And the dish ran away with the spoon.

HOW RIDICULOUS

(*Mother Goose*)

Tom he was a piper's son,
He learned to play when he was young,
But all the tunes that he could play,
Was "Over the hills and far away."

Now Tom with his pipe made such a noise,
That he pleased both girls and boys,
And they stopped to hear him play
"Over the hills and far away."

Tom with his pipe did play with such skill,
That those who heard him could never keep
    still;
Whenever they heard they began for to dance,
Even pigs on their hind legs would after him
    prance.

THE LITTLE KITTENS

Eliza Lee Follen

"Where are you going, my little kittens?"
"We are going to town to get us some mittens."
　"What! Mittens for kittens!
　Do kittens wear mittens?
Who ever saw little kittens with mittens?"

"Where are you going, my little cat?"
"I am going to town to get me a hat."
　"What! A hat for a cat!
　A cat get a hat!
Who ever saw a cat with a hat?"

"Where are you going, my little pig?"
"I am going to town to get me a wig."
　"What! A wig for a pig!
　A pig in a wig!
Who ever saw a pig in a wig?"

THE CATS' TEA-PARTY

Frederick E. Weatherly

Five little pussy-cats, invited out to tea,
Cried: "Mother, let us go—Oh do! for good we'll
　surely be.
We'll wear our bibs and hold our things as you
　have shown us how—
Spoons in right paws, cups in left—and make a
　pretty bow;
We'll always say 'Yes, if you please,' and 'Only
　half of that.' "
"Then go, my darling children," said the happy
　Mother Cat.
The five little pussy-cats went out that night to
　tea.
Their heads were smooth and glossy, their tails
　were swinging free;
They held their things as they had learned, and
　tried to be polite;—
With snowy bibs beneath their chins they were a
　pretty sight.
But, alas, for manners beautiful, and coats as soft
　as silk!
The moment that the little kits were asked to
　take some milk,
They dropped their spoons, forgot to bow, and—
　oh, what do you think?

They put their noses in the cups and all began
　to drink!
Yes, every naughty little kit set up a mew for
　more,
Then knocked their tea-cups over, and scampered
　through the door.

THE DUEL

Eugene Field

The gingham dog and the calico cat
Side by side on the table sat;
'T was half-past twelve, and (what do you think!)
Nor one nor t' other had slept a wink!
　The old Dutch clock and the Chinese plate
　Appeared to know as sure as fate
There was going to be a terrible spat.
　(I wasn't there; I simply state
　What was told to me by the Chinese plate!)

The gingham dog went, "bow-wow-wow!"
And the calico cat replied, "mee-ow!"
The air was littered, an hour or so,
With bits of gingham and calico,
　While the old Dutch clock in the chimney-
　　place
　Up with its hands before its face,
For it always dreaded a family row!
　(Now mind: I'm only telling you
　What the old Dutch clock declares is true!)

The Chinese plate looked very blue,
And wailed, "Oh, dear! what shall we do!"
But the gingham dog and the calico cat
Wallowed this way and tumbled that,
　Employing every tooth and claw
　In the awfullest way you ever saw—
And, oh! how the gingham and calico flew!
　(Don't fancy I exaggerate—
　I got my news from the Chinese plate!)

Next morning, where the two had sat
They found no trace of dog or cat;
And some folks think unto this day
That burglars stole that pair away!
　But the truth about the cat and pup

"The Duel." From *Poems of Childhood* by Eugene Field.
Charles Scribner's Sons, New York, 1904

Is this: they ate each other up!
Now what do you really think of that!
(The old Dutch clock it told me so,
And that is how I came to know.)

THE OWL AND THE PUSSY-CAT

Edward Lear

The Owl and the Pussy-Cat went to sea
   In a beautiful pea-green boat,
They took some honey, and plenty of money
   Wrapped up in a five-pound note.
The Owl looked up to the stars above,
   And sang to a small guitar,
"O lovely Pussy, O Pussy, my love,
   What a beautiful Pussy you are,
          You are,
          You are!
  What a beautiful Pussy you are!"

Pussy said to the Owl, "You elegant fowl,
   How charmingly sweet you sing!
Oh! let us be married, too long we have tarried:
   But what shall we do for a ring?"
They sailed away, for a year and a day,
   To the land where the Bong-tree grows;
And there in a wood a Piggy-wig stood,
   With a ring at the end of his nose,
          His nose,
          His nose,
  With a ring at the end of his nose.

"Dear Pig, are you willing to sell for one shilling
   Your ring?" Said the Piggy, "I will."
So they took it away, and were married next day
   By the Turkey who lives on the hill.
They dined on mince and slices of quince,
   Which they ate with a runcible spoon;
And hand in hand, on the edge of the sand,
   They danced by the light of the moon,
          The moon,
          The moon,
  They danced by the light of the moon.

"The Rum Tum Tugger." From *Old Possum's Book of Practical Cats*, copyright, 1939, by T. S. Eliot. Reprinted by permission of Harcourt, Brace and Company, Inc., and Faber and Faber Limited

THE RUM TUM TUGGER

T. S. Eliot

The Rum Tum Tugger is a Curious Cat:
If you offer him pheasant he would rather have
   grouse.
If you put him in a house he would much prefer
   a flat,
If you put him in a flat then he'd rather have a
   house.
If you set him on a mouse then he only wants a
   rat,
If you set him on a rat then he'd rather chase a
   mouse.
Yes the Rum Tum Tugger is a Curious Cat—
   And there isn't any call for me to shout it:
     For he will do
     As he do do
       And there's no doing anything about it!

The Rum Tum Tugger is a terrible bore:
When you let him in, then he wants to be out;
He's always on the wrong side of every door,
As soon as he's at home, then he'd like to get
   about.
He likes to lie in the bureau drawer,
But he makes such a fuss if he can't get out.
Yes the Rum Tum Tugger is a Curious Cat—
   And it isn't any use for you to doubt it:
     For he will do
     As he do do
       And there's no doing anything about it!

The Rum Tum Tugger is a curious beast:
His disobliging ways are a matter of habit.
If you offer him fish then he always wants a
   feast;
When there isn't any fish then he won't eat
   rabbit.
If you offer him cream then he sniffs and sneers,
For he only likes what he finds for himself;
So you'll catch him in it right up to the ears,
If you put it away on the larder shelf.
The Rum Tum Tugger is artful and knowing,
The Rum Tum Tugger doesn't care for a cud-
   dle;
But he'll leap on your lap in the middle of your
   sewing,
For there's nothing he enjoys like a horrible
   muddle.

Yes the Rum Tum Tugger is a Curious Cat—
    And there isn't any need for me to spout it:
        For he will do
        As he do do
            And there's no doing anything about it!

MACAVITY: THE MYSTERY CAT

T. S. Eliot

Macavity's a Mystery Cat: he's called the Hidden
    Paw—
For he's the master criminal who can defy the
    Law.
He's the bafflement of Scotland Yard, the Flying
    Squad's despair:
For when they reach the scene of crime—*Macav-
    ity's not there!*

Macavity, Macavity, there's no one like Macavity,
He's broken every human law, he breaks the law
    of gravity.
His powers of levitation would make a fakir
    stare,
And when you reach the scene of crime—*Macav-
    ity's not there!*
You may seek him in the basement, you may
    look up in the air—
But I tell you once and once again, *Macavity's
    not there!*

Macavity's a ginger cat, he's very tall and thin;
You would know him if you saw him, for his eyes
    are sunken in.
His brow is deeply lined with thought, his head
    is highly domed;
His coat is dusty from neglect, his whiskers are
    uncombed.
He sways his head from side to side, with move-
    ments like a snake;
And when you think he's half asleep, he's always
    wide awake.

Macavity, Macavity, there's no one like Macavity,
For he's a fiend in feline shape, a monster of
    depravity.

"Macavity: The Mystery Cat." *Doesn't Mr. Eliot have
wonderful names for his cats? From Old Possum's Book of
Practical Cats,* copyright, 1939, by **T. S. Eliot.** Reprinted
by permission of Harcourt, Brace & Company, Inc., and
Faber and Faber Limited

You may meet him in a by-street, you may see
    him in the square—
But when a crime's discovered, then *Macavity's
    not there!*

He's outwardly respectable. (They say he cheats
    at cards.)
And his footprints are not found in any file of
    Scotland Yard's.
And when the larder's looted, or the jewel-case is
    rifled,
Or when the milk is missing, or another Peke's
    been stifled,
Or the greenhouse glass is broken, and the trellis
    past repair—
Ay, there's the wonder of the thing! *Macavity's
    not there!*

And when the Foreign Office find a Treaty's gone
    astray,
Or the Admiralty lose some plans and drawings
    by the way,
There may be a scrap of paper in the hall or on
    the stair—
But it's useless to investigate—*Macavity's not
    there!*
And when the loss has been disclosed, the Secret
    Service say:
"It *must* have been Macavity!"—but he's a mile
    away.
You'll be sure to find him resting, or a-licking of
    his thumbs,
Or engaged in doing complicated long division
    sums.

Macavity, Macavity, there's no one like Macavity,
There never was a Cat of such deceitfulness and
    suavity.
He always has an alibi, and one or two to spare:
At whatever time the deed took place—MACAV-
    ITY WASN'T THERE!
And they say that all the Cats whose wicked
    deeds are widely known,
(I might mention Mungojerrie, I might mention
    Griddlebone)
Are nothing more than agents for the Cat who
    all the time
Just controls their operations: the Napoleon of
    Crime!

(Mother Goose)

Sing a song of sixpence,
    A pocket full of rye;
Four-and-twenty blackbirds
    Baked in a pie!

When the pie was opened
    The birds began to sing;
Was not that a dainty dish
    To set before the king?

The king was in his counting-house
    Counting out his money;
The queen was in the parlor,
    Eating bread and honey.

The maid was in the garden,
    Hanging out the clothes;
When down came a blackbird
    And snapped off her nose.

(Mother Goose)

Hickory, dickory, dock!
    The mouse ran up the clock;
      The clock struck one,
      And down he run,
Hickory, dickory, dock!

(Mother Goose)

A farmer went trotting upon his gray mare;
    Bumpety, bumpety, bump!
With his daughter behind him so rosy and fair;
    Lumpety, lumpety, lump!

A raven cried "Croak!" and they all tumbled
    down,
    Bumpety, bumpety, bump!
The mare broke her knees, and the farmer his
    crown,
    Lumpety, lumpety, lump!

The mischievous raven flew laughing away,
    Bumpety, bumpety, bump!
And vowed he would serve them the same the
    next day,
    Lumpety, lumpety, lump!

(Mother Goose)

I saw a ship a-sailing,
    A-sailing on the sea;
And, oh! it was all laden
    With pretty things for thee!

There were comfits in the cabin,
    And apples in the hold;
The sails were made of silk,
    And the masts were made of gold.

The four-and-twenty sailors
    That stood between the decks,
Were four-and-twenty white mice
    With chains about their necks.

The captain was a duck,
    With a packet on his back;
And when the ship began to move,
    The captain said, "Quack! Quack!"

KINDNESS TO ANIMALS
Laura E. Richards

Riddle cum diddle cum dido,
    My little dog's name is Fido;
      I bought him a wagon,
      And hitched up a dragon,
And off we both went for a ride, oh!

Riddle cum riddle cum doodle,
    My little cat's name is Toodle;
      I curled up her hair,
      But she only said, "There!
You have made me look *just* like a poodle!"

"A farmer went trotting upon his gray mare." *This is fun to do with either two or three speaking choirs. See May Hill Arbuthnot,* Children and Books, *p. 215, and also record album* Poetry Time.
"Kindness to Animals." From *Tirra Lirra* by Laura E. Richards. Copyright 1918, 1930, 1932 by Laura E. Rich-

ards. By permission of Little, Brown & Co.
"Higgledy, piggledy! see how they run!" From *Under the Window* by Kate Greenaway. Frederick Warne and Company, New York and London, 1910
"My Donkey." *Could this wise little donkey be faking his pains to win sympathy and presents? Charming for*

Riddle cum diddle cum dinky,
My little pig's name is Winkie;
  I keep him quite clean
  With the washing machine,
And I rinse him all off in the sinkie.

Kate Greenaway

Higgledy, piggledy! see how they run!
Hopperty, popperty! what is the fun?
Has the sun or the moon tumbled into the sea?
What is the matter, now? Pray tell it me!

Higgledy, piggledy! how can I tell?
Hopperty, popperty! hark to the bell!
The rats and the mice even scamper away;
Who can say what may not happen to-day?

MY DONKEY

(French)

Rose Fyleman

My donkey, my dear,
Had a pain in his head;
A kind lady gave him
A bonnet of red,
And little shoes of lavender,
Lav—lav—lavender,
And little shoes of lavender
To keep him from the cold.

My donkey, my dear,
Had a pain in his throat;
A kind lady gave him
A button-up coat,
And little shoes of lavender,
Lav—lav—lavender,
And little shoes of lavender
To keep him from the cold.

My donkey, my dear,
Had a pain in his chest;
A kind lady gave him
A thick woolly vest,
And little shoes of lavender,
Lav—lav—lavender,
And little shoes of lavender,
To keep him from the cold.

ALL WOOL

Abbie Farwell Brown

I've noticed how the woolly lamb
  Dislikes the rain and dew.
I wonder if he fears to damp
  His little garments through?

How very horrid it would be
  If they should shrink when wet!
He cannot take his woollies off
  And wear another set.

His legs would be so bare and cold,
  An ugly sight to see!
The flock would bleat, "Bah! Bah!" at him.
  How sheepish he would be!

THE PURPLE COW

Gelett Burgess

I never saw a Purple Cow,
  I never hope to see one;
But I can tell you, anyhow,
  I'd rather see than be one.

(American Mother Goose)

How much wood would a wood-chuck chuck
If a wood-chuck could chuck wood?
He would chuck as much wood as a wood-chuck
  would chuck,
If a wood-chuck could chuck wood.

choral speaking. From *Picture Rhymes from Foreign Lands*. Copyright 1935 by Rose Fyleman. Reprinted by permission of J. B. Lippincott Company
"All Wool." From *Songs of Sixpence* by Abbie Farwell Brown. Reprinted by permission of and arrangement with Houghton Mifflin Company, the authorized publishers

"The Purple Cow." From *The Burgess Nonsense Book* by Gelett Burgess. J. B. Lippincott Company, New York, 1901. Used by permission of the author
"How much wood would a wood-chuck chuck." From *The American Mother Goose* compiled by Ray Wood. Copyright 1940 by J. B. Lippincott Company

THE TREE TOAD

Monica Shannon

The Tree Toad is a creature neat,
With tidy rubbers on his feet.
Embarrassment is all he knows—
His color comes, his color goes.

The Tree Toad is quite small, at least,
Unless his girth has just increased.
The truth is always hard to seek,
For things are changing every week.

ONLY MY OPINION

Monica Shannon

Is a caterpillar ticklish?
    Well, it's always my belief
That he giggles, as he wiggles
    Across a hairy leaf.

THE BUMBLEBEAVER

Kenyon Cox

A cheerful and industrious beast,
    He's always humming as he goes
To make mud-houses with his tail
    Or gather honey with his nose.

Although he flits from flower to flower
    He's not at all a gay deceiver.
We might take lessons by the hour
    From busy, buzzy Bumblebeaver.

ALAS, ALACK

Walter de la Mare

Ann, Ann!
    Come! Quick as you can!
There's a fish that *talks*
    In the frying-pan.

Out of the fat,
    As clear as glass,
He put up his mouth
    And moaned "Alas!"
Oh, most mournful,
    "Alas, alack!"
Then turned to his sizzling,
    And sank him back.

SOME FISHY NONSENSE

Laura E. Richards

Timothy Tiggs and Tomothy Toggs,
They both went a-fishing for pollothywogs;
    They both went a-fishing
    Because they were wishing
To see how the creatures would turn into frogs.

Timothy Tiggs and Tomothy Toggs,
They both got stuck in the bogothybogs;
    They caught a small minnow,
    And said 't was a sin oh!
That things with no legs should pretend to be
    frogs.

THERE ONCE WAS A PUFFIN

Florence Page Jaques

Oh, there once was a Puffin
Just the shape of a muffin,
And he lived on an island
In the
    bright
        blue
            sea!

He ate little fishes,
That were most delicious,
And he had them for supper
And he
    had
        them
            for tea.

"The Tree Toad." From *Goose Grass Rhymes* by Monica Shannon. Copyright 1930 by Doubleday & Company, Inc.

"Only My Opinion." From *Goose Grass Rhymes* by Monica Shannon. Copyright 1930 by Doubleday & Company, Inc.

"The Bumblebeaver." *There are several of these "Mixed Beasts"* (pp. 119 and 121) . *Perhaps you could mix a few of your own. Theodore Seuss Geisel has done it wonderfully in* If I Ran the Zoo. From *Mixed Beasts* by Kenyon Cox. Reprinted by permission of Dodd, Mead & Company

"Alas, Alack!" From *Collected Poems, 1901–1918,* by Walter de la Mare. Copyright, 1920, by Henry Holt and

But this poor little Puffin,
He couldn't play nothin',
For he hadn't anybody
To
  play
    with
      at all.

So he sat on his island,
And he cried for awhile, and
He felt very lonely,
And he
  felt
    very
      small.

Then along came the fishes,
And they said, "If you wishes,
You can have us for playmates,
Instead
  of
    for
      tea!"

So they now play together,
In all sorts of weather,
And the puffin eats pancakes,
Like you
  and
    like
      me.

THREE LITTLE PUFFINS

Eleanor Farjeon

Three little puffins
  Were partial to muffins,
As partial as partial can be.
  They wouldn't eat nuffin
  But hot buttered muffin
For breakfast and dinner and tea.

Pantin' and puffin'
  And chewin' and chuffin'
They just went on stuffin', dear me!
  Till the three little puffins
  Were chockful of muffins
And puffy as puffy can be,
        All three
  Were puffy as puffy can be.

THE OCTOPUS

Ogden Nash

Tell me, O Octopus, I begs,
Is those things arms, or is they legs?
I marvel at thee, Octopus;
If I were thou, I'd call me Us.

THE OCTOPUSSYCAT

Kenyon Cox

I love Octopussy, his arms are so long;
There's nothing in nature so sweet as his song.
'Tis true I'd not touch him—no, not for a farm!
If I keep at a distance he'll do me no harm.

Lewis Carroll

How doth the little crocodile
  Improve his shining tail,
And pour the waters of the Nile
  On every golden scale!

How cheerfully he seems to grin,
  How neatly spreads his claws,
And welcomes little fishes in,
  With gently smiling jaws!

Lewis Carroll

"The time has come," the Walrus said,
"To talk of many things:
Of shoes—and ships—and sealing-wax—
Of cabbages—and kings—
And why the sea is boiling hot—
And whether pigs have wings."

THE MONKEYS AND THE CROCODILE

Laura E. Richards

Five little monkeys
Swinging from a tree;
Teasing Uncle Crocodile,
Merry as can be.
Swinging high, swinging low,
Swinging left and right:
"Dear Uncle Crocodile,
Come and take a bite!"

Five little monkeys
Swinging in the air;
Heads up, tails up,
Little do they care.
Swinging up, swinging down,
Swinging far and near:
"Poor Uncle Crocodile,
Aren't you hungry, dear?"

Four little monkeys
Sitting in the tree;
Heads down, tails down,
Dreary as can be.
Weeping loud, weeping low,
Crying to each other:
"Wicked Uncle Crocodile,
To gobble up our brother!"

SO MANY MONKEYS

Marion Edey and Dorothy Grider

Monkey Monkey Moo!
Shall we buy a few?
Yellow monkeys,
Purple monkeys,
Monkeys red and blue.

Be a monkey, do!
Who's a monkey, *who?*
He's a monkey,
She's a monkey,
You're a monkey, too!

THE SHIP OF RIO

Walter de la Mare

There was a ship of Rio
Sailed out into the blue,
And nine and ninety monkeys
Were all her jovial crew.
From bo'sun to the cabin boy,
From quarter to caboose,
There weren't a stitch of calico
To breech 'em—tight or loose;
From spar to deck, from deck to keel,
From barnacle to shroud,
There weren't one pair of reach-me-downs
To all that jabbering crowd.
But wasn't it a gladsome sight,
When roared the deep-sea gales,
To see them reef her fore and aft,
A-swinging by their tails!
Oh, wasn't it a gladsome sight,
When glassy calm did come,
To see them squatting tailor-wise
Around a keg of rum!
Oh, wasn't it a gladsome sight,
When in she sailed to land,

"The Monkeys and the Crocodile." *To bring out the mock tragedy of the last verse keep the first two, with the five monkeys, light and gay. And then, the last verse is all contrasts—four instead of five monkeys, and instead of their taunting challenge to Mr. Crocodile, a reproachful last two lines. From* Tirra Lirra *by Laura E. Richards. Little, Brown & Company, Boston, 1932*
"So Many Monkeys." Reprinted from *Open the Door*

by Marion Edey and Dorothy Grider. Copyright 1949 by Marion Edey and Dorothy Grider. Used by permission of the publishers, Charles Scribner's Sons
"The Ship of Rio." From *Collected Poems, 1901–1918,* by Walter de la Mare. Copyright, 1920, by Henry Holt and Company, Inc. Copyright, 1948, by Walter de la Mare. Reprinted by permission of the publishers
"Habits of the Hippopotamus." From *Gaily the Trouba-*

To see them all a-scampering skip
For nuts across the sand!

HABITS OF THE HIPPOPOTAMUS

Arthur Guiterman

The hippopotamus is strong
  And huge of head and broad of bustle;
The limbs on which he rolls along
  Are big with hippopotomuscle.

He does not greatly care for sweets
  Like ice cream, apple pie, or custard,
But takes to flavor what he eats
  A little hippopotomustard.

The hippopotamus is true
  To all his principles, and just;
He always tries his best to do
  The things one hippopotomust.

He never rides in trucks or trams,
  In taxicabs or omnibuses,
And so keeps out of traffic jams
  And other hippopotomusses.

THE KANGAROOSTER

Kenyon Cox

His tail is remarkably long
And his legs are remarkably strong;
  But the strength and the length of his legs and
    his tail
Are as naught to the strength of his song.

He picks up his food with his bill;
He bounds over valley and hill;
  But the height of his bounds can't compare
    with the sounds
He lets out when he crows with a will.

Zhenya Gay

When a goose meets a moose
At the house of a mouse
I wonder if all three
Sit down and drink tea.

GRIZZLY BEAR

Mary Austin

If you ever, ever, ever meet a grizzly bear,
You must never, never, never ask him *where*
He is going,
Or *what* he is doing;
For if you ever, ever, dare
To stop a grizzly bear,
You will never meet *another* grizzly bear.

RACCOON

William Jay Smith

One summer night a little Raccoon,
Above his left shoulder, looked at the new moon.
    He made a wish;
    He said: "I wish
    I were a Catfish,
    A Blowfish, a Squid,
    A Katydid,
    A Beetle, a Skink,
    An Ostrich, a pink
    Flamingo, a Gander,
    A Salamander,
    A Hippopotamus,
    A Duck-billed Platypus,
    A Gecko, a Slug,
    A Water Bug,
    A pug-nosed Beaver,
    Anything whatever
Except what I am, a little Raccoon!"

Above his left shoulder, the Evening Star
Listened and heard the little Raccoon
      Who wished on the moon;
      And she said: "Why wish
      You were a Catfish,
      A Blowfish, a Squid,
      A Katydid,
      A Beetle, a Skink,
      An Ostrich, a pink
      Flamingo, a Gander,
      A Salamander,
      A Hippopotamus,
      A Duck-billed Platypus,
      A Gecko, a Slug,
      A Water Bug,
      A pug-nosed Beaver,
      Anything whatever?
Why must you change?" said the Evening Star,
"When you are perfect as you are?
I know a boy who wished on the moon
That *he* might be a little Raccoon!"

HOW TO TELL THE WILD ANIMALS

Carolyn Wells

If ever you should go by chance
  To jungles in the East;
And if there should to you advance
  A large and tawny beast,
If he roars at you as you're dyin'
You'll know it is the Asian Lion.

Or if some time when roaming round,
  A noble wild beast greets you,
With black stripes on a yellow ground,
  Just notice if he eats you.
This simple rule may help you learn
The Bengal Tiger to discern.

If strolling forth, a beast you view,
  Whose hide with spots is peppered,
As soon as he has lept on you,

You'll know it is the Leopard.
'Twill do no good to roar with pain,
He'll only lep and lep again.

If when you're walking round your yard,
  You meet a creature there,
Who hugs you very, very hard,
  Be sure it is the Bear.
If you have any doubt, I guess
He'll give you just one more caress.

Though to distinguish beasts of prey
  A novice might nonplus,
The Crocodiles you always may
  Tell from Hyenas thus:
Hyenas come with merry smiles;
But if they weep, they're Crocodiles.

The true Chameleon is small,
  A lizard sort of thing;
He hasn't any ears at all,
  And not a single wing.
If there is nothing on the tree,
'Tis the Chameleon you see.

(American Mother Goose)

I asked my mother for fifteen cents
To see the elephant jump the fence,
He jumped so high that he touched the sky
And never came back 'till the Fourth of July.

ELETELEPHONY

Laura E. Richards

Once there was an elephant,
Who tried to use the telephant—
No! no! I mean an elephone
Who tried to use the telephone—
(Dear me! I am not certain quite
That even now I've got it right.)

"How to Tell the Wild Animals." From *Baubles* by Carolyn Wells. Reprinted by permission of Dodd, Mead & Company

"I asked my mother for fifteen cents." From *The American Mother Goose* compiled by Ray Wood. Copyright 1940 by J. B. Lippincott Company

Howe'er it was, he got his trunk
Entangled in the telephunk;
The more he tried to get it free,
The louder buzzed the telephee—
(I fear I'd better drop the song
Of elephop and telephong!)

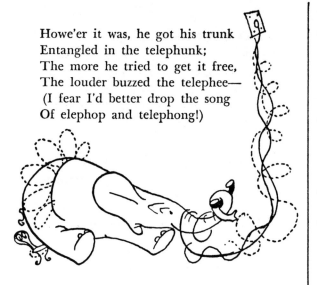

JABBERWOCKY

Lewis Carroll

'Twas brillig, and the slithy toves
  Did gyre and gimble in the wabe:
All mimsy were the borogoves,
    And the mome raths outgrabe.

"Beware the Jabberwock, my son!
  The jaws that bite, the claws that catch!
Beware the Jubjub bird, and shun
    The frumious Bandersnatch!"

He took his vorpal sword in hand:
  Long time the manxome foe he sought—
So rested he by the Tumtum tree,
    And stood awhile in thought.

And, as in uffish thought he stood,
  The Jabberwock, with eyes of flame,
Came whiffling through the tulgey wood,
    And burbled as it came!

One, two! One, two! And through and through
  The vorpal blade went snicker-snack!
He left it dead, and with its head
    He went galumphing back.

"And hast thou slain the Jabberwock?
  Come to my arms, my beamish boy!

O frabjous day! Callooh! Callay!"
  He chortled in his joy.

'Twas brillig, and the slithy toves
  Did gyre and gimble in the wabe:
All mimsy were the borogoves,
    And the mome raths outgrabe.

THE SPANGLED PANDEMONIUM

Palmer Brown

  The Spangled Pandemonium
  Is missing from the zoo.
  He bent the bars the barest bit,
  And slithered glibly through.

  He crawled across the moated wall,
  He climbed the mango tree,
  And when his keeper scrambled up,
  He nipped him in the knee.

  To all of you, a warning
  Not to wander after dark,
  Or if you must, make very sure
  You stay out of the park.

  For the Spangled Pandemonium
  Is missing from the zoo,
  And since he nipped his keeper,
  He would just as soon nip you!

A CENTIPEDE

Unknown

  A centipede was happy quite,
  Until a frog in fun
  Said, "Pray, which leg comes after which?"
  This raised her mind to such a pitch,
  She lay distracted in a ditch,
  Considering how to run.

ANTONIO
Laura E. Richards

Antonio, Antonio,
Was tired of living alonio.
    He thought he would woo
    Miss Lissamy Lou,
Miss Lissamy Lucy Molonio.

Antonio, Antonio,
Rode off on his polo-ponio.
    He found the fair maid
    In a bowery shade,
A-sitting and knitting alonio.

Antonio, Antonio,
Said, "If you will be my ownio,
    I'll love you true,
    And I'll buy for you,
An icery creamery conio!"

"Oh, nonio, Antonio!
You're far too bleak and bonio!
    And all that I wish,
    You singular fish,
Is that you will quickly begonio."

Antonio, Antonio,
He uttered a dismal moanio;
    Then ran off and hid
    (Or I'm told that he did)
In the Antarctical Zonio.

STATELY VERSE
Unknown

If Mary goes far out to sea,
    By wayward breezes fanned,
I'd like to know—can you tell me?—
    Just where would Maryland?

If Tenny went high up in air
    And looked o'er land and lea,
Looked here and there and everywhere,
    Pray what would Tennessee?

I looked out of the window and
    Saw Orry on the lawn;
He's not there now, and who can tell
    Just where has Oregon?

Two girls were quarrelling one day
    With garden tools, and so
I said, "My dears, let Mary rake
    And just let Idaho."

A friend of mine lived in a flat
    With half a dozen boys;
When he fell ill I asked him why.
    He said: "I'm Illinois."

An English lady had a steed.
    She called him 'Ighland Bay.
She rode for exercise, and thus
    Rhode Island every day.

DIAMOND CUT DIAMOND
Ewart Milne

Two cats
One up a tree
One under the tree
The cat up a tree is he
The cat under the tree is she
The tree is witch elm, just incidentally.
He takes no notice of she, she takes no notice of he.
He stares at the woolly clouds passing, she stares at the tree.
There's been a lot written about cats, by Old Possum, Yeats and Company
But not Alfred de Musset or Lord Tennyson or Poe or anybody
Wrote about one cat under, and one cat up, a tree.
God knows why this should be left for me
Except I like cats as cats be
Especially one cat up
And one cat under
A witch elm
Tree.

THE OSTRICH IS A SILLY BIRD

Mary E. Wilkins Freeman

The ostrich is a silly bird,
   With scarcely any mind.
He often runs so very fast,
   He leaves himself behind.

And when he gets there, has to stand
   And hang about till night,
Without a blessed thing to do
   Until he comes in sight.

RELATIVITY

Anonymous

There was a young lady named Bright,
Who traveled much faster than light.
   She started one day
   In the relative way,
And returned on the previous night.

(Mother Goose)

Mary, Mary, quite contrary,
   How does your garden grow?
Silver bells and cockle-shells,
   And pretty maids all in a row.

(Mother Goose)

Little Boy Blue, come blow your horn;
The sheep's in the meadow, the cow's in the corn.
Where's the little boy that looks after the sheep?
He's under the haystack, fast asleep.

(Mother Goose)

Wee Willie Winkie runs through the town,
Upstairs and downstairs, in his nightgown;
Rapping at the window, crying through the lock,
   "Are the children in their beds?
   Now it's eight o'clock."

"Antonio." By Laura E. Richards. By permission of Trustee u/w Laura E. Richards
"Diamond Cut Diamond" is reproduced from a volume of verse by Ewart Milne published under the title *Dia-*

(Mother Goose)

Jack and Jill went up the hill
   To fetch a pail of water.
Jack fell down and broke his crown
   And Jill came tumbling after.

Up Jack got and home he did trot
   As fast as he could caper.
He went to bed to mend his head
   In vinegar and brown paper.

(Mother Goose)

Little Miss Muffet
Sat on a tuffet,
Eating of curds and whey;
   There came a big spider,
   And sat down beside her,
And frightened Miss Muffet away.

(Mother Goose)

Little Bo-Peep has lost her sheep,
And can't tell where to find them;
Leave them alone, and they'll come home,
And bring their tails behind them.

Little Bo-Peep fell fast asleep,
And dreamt she heard them bleating;
But when she awoke, she found it a joke,
For still they all were fleeting.

Then up she took her little crook,
Determined for to find them;
She found them indeed, but it made her heart
   bleed,
For they'd left all their tails behind 'em!

It happened one day, as Bo-Peep did stray
Unto a meadow hard by—
There she espied their tails, side by side,
All hung on a tree to dry.

She heaved a sigh and wiped her eye,
And over the hillocks she raced;
And tried what she could, as a shepherdess
   should,
That each tail should be properly placed.

mond Cut Diamond by The Bodley Head, Ltd.
"The Ostrich is a Silly Bird." By Mary E. Wilkins Freeman. From *Harper's Magazine*, August 1905. Reprinted by permission of the publishers

THE BONNIE CRAVAT

(*Mother Goose*)

Jennie, come tie my,
Jennie, come tie my,
Jennie, come tie my bonnie cravat;
I've tied it behind,
I've tied it before,
I've tied it so often, I'll tie it no more.

(*Mother Goose*)

Ding, dong, bell!
Pussy's in the well!
Who put her in?
Little Johnny Green.
Who pulled her out?
Little Johnny Stout.

What a naughty boy was that
To try to drown poor pussy cat
Which never did him any harm,
But killed the mice in his father's barn!

(*Mother Goose*)

A diller, a dollar, a ten o'clock scholar!
What makes you come so soon?
You used to come at ten o'clock,
But now you come at noon.

(*Mother Goose*)

Bye, baby bunting,
Father's gone a-hunting,
Mother's gone a-milking,
Sister's gone a-silking,
And brother's gone to buy a skin
To wrap the baby bunting in.

(*Mother Goose*)

There was an old woman who lived in a shoe;
She had so many children she didn't know what
to do;
She gave them some broth without any bread;
She whipped them all soundly and put them to
bed.

(*Mother Goose*)

"Old woman, old woman, shall we go a-shearing?"
"Speak a little louder, sir, I am very thick of
hearing."
"Old woman, old woman, shall I kiss you
dearly?"
"Thank you, kind sir, I hear you very clearly."

(*Mother Goose*)

Hark, hark! the dogs do bark!
Beggars are coming to town:
Some in jags, and some in rags,
And some in velvet gown.

(*American Mother Goose*)

There was an old man named Michael Finnegan,
He grew a long beard right on his chinnigan,
Along came a wind and blew it in again—
Poor old Michael Finnegan.

(*Mother Goose*)

There was an old woman, as I've heard tell,
She went to market her eggs to sell;
She went to market all on a market-day,
And she fell asleep on the king's highway.

There came by a peddler whose name was Stout;
He cut her petticoats all round about;
He cut her petticoats up to the knees,
Which made the old woman to shiver and freeze.

When this little woman first did wake,
She began to shiver and she began to shake;
She began to wonder and she began to cry,
"Oh! deary, deary me, this is none of I!

"But if it be I, as I do hope it be,
I've a little dog at home, and he'll know me;
If it be I, he'll wag his little tail,
And if it be not I, he'll loudly bark and wail."

"The Bonnie Cravat." *This seems to demand a duet
performance—either by one boy and one girl or by two
verse choirs.*
"There was an old man named Michael Finnegan."
From *The American Mother Goose* compiled by Ray
Wood. Copyright 1940 by J. B. Lippincott Company
"There was a Young Lady whose chin." *These are only*

Home went the little woman all in the dark;
Up got the little dog, and he began to bark;
He began to bark, so she began to cry,
"Oh! deary, deary me, this is none of I!"

Edward Lear

There was a Young Lady whose chin
Resembled the point of a pin;
So she had it made sharp, and purchased a harp,
And played several tunes with her chin.

Edward Lear

There was an Old Man in a tree,
Who was horribly bored by a Bee;
When they said, "Does it buzz?"
    he replied, "Yes, it does!
It's a regular brute of a Bee."

Edward Lear

There was an Old Man with a beard,
Who said, "It is just as I feared!—
Two Owls and a Hen, four Larks and a Wren,
Have all built their nests in my beard."

Edward Lear

There was a Young Lady of Norway,
Who casually sat in a doorway;
When the door squeezed her flat,
    she exclaimed, "What of that?"
This courageous Young Lady of Norway.

JONATHAN

(*Dutch*)
Rose Fyleman

Jonathan Gee
Went out with his cow;
    He climbed up a tree

And sat on a bough.
    He sat on a bough
    And it broke in half,
        And John's old cow
        Did nothing but laugh.

Kate Greenaway

Tommy was a silly boy,
    "I can fly," he said;
He started off, but very soon,
    He tumbled on his head.

His little sister Prue was there,
    To see how he would do it;
She knew that, after all his boast,
    Full dearly Tom would rue it!

TIMOTHY BOON

Ivy O. Eastwick

Timothy Boon
Bought a balloon
Blue as the sky,
Round as the moon.
"Now I will try
To make it fly
Up to the moon,
Higher than high!"
Timothy said,
Nodding his head.

Timothy Boon
Sent his balloon
Up through the skies,
Up to the moon.
But a strong breeze
Stirred in the trees,
Rocked the bright moon,
Tossed the great seas,
And, with its mirth,
Shook the whole earth.

a few of Lear's many limericks. Look at his The Complete Nonsense Book *and you may feel inspired to try writing some limericks of your own.*
"Jonathan." From *Picture Rhymes from Foreign Lands.* Copyright 1935 by Rose Fyleman. Reprinted by permission of J. B. Lippincott Company

"Tommy was a silly boy." From *Under the Window* by Kate Greenaway. Frederick Warne and Company, New York and London, 1910
"Timothy Boon." Taken from *Fairies and Suchlike,* by Ivy O. Eastwick, published and copyright, 1946, by E. P. Dutton & Co., Inc., New York

Timothy Boon,
And his balloon,
Caught by the breeze
Flew to the moon;
Up past the trees,
Over the seas,
Up to the moon—
Swift as you please!—
And, ere I forget,
They have not come down yet!

THE STORY OF JOHNNY HEAD-IN-AIR

Heinrich Hoffman

As he trudg'd along to school,
It was always Johnny's rule
To be looking at the sky
And the clouds that floated by;
But what just before him lay,
In his way,
Johnny never thought about;
So that every one cried out—
"Look at little Johnny there,
Little Johnny Head-in-Air!"

Running just in Johnny's way,
Came a little dog one day;
Johnny's eyes were still astray
Up on high,
In the sky;
And he never heard them cry—
"Johnny, mind, the dog is nigh!"
Bump!
Dump!
Down they fell, with such a thump,
Dog and Johnny in a lump!

Once, with head as high as ever,
Johnny walk'd beside the river.
Johnny watch'd the swallows trying
Which was cleverest at flying.
Oh! what fun!
Johnny watch'd the bright round sun
Going in and coming out;
This was all he thought about.
So he strode on, only think!
To the river's very brink,
Where the bank was high and steep,
And the water very deep;

And the fishes, in a row,
Stared to see him coming so.

One step more! Oh! sad to tell!
Headlong in Poor Johnny fell.
And the fishes, in dismay,
Wagg'd their tails and ran away.

There lay Johnny on his face,
With his nice red writing-case;
But, as they were passing by,
Two strong men had heard him cry;
And, with sticks, these two strong men
Hook'd poor Johnny out again.
Oh! you should have seen him shiver
When they pull'd him from the river.
He was in a sorry plight!
Dripping wet, and such a fright!
Wet all over, everywhere,
Clothes, and arms, and face, and hair;
Johnny never will forget
What it is to be so wet.

And the fishes, one, two, three,
Are come back again, you see,
Up they came the moment after,
To enjoy the fun and laughter.
Each popp'd out his little head,
And, to tease poor Johnny, said,
"Silly little Johnny, look,
You have lost your writing-book!"

THE STORY OF AUGUSTUS

Heinrich Hoffmann

Augustus was a chubby lad;
Fat ruddy cheeks Augustus had;
And every body saw with joy
The plump and hearty healthy boy.
He ate and drank as he was told,
And never let his soup get cold.
But one day, one cold winter's day,
He scream'd out—"Take the soup away!
O take the nasty soup away!
I won't have any soup to-day."

"The Story of Johnny Head-in-Air" and "The Story of Augustus." *These two selections from the famous old book* Slovenly Peter *are fun to illustrate verse by verse. They make lively comic strips.*
"Godfrey Gordon Gustavus Gore." *Did you ever notice how often nonsense verse turns upon a humorous-sound-*

Next day, now look, the picture shows
How lank and lean Augustus grows!
Yet, though he feels so weak and ill,
The naughty fellow cries out still—
"Not any soup for me, I say:
O take the nasty soup away!
I won't have any soup to-day."

The third day comes; Oh what a sin!
To make himself so pale and thin.
Yet, when the soup is put on table,
He screams, as loud as he is able,—
"Not any soup for me, I say:
O take the nasty soup away!
I won't have any soup to-day."

Look at him, now the fourth day's come!
He scarcely weighs a sugar-plum;
He's like a little bit of thread,
And on the fifth day, he was—dead!

GODFREY GORDON GUSTAVUS GORE

William Brighty Rands

Godfrey Gordon Gustavus Gore—
No doubt you have heard the name before—
Was a boy who never would shut a door!

The wind might whistle, the wind might roar,
And teeth be aching and throats be sore,
But still he never would shut the door.

His father would beg, his mother implore,
"Godfrey Gordon Gustavus Gore,
We really *do* wish you would shut the door!"

Their hands they wrung, their hair they tore;
But Godfrey Gordon Gustavus Gore
Was deaf as the buoy out at the Nore.

When he walked forth the folks would roar,
"Godfrey Gordon Gustavus Gore,
Why don't you think to shut the door?"

They rigged out a Shutter with sail and oar,
And threatened to pack off Gustavus Gore
On a voyage of penance to Singapore.

But he begged for mercy, and said, "No more!
Pray do not send me to Singapore
On a Shutter, and then I will shut the door!"

"You will?" said his parents; "then keep on
    shore!
But mind you do! For the plague is sore
Of a fellow that never will shut the door,
Godfrey Gordon Gustavus Gore!"

MOMOTARA

(*Japanese*)

Rose Fyleman

Where did Momotara go,
With a hoity-toity-tighty?
He went to lay the giants low,
The wicked ones and mighty.

What did Momotara take?
His monkey, dog and pheasant,
Some dumplings and an almond cake,
Which made the journey pleasant.

How did Momotara fare
Upon the fearful meeting?
He seized the giants by the hair
And gave them all a beating.

ing combination of consonants? You can't say this mouth-filling name in a hurry.

"Momotara." This is about a famous Japanese folk tale. It lends itself to choral speaking with two choirs, one for the question and one for the answer. But note the changing atmosphere of the stanzas or the poem will become monotonous. Stanzas one and three are "fearful" indeed. Stanza two is pleasant enough, stanza four full of beautiful things, and the last stanza a gay, brisk conclusion. From Picture Rhymes from Foreign Lands. Copyright 1935 by Rose Fyleman. Reprinted by permission of J. B. Lippincott Company

What did Momotara bring?
Oh, more than you could measure:
A silver coat, a golden ring
And a waggon-load of treasure.

What did Momotara do?
He sat himself astride it;
The monkey pushed, the pheasant drew
And the little dog ran beside it.

AMBITION

Edith Agnew

When I am grown an *hombre*
I shall have another *nombre,*
They won't call me "Ramonito" any more;
But they'll call me *"caballero,"*
And I'll wave my wide *sombrero*
At all the señoritas I adore.

I've extravagant ideas:
Butter on all my *tortillas,*
And as much chokeberry jelly as I dare!
I will buy red combs for Mother—
She shall wear them, and no other—
With shiny stones to lie against her hair.

There will not be any, any,
That can use the words so many,
Or make speech so long as mine when I am big;
And for my songs I'll borrow
Uncle Pablo's good *guitarra.*—
But now I have to go and feed the pig.

CURIOUS SOMETHING

Winifred Welles

If I could smell smells with my ears,
If sounds came buzzing in my nose,
If in my lips were looks and tears,
Tongues in my eyes, do you suppose
That I should have this kind of face,
Or something curious in its place?

PHIZZOG

Carl Sandburg

This face you got,
This here phizzog you carry around,
You never picked it out for yourself, at all, at all
    —did you?
This here phizzog—somebody handed it to you
    —am I right?
Somebody said, "Here's yours, now go see what
    you can do with it."
Somebody slipped it to you and it was like a
    package marked:
"No goods exchanged after being taken away"—
This face you got.

THE TWINS

Henry Sambrooke Leigh

In form and feature, face and limb,
    I grew so like my brother
That folks got taking me for him
    And each for one another.
It puzzled all our kith and kin,
    It reach'd an awful pitch;
For one of us was born a twin
    And not a soul knew which.

One day (to make the matter worse),
    Before our names were fix'd,
As we were being wash'd by nurse,
    We got completely mix'd.
And thus, you see, by Fate's decree,
    (Or rather nurse's whim),
My brother John got christen'd *me,*
    And I got christen'd *him.*

This fatal likeness even dogg'd
    My footsteps when at school,
And I was always getting flogg'd—
    For John turn'd out a fool.
I put this question hopelessly
    To every one I knew,—

"Ambition." From *The Songs of Marcelino* by Edith Agnew. Ward Anderson Printing Company, Albuquerque, New Mexico, 1940. Used by permission of the author
"Curious Something." From *Skipping Along Alone* by Winifred Welles. The Macmillan Company, New York,

1931. Used by permission of James Welles Shearer
"Phizzog." From *Early Moon* by Carl Sandburg, copyright, 1930, by Harcourt, Brace and Company, Inc.
"Felicia Ropps." *Have you met her? And have you any other candidates for Goopdom? Maybe people who won't*

What *would* you do, if you were me,
  To prove that you were *you?*

Our close resemblance turn'd the tide
  Of my domestic life;
For somehow my intended bride
  Became my brother's wife.
In short, year after year the same
  Absurd mistake went on;
And when I died—the neighbors came
  And buried brother John!

FELICIA ROPPS

Gelett Burgess

Funny, how Felicia Ropps
Always handles things in shops!
Always pinching, always poking,
Always feeling, always stroking
Things she has no right to touch!
Goops like that annoy me much!

MRS. SNIPKIN AND
MRS. WOBBLECHIN

Laura E. Richards

Skinny Mrs. Snipkin,
  With her little pipkin,
Sat by the fireside a-warming of her toes.
  Fat Mrs. Wobblechin,
  With her little doublechin,
Sat by the window a-cooling of her nose.

  Says this one to that one,
  "Oh! you silly fat one,
Will you shut the window down? You're freezing
    me to death!"

Says that one to t' other one,
  "Good gracious, how you bother one!
There isn't air enough for me to draw my pre-
  cious breath!"

  Skinny Mrs. Snipkin,
  Took her little pipkin,
Threw it straight across the room as hard as she
    could throw;
  Hit Mrs. Wobblechin
  On her little doublechin,
And out of the window a-tumble she did go.

GOING TOO FAR

Mildred Howells

A woman who lived in Holland, of old,
Polished her brass till it shone like gold.
She washed her pig after all his meals
In spite of his energetic squeals.
She scrubbed her doorstep into the ground,
And the children's faces, pink and round,
She washed so hard that in several cases
She polished their features off their faces—
Which gave them an odd appearance, though
She thought they were really neater so!
Then her passion for cleaning quickly grew,
And she scrubbed and polished the village
    through,
Until, to the rage of all the people,
She cleaned the weather-vane off the steeple.
As she looked at the sky one summer's night
She thought that the stars shone out less bright;
And she said with a sigh, "If I were there,
I'd rub them up till the world should stare."
That night a storm began to brew,
And a wind from the ocean blew and blew
Till, when she came to her door next day
It whisked her up, and blew her away—
Up and up in the air so high
That she vanished, at last, in the stormy sky.
Since then it's said that each twinkling star
And the big white moon, shine brighter far.
But the neighbors shake their heads in fear
She may rub so hard they will disappear!

MR. PYME

Harry Behn

Once upon a time
Old Mr. Pyme
Lived all alone
Under a stone.

When the rain fell
He rang a bell,
When the sun shined
He laughed and dined

And floated to town
On thistledown,
And what a nice time
Had Mr. Pyme!

JONATHAN BING

Beatrice Curtis Brown

Poor old Jonathan Bing
Went out in his carriage to visit the King,
But everyone pointed and said, "Look at that!
Jonathan Bing has forgotten his hat!"
(He'd forgotten his hat!)

Poor old Jonathan Bing
Went home and put on a new hat for the King,
But up by the palace a soldier said, "Hi!
You can't see the King; you've forgotten your
    tie!"
(He'd forgotten his tie!)

Poor old Jonathan Bing,
He put on a *beautiful* tie for the King,
But when he arrived an Archbishop said, "Ho!
You can't come to court in pyjamas, you know!"

Poor old Jonathan Bing
Went home and addressed a short note to the
    King:

If you please will excuse me
I won't come to tea;
For home's the best place for
All people like me!

OLD QUIN QUEERIBUS

Nancy Byrd Turner

Old Quin Queeribus—
    He loved his garden so,
He wouldn't have a rake around,
    A shovel or a hoe.

For each potato's eyes he bought
    Fine spectacles of gold,
And mufflers for the corn, to keep
    Its ears from getting cold.

On every head of lettuce green—
    What do you think of that?—
And every head of cabbage, too,
    He tied a garden hat.

Old Quin Queeribus—
    He loved his garden so,
He couldn't eat his growing things,
    He only let them grow!

Lewis Carroll

"You are old, Father William," the young man
    said,
    "And your hair has become very white;
And yet you incessantly stand on your head—
    Do you think, at your age, it is right?"

"In my youth," Father William replied to his
    son,
    "I feared it might injure the brain;

"Mr. Pyme." From *The Little Hill*, copyright, 1949, by Harry Behn. Reprinted by permission of Harcourt, Brace and Company, Inc.

"Jonathan Bing." From *Jonathan Bing and Other Verses* by Beatrice Curtis Brown. Oxford University Press, New York, 1936. Copyright 1936 by Beatrice Curtis Brown. Reprinted by permission of the author

"Old Quin Queeribus." From *Zodiac Town* by Nancy

But, now that I'm perfectly sure I have none,
  Why, I do it again and again."

"You are old," said the youth, "as I mentioned before.
  And have grown most uncommonly fat;
Yet you turned a back-somersault in at the door—
  Pray, what is the reason of that?"

"In my youth," said the sage, as he shook his grey locks,
  "I kept all my limbs very supple
By the use of this ointment—one shilling the box—
  Allow me to sell you a couple?"

"You are old," said the youth, "and your jaws are too weak
  For anything tougher than suet;
Yet you finished the goose, with the bones and the beak—
  Pray, how did you manage to do it?"

"In my youth," said his father, "I took to the law,
  And argued each case with my wife;
And the muscular strength, which it gave to my jaw
  Has lasted the rest of my life."

"You are old," said the youth, "one would hardly suppose
  That your eye was as steady as ever;
Yet you balanced an eel on the end of your nose—
  What made you so awfully clever?"

"I have answered three questions, and that is enough,"
  Said his father. "Don't give yourself airs!
Do you think I can listen all day to such stuff?
  Be off, or I'll kick you down-stairs!"

Byrd Turner. By permission of Little, Brown & Co.
  "The Pirate Don Durk of Dowdee." *Here is another name concocted out of a delightful combination of con-*

THE PIRATE DON DURK OF DOWDEE

Mildred Plew Meigs

Ho, for the Pirate Don Durk of Dowdee!
He was as wicked as wicked could be,
But oh, he was perfectly gorgeous to see!
  The Pirate Don Durk of Dowdee.

His conscience, of course, was as black as a bat,
But he had a floppety plume on his hat
And when he went walking it jiggled—like that!
  The plume of the Pirate Dowdee.

His coat it was crimson and cut with a slash,
And often as ever he twirled his mustache
Deep down in the ocean the mermaids went splash,
  Because of Don Durk of Dowdee.

Moreover, Dowdee had a purple tattoo,
And stuck in his belt where he buckled it through
Were a dagger, a dirk and a squizzamaroo,
  For fierce was the Pirate Dowdee.

So fearful he was he would shoot at a puff,
And always at sea when the weather grew rough
He drank from a bottle and wrote on his cuff,
  Did Pirate Don Durk of Dowdee.

sonants. Do you think of any others? From *Child Life*,
March 1923. Child Life, Inc., Boston. By permission of
Marion Plew Ruckel

Oh, he had a cutlass that swung at his thigh
And he had a parrot called Pepperkin Pye,
And a zigzaggy scar at the end of his eye
    Had Pirate Don Durk of Dowdee.

He kept in a cavern, this buccaneer bold,
A curious chest that was covered with mould,
And all of his pockets were jingly with gold!
    Oh jing! went the gold of Dowdee.

His conscience, of course, it was crook'd like a
    squash,
But both of his boots made a slickery slosh,
And he went through the world with a wonder-
    ful swash,
    Did Pirate Don Durk of Dowdee.

It's true he was wicked as wicked could be,
His sins they outnumbered a hundred and three,
But oh, he was perfectly gorgeous to see,
    The Pirate Don Durk of Dowdee.

THE JUMBLIES

Edward Lear

They went to sea in a sieve, they did;
    In a sieve they went to sea:
In spite of all their friends could say,
On a winter's morn, on a stormy day,
    In a sieve they went to sea.
And when the sieve turned round and round,
And every one cried, "You'll all be drowned!"
They called aloud, "Our sieve ain't big;
But we don't care a button, we don't care a fig:
    In a sieve we'll go to sea!"
        Far and few, far and few,
            Are the lands where the Jumblies live:
            Their heads are green, and their hands are
                blue;
            And they went to sea in a sieve.

They sailed away in a sieve, they did,
    In a sieve they sailed so fast,
With only a beautiful pea-green veil
Tied with a ribbon, by way of a sail,

"The Jumblies." *These outrageous Jumblies are annoy-
ing because they do things they shouldn't do and come
through all right.*

To a small tobacco-pipe mast.
And every one said who saw them go,
"Oh! won't they be soon upset, you know?
For the sky is dark, and the voyage is long;
And, happen what may, it's extremely wrong
    In a sieve to sail so fast."
        Far and few, far and few,
            Are the lands where the Jumblies live:
            Their heads are green, and their hands are
                blue;
            And they went to sea in a sieve.

The water it soon came in, it did;
    The water it soon came in:
So, to keep them dry, they wrapped their feet
In a pinky paper all folded neat;
    And they fastened it down with a pin.
And they passed the night in a crockery-jar;
And each of them said, "How wise we are!
Though the sky be dark, and the voyage be long,
Yet we never can think we were rash or wrong,
    While round in our sieve we spin."
        Far and few, far and few,
            Are the lands where the Jumblies live:
            Their heads are green, and their hands are
                blue;
            And they went to sea in a sieve.

And all night long they sailed away;
    And when the sun went down,
They whistled and warbled a moony song,
To the echoing sound of a coppery gong,
    In the shade of the mountains brown.
"O Timballoo! How happy we are
When we live in a sieve and a crockery-jar!
And all night long, in the moonlight pale,
We sail away with a pea-green sail
    In the shade of the mountains brown."
        Far and few, far and few,
            Are the lands where the Jumblies live:
            Their heads are green, and their hands are
                blue;
            And they went to sea in a sieve.

They sailed to the Western Sea, they did,—
    To a land all covered with trees:
And they bought an owl, and a useful cart,
And a pound of rice, and a cranberry-tart,
    And a hive of silvery bees;

And they bought a pig, and some green jackdaws,
And a lovely monkey with lollipop paws,
And forty bottles of ring-bo-ree,
   And no end of Stilton cheese.
     Far and few, far and few,
      Are the lands where the Jumblies live:
     Their heads are green, and their hands are
       blue;
      And they went to sea in a sieve.

And in twenty years they all came back,—
  In twenty years or more;
And every one said, "How tall they've grown!

For they've been to the Lakes, and the Torrible
  Zone,
   And the hills of the Chankly Bore."
And they drank their health, and gave them a
  feast
Of dumplings made of beautiful yeast;
And every one said, "If we only live,
We, too, will go to sea in a sieve,
  To the hills of the Chankly Bore."
    Far and few, far and few,
     Are the lands where the Jumblies live:
    Their heads are green, and their hands are
     blue;
     And they went to sea in a sieve.

FAIRIES

Hilda Conkling

I cannot see fairies.
I dream them.
There is no fairy can hide from me;
I keep on dreaming till I find him:
There you are, Primrose! I see you, Black Wing!

HAVE YOU WATCHED THE FAIRIES?

Rose Fyleman

Have you watched the fairies when the rain is
    done
Spreading out their little wings to dry them in
    the sun?
    I have, I have! Isn't it fun?

Have you heard the fairies all among the limes
Singing little fairy tunes to little fairy rhymes?
    I have, I have, lots and lots of times!

Have you seen the fairies dancing in the air,
And dashing off behind the stars to tidy up their
    hair?
    I have, I have; I've been there!

MAGIC AND MAKE BELIEVE

I KEEP THREE WISHES READY

Annette Wynne

I keep three wishes ready,
Lest I should chance to meet,
Any day a fairy
Coming down the street.

I'd hate to have to stammer,
Or have to think them out,
For it's very hard to think things up
When a fairy is about.

And I'd hate to lose my wishes,
For fairies fly away,
And perhaps I'd never have a chance
On any other day.

So I keep three wishes ready,
Lest I should chance to meet,
Any day a fairy
Coming down the street.

COULD IT HAVE BEEN A SHADOW?

Monica Shannon

What ran under the rosebush?
  What ran under the stone?
Could it have been a shadow,
  Running away alone?
Maybe a fairy's shadow,
  Slipping away at dawn
To guard a gleaming pot of gold
  For a busy leprechaun.

THE BEST GAME THE FAIRIES PLAY

Rose Fyleman

The best game the fairies play,
  The best game of all,
Is sliding down steeples—
  (You know they're very tall.)
You fly to the weathercock,
  And when you hear it crow
You fold your wings and clutch your things
  And then let go!

They have a million other games—
  Cloud-catching's one,
And mud-mixing after rain
  Is heaps and heaps of fun;
But when you go and stay with them
  Never mind the rest,
Take my advice—they're very nice,
  But steeple-sliding's best!

YESTERDAY IN OXFORD STREET

Rose Fyleman

Yesterday in Oxford Street, oh, what d'you think,
  my dears?
I had the most exciting time I've had for years
  and years;
The buildings looked so straight and tall, the sky
  was blue between,
And, riding on a motor-bus, I saw the fairy
  queen!

Sitting there upon the rail and bobbing up and
  down,
The sun was shining on her wings and on her
  golden crown;
And looking at the shops she was, the pretty silks
  and lace—
She seemed to think that Oxford Street was quite
  a lovely place.

And once she turned and looked at me, and
    waved her little hand;
But I could only stare and stare—oh, would she
    understand?
I simply couldn't speak at all, I simply couldn't
    stir,
And all the rest of Oxford Street was just a shin-
    ing blur.

Then suddenly she shook her wings—a bird had
    fluttered by—
And down into the street she looked and up into
    the sky;
And perching on the railing on a tiny fairy
    toe,
She flashed away so quickly that I hardly saw
    her go.

I never saw her any more, altho' I looked all
    day;
Perhaps she only came to peep, and never meant
    to stay:
But oh, my dears, just think of it, just think what
    luck for me,
That she should come to Oxford Street, and I be
    there to see!

FOR A MOCKING VOICE

Eleanor Farjeon

Who   calls?   Who   calls?   Who?
Did you call?   Did you?—
I call!   I call!   I!
Follow where I fly.—
Where?   O where?   O where?
On Earth or in the Air?—
Where you come, I'm gone!
Where you fly, I've flown!—
Stay! ah, stay! ah, stay,
Pretty Elf, and play!
Tell me where you are—
Ha, ha, ha, ha, ha!

WHEN A RING'S AROUND THE MOON

Mary Jane Carr

The wee folk will be tripping,
    In their silver dancing shoon,
Ring-around-the-meadow,
    When a ring's around the moon:

Curtsy to the right and left,
    And curtsy to the middle—
The fiddler will be fiddling
    On his tiny fairy fiddle;

In and out and round about,
    A magic circle making;
The pipers will be piping
    Till their tiny throats are aching.

Oh, few may watch the wee ones dance,
    For fairy guards are spying,
And down beneath the grasses
    All the dancers will be hieing;

But hearken well, what time you see
    A ring around the moon;
And you will hear the music
    Of the wee folks' dancing tune.

MIDSUMMER MAGIC

Ivy O. Eastwick

Midsummer Eve, a year ago, my mother she com-
    manded,
"Now don't you go a'running down to Ragwort
    Meadow!
And don't you go a'plucking of the bracken-seed
    or nightshade;
Stay out of the moonlight, mind! and keep out of
    the shadow,
    For they say that the Ragtag,
                Bobtail,
                Merry-derry
                Fairy-men
Tonight will go a'dancing down in Ragwort
    Meadow!"

Midsummer Eve, a year ago, my mother she commanded,

"Now don't you go a'playing down in Ragwort Meadow!

Keep away from thorn-tree, from adders' tongue and henbane!

Keep away from moonlight and don't venture in the shadow,

   For they say that the Ragtag,
               Bobtail,
               Merry-derry
               Fairy-men

Are out a'snaring mortals down in Ragwort Meadow."

I wouldn't heed my mother's words! I wouldn't heed her warning!

I ran through the moonlight, through the starlight and the shadow!

And I never stopped a'running though my breath came quick and gasping,

Till I reached the very middle of Ragwort Meadow,

   And there I heard the Ragtag,
               Bobtail,
               Merry-derry
               Fairy-men

A'laughing fit to kill themselves in Ragwort Meadow.

I heard 'em! But I couldn't see, no! not a little sight of 'em!

I pulled a curly bracken-leaf a'growing in the meadow,

I scratched out all the bracken-seeds and rubbed them on my eyelids—

The moon gave brilliant sunlight! There wasn't any shadow!

   And there I saw the Ragtag,
               Bobtail,
               Merry-derry
               Fairy-men

A'dancing round me in a ring in Ragwort Meadow.

Half-a-hundred fairy-men and half-a-score of rabbits;

Half-a-dozen squirrels down in Ragwort Meadow,

Dancing round me in a ring—you never saw the like of it!—

Underneath the daylight which the bright moon shed! Oh!

   A blessing on the Ragtag,
               Bobtail,
               Merry-derry
               Fairy-men

Who showed themselves to me down in Ragwort Meadow.

CRAB-APPLE

Ethel Talbot

I dreamed the Fairies wanted me
   To spend my birth-night with them all;
And I said, "Oh, but you're so wee
   And I am so tremendous tall,
What could we do?"
   "Crab-apple stem!"
Said they, and I was just like them.

And then, when we were all the same,
   The party and the fun began;
They said they'd teach me a new game
   Of "Dew-ponds." "I don't think I can
Play that," I said.
   "Crab-apple blue!"
Said they, and I could play it too.

And then, when we had played and played,
   The Fairies said that we would dance;
And I said, "Oh, but I'm afraid
   That I've no shoes." I gave a glance
At my bare toes.
   "Crab-apple sweet!"
Said they, and shoes were on my feet.

And then we danced away, away,
   Until my birth-night all was done;

their laughter but could not see them until she rubbed her eyes with "bracken" seed. That is fern seed and is supposed to have magic power like the other flowers and trees the mother mentions. Taken from Fairies and Suchlike, by

Ivy O. Eastwick, published and copyright, 1946, by E. P. Dutton & Co., Inc., New York

"Crab-Apple." *Oh, what a dream!* From *Punch.* Reproduced by permission of the Proprietors of *Punch*

And I said, "I'll go home to-day;
    And thank you for my lovely fun,
I'll come again."
    "Crab-apple red!"
Said they, and I woke up in bed.

STOCKING FAIRY

Winifred Welles

In a hole of the heel of an old brown stocking,
A little old Fairy sits rocking and rocking,
And scolding and pointing and squeaking and
    squinting,
Brown as a nut, a bright eye glinting,
She tugs at a thread, she drags up a needle,
She stamps and she shrills, she commences to
    wheedle,
To whine of the cold, in a fine gust of temper
She beats on my thumb, and then with a whim-
    per
She sulks in her shawl, she says I've forgotten
I promised to make her a lattice of cotton,
A soft, woven window, cozy yet airy,
Where she could sit rocking and peeking—Hush,
    Fairy,
Tush, Fairy, sit gently, look sweetly,
I'll do what I said, now, and close you in neatly.

THE PLUMPUPPETS

Christopher Morley

When little heads weary have gone to their bed,
When all the good nights and the prayers have
    been said,
Of all the good fairies that send bairns to rest
The little Plumpuppets are those I love best.

If your pillow is lumpy, or hot, thin and flat,
The little Plumpuppets know just what
    they're at;
They plump up the pillow, all soft, cool and
    fat—
    The little Plumpuppets plump-up it!

The little Plumpuppets are fairies of beds:
They have nothing to do but to watch sleepy
    heads;
They turn down the sheets and they tuck you in
    tight,
And they dance on your pillow to wish you good
    night!

No matter what troubles have bothered the day,
Though your doll broke her arm or the pup ran
    away;
Though your handies are black with the ink that
    was spilt—
Plumpuppets are waiting in blanket and quilt.

If your pillow is lumpy, or hot, thin and flat,
The little Plumpuppets know just what
    they're at;
They plump up the pillow, all soft, cool and
    fat—
    The little Plumpuppets plump-up it!

THE ROCK-A-BY LADY

Eugene Field

The Rock-a-By Lady from Hushaby street
    Comes stealing; comes creeping;
The poppies they hang from her head to her feet,
And each hath a dream that is tiny and fleet—
She bringeth her poppies to you, my sweet,
    When she findeth you sleeping!

There is one little dream of a beautiful drum—
    "Rub-a-dub!" it goeth;
There is one little dream of a big sugar-plum,
And lo! thick and fast the other dreams come

"Stocking Fairy." *The staccato thud of these words cre-*
ates the picture of this cross, crabby old fairy as much as
the words themselves. After all her scolding, notice the
quiet, soothing ending. From Skipping Along Alone by
Winifred Welles. The Macmillan Company, New York,
1931. Used by permission of James Welles Shearer

"The Plumpuppets." From *The Rocking Horse*. Copy-
right 1918, 1946 by Christopher Morley. Published by J. B.
Lippincott Company
"The Rock-a-By Lady." From *Poems of Childhood* by
Eugene Field. Charles Scribner's Sons, New York, 1904

Of popguns that bang, and tin tops that hum,
  And a trumpet that bloweth!

And dollies peep out of those wee little dreams
  With laughter and singing;
And boats go a-floating on silvery streams,
And the stars peek-a-boo with their own misty
    gleams,
And up, up, and up, where the Mother Moon
    beams,
  The fairies go winging!

Would you dream all these dreams that are tiny
    and fleet?
  They'll come to you sleeping;
So shut the two eyes that are weary, my sweet,
For the Rock-a-By Lady from Hushaby street,
With poppies that hang from her head to her
    feet,
  Comes stealing; comes creeping.

THE HORSEMAN
Walter de la Mare

I heard a horseman
  Ride over the hill;
The moon shone clear,
  The night was still;
His helm was silver,
  And pale was he;
And the horse he rode
  Was of ivory.

KIPH
Walter de la Mare

My Uncle Ben, who's been
To Bisk, Bhir, Biak—
Been, and come back:
To Tab, Tau, Tze, and Tomsk,
And home, by Teneriffe:
Who, brown as desert sand,
Gaunt, staring, slow and stiff,
Has chased the Unicorn
And Hippogriff,
Gave me a smooth, small, shining stone,
Called *Kiph.*

"Look'ee, now, Nevvy mine,"
He told me—*"If*
You'd wish a wish,
Just rub this smooth, small, shining stone,
Called *Kiph."*

Hide it did I,
In a safe, secret spot;
Slept, and the place
In dreams forgot.

One wish *alone*
Now's mine: Oh, if
I could but find again
That stone called *Kiph!*

THE GNOME
Harry Behn

I saw a gnome
As plain as plain
Sitting on top
Of a weathervane.

He was dressed like a crow
In silky black feathers,
And there he sat watching
All kinds of weathers.

He talked like a crow too,
Caw caw caw,
When he told me exactly
What he saw,

Snow to the north of him
Sun to the south,
And he spoke with a beaky
Kind of a mouth.

But he wasn't a crow,
That was plain as plain
'Cause crows never sit
On a weathervane.

What I saw was simply
A usual gnome
Looking things over
On his way home.

"The Horseman" and "Kiph." From *Rhymes and Verses* by Walter de la Mare. Published by Henry Holt & Company, Inc., New York, 1947. By permission of the literary trustees of Walter de la Mare and The Society of Authors, London, as their representatives

"The Gnome." From *Windy Morning* by Harry Behn. Copyright 1953 by Harry Behn. Reprinted by permission of Harcourt, Brace and Company, Inc., New York

THE GOBLIN

(*French*)

Rose Fyleman

A goblin lives in *our* house, in *our* house, in *our*
    house,
A goblin lives in *our* house all the year round.
He bumps
And he jumps
And he thumps
And he stumps.
He knocks
And he rocks
And he rattles at the locks.
A goblin lives in *our* house, in *our* house, in *our*
    house,
A goblin lives in *our* house all the year round.

A GOBLINADE

Florence Page Jaques

A green hobgoblin,
    Small but quick,
Went out walking
    With a black thorn stick.

He was full of mischief,
    Full of glee.
He frightened all
    That he could see.

He saw a little maiden
    In a wood.
He looked as fierce as
    A goblin should.

He crept by the hedge row,
    He said, "Boo!"
"Boo!" laughed the little girl,
    "How are you?"

"What!" said the goblin,
    "Aren't you afraid?"
"I think you're funny,"
    Said the maid.

"Ha!" said the goblin,
    Sitting down flat.
"You think I'm funny?
    I don't like that.

"I'm very frightening.
    You should flee!"
"You're cunning," she said,
    "As you can be!"

Then she laughed again, and
    Went away.
But the goblin stood there
    All that day.

A beetle came by, and
    "Well?" it said.
But the goblin only
    Shook his head.

"For I am funny,"
    He said to it.
"I thought I was alarming,
    And I'm not a bit.

"If I'm amusing,"
    He said to himself,
"I won't be a goblin,
    I'll be an elf!

"For a goblin must be goblin
    All the day,
But an elf need only
    Dance and play."

So the little green goblin
    Became an elf.
And he dances all day, and
    He likes himself.

"The Goblin." *The words suggest in their sound the awkward, thumping movements of the goblin. For verse choir see May Hill Arbuthnot,* Children and Books, *p. 215.* From Picture Rhymes from Foreign Lands. *Copyright 1935* by Rose Fyleman. Reprinted by permission of J. B. Lippin-cott Company

"A Goblinade." From *Child Life*, October 1927. Child Life, Inc., Boston. By permission of the author

"Overheard on a Saltmarsh." *Here is a long conversation between a nymph and a goblin with never a "he said" or*

OVERHEARD ON A SALTMARSH

Harold Monro

Nymph, nymph, what are your beads?

Green glass, goblin. Why do you stare at them?

Give them me.

No.

Give them me. Give them me.

No.

Then I will howl all night in the reeds,
Lie in the mud and howl for them.

Goblin, why do you love them so?

They are better than stars or water,
Better than voices of winds that sing,
Better than any man's fair daughter,
Your green glass beads on a silver ring.

Hush, I stole them out of the moon.

Give me your beads, I desire them.

No.

I will howl in a deep lagoon
For your green glass beads, I love them so.
Give them me. Give them.

No.

THE LITTLE ELFMAN

John Kendrick Bangs

I met a little Elfman once,
  Down where the lilies blow.
I asked him why he was so small,
  And why he didn't grow.

*"she said" to tell you who is speaking. Yet if you read it
aloud it is perfectly clear and a delightful poem for verse
choirs or individual reading. From Children of Love by
Harold Monro. The Poetry Bookshop, London, 1913. Used
by permission of Alida Monro*

He slightly frowned, and with his eye
  He looked me through and through—
"I'm just as big for me," said he,
  "As you are big for you!"

THE ELF AND THE DORMOUSE

Oliver Herford

Under a toadstool
  Crept a wee Elf,
Out of the rain
  To shelter himself.

Under the toadstool,
  Sound asleep,
Sat a big Dormouse
  All in a heap.

Trembled the wee Elf,
  Frightened, and yet
Fearing to fly away
  Lest he get wet.

To the next shelter—
  Maybe a mile!
Sudden the wee Elf
  Smiled a wee smile,

"The Little Elfman." By permission of Mary Gray Bangs
for the Estate of John Kendrick Bangs
"The Elf and the Dormouse." From *Artful Anticks* by
Oliver Herford. Reprinted by permission of Appleton-
Century-Crofts, Inc.

Tugged till the toadstool
Toppled in two.
Holding it over him
Gaily he flew.

Soon he was safe home
Dry as could be.
Soon woke the Dormouse—
"Good gracious me!

Where is my toadstool?"
Loud he lamented.
—And that's how umbrellas
First were invented.

HOW TO TELL GOBLINS FROM ELVES

Monica Shannon

The Goblin has a wider mouth
Than any wondering elf.
The saddest part of this is that
He brings it on himself.
For hanging in a willow clump
In baskets made of sheaves,
You may see the baby goblins
Under coverlets of leaves.

They suck a pink and podgy foot,
(As human babies do),
And then they suck the other one,
Until they're sucking two.
And so it is that goblins' mouths
Keep growing very round.
So you can't mistake a goblin,
When a goblin you have found.

THE MAN WHO HID HIS OWN FRONT DOOR

Elizabeth MacKinstry

There was a little, Elvish man
Who lived beside a moor,

A shy, secretive, furtive soul
Who hid his own front door.

He went and hid his door beneath
A pink laburnum bush:
The neighbors saw the curtains blow,
They heard a singing thrush.

The Banker came and jingled gold,
It did not serve him there;
The honey-colored walls uprose
Unbroken and foresquare.

The Mayor called, the Misses Pitt
With cordials and game pie;
There was not any door at all,
They had to pass him by!

But ah! my little sister.
Her eyes were wild and sweet,
She wore blue faded calico,
And no shoes on her feet.

She found the wandering door in place
And easily went through
Into a strange and mossy Hall
Where bowls of old Delft blue

Held feasts of blackberries, like gems
In webs of shining dew—
*There stood that little Elvish man
And smiled to see her, too!*

(*Mother Goose*)

I had a little nut tree, nothing would it bear
But a silver nutmeg and a golden pear;
The king of Spain's daughter came to visit me,
And all for the sake of my little nut tree.
I skipped over water, I danced over sea,
And all the birds in the air couldn't catch me.

"How to Tell Goblins from Elves." From *Goose Grass Rhymes* by Monica Shannon. Copyright 1930 by Doubleday & Company, Inc.
"The Man Who Hid His Own Front Door." *Perhaps there is a moral to this charming verse. Perhaps it is a little like "Midsummer Magic," p. 138.* From *Gaily We Parade*. The Macmillan Company, New York, 1940. Used by permission of the author
"Sleepyhead." From *Collected Poems, 1901–1918*, by Walter de la Mare. Copyright, 1920, by Henry Holt and Company, Inc. Copyright, 1948, by Walter de la Mare. Reprinted by permission of the publishers

SLEEPYHEAD

Walter de la Mare

As I lay awake in the white moonlight,
I heard a faint singing in the wood,
  "Out of bed,
  Sleepyhead,
  Put your white foot now,
  Here are we,
  Neath the tree
  Singing round the root now!"

I looked out of window, in the white moonlight,
The trees were like snow in the wood—
  "Come away,
  Child, and play
  Light with the gnomies;
  In a mound,
  Green and round,
  That's where their home is.

  "Honey sweet,
  Curds to eat,
  Cream and fruménty,
  Shells and beads,
  Poppy seeds,
  You shall have plenty."

But soon as I stooped in the dim moonlight
To put on my stocking and my shoe,
The sweet, sweet singing died sadly away,
And the light of the morning peeped through:
Then instead of the gnomies there came a red
    robin
To sing of the buttercups and dew.

SOME ONE

Walter de la Mare

  Some one came knocking
    At my wee, small door;
  Some one came knocking,
    I'm sure—sure—sure;

"Some One." *This is as hushed as the mystery it describes. And who or what was it, do you think? From Collected Poems, 1901–1918, by Walter de la Mare.* Copyright, 1920, by Henry Holt and Company, Inc. Copyright, 1948, by Walter de la Mare. Reprinted by permission of the publishers

  I listened, I opened,
    I looked to left and right,
  But nought there was a-stirring
    In the still dark night;
  Only the busy beetle
    Tap-tapping in the wall,
  Only from the forest
    The screech-owl's call,
  Only the cricket whistling
    While the dew drops fall,
  So I know not who came knocking,
    At all, at all, at all.

William Shakespeare

  Where the bee sucks, there suck I:
  In a cowslip's bell I lie;
  There I couch when owls do cry.
  On the bat's back I do fly
  After summer merrily.
Merrily, merrily, shall I live now
Under the blossom that hangs on the bough.

THE BAGPIPE MAN

Nancy Byrd Turner

The bagpipe man came over our hill
  When no one knew he was anywhere round,
With a whirl and a skirl, a toot and a trill;
  And we all went scampering after the sound.
We cried, "Oh, tell us, what do you play?
  What do you play so queer, so queer?"
And he skipped a couple of notes to say,
  "But tell me, what do ye hear?"
Then one of us heard a trumpet sweet,
  And the tramp, tramp, tramp of marching
    men;
And one of us heard the dancing feet
  Of fairies down in a dusky glen;
And one of us called it a bird in June,
  And one, a river that ran and ran.
But he never would tell us the name of his tune,
  The funny old bagpipe man!

"Where the bee sucks, there suck I." From *The Tempest*, Act V, Sc. 1
"The Bagpipe Man." From *Magpie Lane* by Nancy Byrd Turner, copyright, 1927, by Harcourt, Brace and Company, Inc.

THE BALLAD OF
THE HARP-WEAVER

Edna St. Vincent Millay

"Son," said my mother,
  When I was knee-high,
"You've need of clothes to cover you,
  And not a rag have I.

"There's nothing in the house
  To make a boy breeches,
Nor shears to cut a cloth with
  Nor thread to take stitches.

"There's nothing in the house
  But a loaf-end of rye,
And a harp with a woman's head
  Nobody will buy,"
And she began to cry.

That was in the early fall.
  When came the late fall,
"Son," she said, "the sight of you
  Makes your mother's blood crawl,—

"Little skinny shoulder-blades
  Sticking through your clothes!
And where you'll get a jacket from
  God above knows.

"It's lucky for me, lad,
  Your daddy's in the ground,
And can't see the way I let
  His son go around!"
And she made a queer sound.

That was in the late fall.
  When the winter came,
I'd not a pair of breeches
  Nor a shirt to my name.

I couldn't go to school,
  Or out of doors to play.
And all the other little boys
  Passed our way.

"Son," said my mother,
  "Come, climb into my lap,
And I'll chafe your little bones
  While you take a nap."

And, oh, but we were silly
  For half an hour or more,
Me with my long legs
  Dragging on the floor,

A-rock-rock-rocking
  To a mother-goose rhyme!
Oh, but we were happy
  For half an hour's time!

But there was I, a great boy,
  And what would folks say
To hear my mother singing me
  To sleep all day,
  In such a daft way?

Men say the winter
  Was bad that year;
Fuel was scarce,
  And food was dear.

A wind with a wolf's head
  Howled about our door,
And we burned up the chairs
  And sat upon the floor.

All that was left us
  Was a chair we couldn't break,
And the harp with a woman's head
  Nobody would take,
  For song or pity's sake.

The night before Christmas
  I cried with the cold,
I cried myself to sleep
  Like a two-year-old.

And in the deep night
  I felt my mother rise,
And stare down upon me
  With love in her eyes.

I saw my mother sitting
  On the one good chair,
A light falling on her
  From I couldn't tell where,

Looking nineteen,
    And not a day older,
And the harp with a woman's head
    Leaned against her shoulder.

Her thin fingers, moving
    In the thin, tall strings,
Were weav-weav-weaving
    Wonderful things.

Many bright threads,
    From where I couldn't see,
Were running through the harp-strings
    Rapidly,

And gold threads whistling
    Through my mother's hand.
I saw the web grow,
    And the pattern expand.

She wove a child's jacket,
    And when it was done
She laid it on the floor
    And wove another one.

She wove a red cloak
    So regal to see,
"She's made it for a king's son,"
    I said, "and not for me."
    But I knew it was for me.

She wove a pair of breeches
    Quicker than that!
She wove a pair of boots
    And a little cocked hat.

She wove a pair of mittens,
    She wove a little blouse,
She wove all night
    In the still, cold house.

She sang as she worked,
    And the harp-strings spoke;
Her voice never faltered,
    And the thread never broke.
    And when I awoke,—

There sat my mother
    With the harp against her shoulder,
Looking nineteen
    And not a day older,

A smile about her lips,
    And a light about her head,
And her hands in the harp-strings
    Frozen dead.

And piled up beside her
    And toppling to the skies,
Were the clothes of a king's son,
    Just my size.

TILLIE

Walter de la Mare

Old Tillie Turveycombe
Sat to sew,
Just where a patch of fern did grow;
There, as she yawned,
And yawn wide did she,
Floated some seed
Down her gull-e-t;
And look you once,
And look you twice,
Poor old Tillie
Was gone in a trice.
But oh, when the wind
Do a-moaning come,
'Tis poor old Tillie
Sick for home;
And oh, when a voice
In the mist do sigh,
Old Tillie Turveycombe's
Floating by.

"Tillie." *Here is the magic of fern seed again. Poor old Tillie! See the introduction, p. xix.* From *Collected Poems, 1901–1918,* by Walter de la Mare. Copyright, 1920, by Henry Holt and Company, Inc. Copyright, 1948, by Walter de la Mare. Reprinted by permission of the publishers

BERRIES

Walter de la Mare

There was an old woman
  Went blackberry picking
Along the hedges
  From Weep to Wicking.
Half a pottle—
  No more she had got,
When out steps a Fairy
  From her green grot;

And says, "Well, Jill,
  Would 'ee pick 'ee mo?"
And Jill, she curtseys,
  And looks just so.
"Be off," says the Fairy,
  "As quick as you can,
Over the meadows
  To the little green lane,
That dips to the hayfields
  Of Farmer Grimes:
I've berried those hedges
  A score of times;
Bushel on bushel
  I'll promise 'ee, Jill,
This side of supper
  If 'ee pick with a will."
She glints very bright,
  And speaks her fair;
Then lo, and behold!
  She had faded in air.

Be sure Old Goodie
  She trots betimes
Over the meadows
  To Farmer Grimes.
And never was queen
  With jewellery rich
As those same hedges
  From twig to ditch;
Like Dutchmen's coffers,
  Fruit, thorn, and flower—

They shone like William
  And Mary's bower.
And be sure Old Goodie
  Went back to Weep
So tired with her basket
  She scarce could creep.

When she comes in the dusk
  To her cottage door,
There's Towser wagging
  As never before,
To see his Missus
  So glad to be
Come from her fruit-picking
  Back to he.
As soon as next morning
  Dawn was grey,
The pot on the hob
  Was simmering away;
And all in a stew
  And a hugger-mugger
Towser and Jill
  A-boiling of sugar,
And the dark clear fruit
  That from Faërie came,
For syrup and jelly
  And blackberry jam.

Twelve jolly gallipots
  Jill put by;
And one little teeny one,
  One inch high;
And that she's hidden
  A good thumb deep,
Halfway over
  From Wicking to Weep.

BEHIND THE WATERFALL
Winifred Welles

A little old woman
In a thin white shawl,
Stepped straight through the column
Of the silver waterfall,
As if the fall of water
Were not anything at all.
I saw her crook her finger,
I heard her sweetly call.
Over stones all green and glossy
I fled and did not fall;
I ran along the river
And through the waterfall,
And that heavy curve of water
Never hindered me at all.
The little old woman
In the thin white shawl
Took my hand and laughed and led me
Down a cool, still hall,
Between two rows of pillars
That were glistening and tall.
At her finger's tap swung open
A wide door in the wall,
And I saw the crystal city
That's behind the waterfall.

THE LITTLE GREEN ORCHARD
Walter de la Mare

Some one is always sitting there,
    In the little green orchard;
Even when the sun is high,
In noon's unclouded sky,
And faintly droning goes
The bee from rose to rose,
Some one in shadow is sitting there,
    In the little green orchard.

Yes, and when twilight's falling softly
    On the little green orchard;

When the grey dew distils
And every flower-cup fills;
When the last blackbird says,
    "What—what!" and goes her way—ssh!
I have heard voices calling softly
    In the little green orchard.

Not that I am afraid of being there,
    In the little green orchard;
Why, when the moon's been bright,
Shedding her lonesome light,
And moths like ghosties come,
And the horned snail leaves home:
I've sat there, whispering and listening there,
    In the little green orchard;

Only it's strange to be feeling there,
    In the little green orchard;
Whether you paint or draw,
Dig, hammer, chop, or saw;
When you are most alone.
All but the silence gone . . .
Some one is waiting and watching there,
    In the little green orchard.

SAM
Walter de la Mare

When Sam goes back in memory,
    It is to where the sea
Breaks on the shingle, emerald-green
    In white foam, endlessly;
He says—with small brown eye on mine—
    "I used to keep awake,
And lean from my window in the moon,

Watching those billows break.
And half a million tiny hands,
   And eyes, like sparks of frost,
Would dance and come tumbling into the moon,
   On every breaker tossed.
And all across from star to star,
   I've seen the watery sea,
With not a single ship in sight,
   Just ocean there, and me;
And heard my father snore . . . And once,
   As sure as I'm alive,
Out of those wallowing, moon-flecked waves
   I saw a mermaid dive;
Head and shoulders above the wave,
   Plain as I now see you,
Combing her hair, now back, now front,
   Her two eyes peeping through;
Calling me, 'Sam!'—quietlike—'Sam!' . . .
   But me . . . I never went,
Making believe I kind of thought
   'Twas someone else she meant . . .
Wonderful lovely there she sat,
   Singing the night away,
All in the solitudinous sea
   Of that there lonely bay.
P'raps," and he'd smooth his hairless mouth,
   "P'raps, if 'twere *now*, my son,
P'raps, if I heard a voice say, 'Sam!' . . .
   Morning would find me gone."

FAITH, I WISH I WERE A LEPRECHAUN

Margaret Ritter

Faith, I wish I were a leprechaun
Beneath a hawthorn tree,
A-cobblin' of wee, magic boots,
A-eatin' luscious, lovely fruits;
Oh, fiddle-dum, oh, fiddle-dee,
I wish I were a leprechaun
Beneath a hawthorn tree!

"Faith, I Wish I Were a Leprechaun." *Do you know the fairy shoemaker, the leprechaun, who has to give you his pot of gold if you can keep your eyes on him? From Mirrors by Margaret Ritter. Copyright 1925 by The Macmillan Company and used with their permission*

Faith, I wish I were a leprechaun
Beneath a hawthorn tree,
A-throwin' snuff into the eyes
Of young and old and dull and wise;
Oh, fiddle-dum, oh, fiddle-dee,
I wish I were a leprechaun
Beneath a hawthorn tree!

Faith, I wish I were a leprechaun
Beneath a hawthorn tree,
With no more irksome thing to do
Than sew a small, bewitchin' shoe;
Oh, fiddle-dum, oh, fiddle-dee,
I wish I were a leprechaun
Beneath a hawthorn tree!

THE UNICORN

Ella Young

While yet the Morning Star
Flamed in the sky
A Unicorn went mincing by,
Whiter by far than blossom of the thorn:
His silver horn
Glittered as he danced and pranced
Silver-pale in the silver-pale morn.

The folk that saw him, ran away.

"The Unicorn." *This poem is sheer music. The picture of the strange, bright fairy creature is beautiful but it is the melody of the lines that will haunt you. From The Horn Book March–April, 1939. The Horn Book Inc., Boston.*

Where he went, so gay, so fleet,
Star-like lilies at his feet
Flowered all day,
Lilies, lilies in a throng,
And the wind made for him a song:

But he dared not stay
Over-long!

INTRODUCTION
to SONGS OF INNOCENCE

William Blake

Piping down the valleys wild,
  Piping songs of pleasant glee,
On a cloud I saw a child,
  And he laughing said to me:

"Pipe a song about a Lamb!"
  So I piped with merry cheer.
"Piper, pipe that song again;"
  So I piped; he wept to hear.

"Drop thy pipe, thy happy pipe;
  Sing thy songs of happy cheer!"
So I sang the same again,
  While he wept with joy to hear.

"Piper, sit thee down and write
  In a book, that all may read."
So he vanished from my sight;
  And I plucked a hollow reed,

And I made a rural pen,
  And I stained the water clear,

And I wrote my happy songs
  Every child may joy to hear.

THE SONG OF
WANDERING AENGUS

William Butler Yeats

I went out to the hazel wood,
Because a fire was in my head,
And cut and peeled a hazel wand,
And hooked a berry to a thread;
And when white moths were on the wing,
And moth-like stars were flickering out,
I dropped a berry in a stream
And caught a little silver trout.

When I had laid it on the floor
I went to blow the fire aflame,
But something rustled on the floor,
And some one called me by my name:
It had become a glimmering girl
With apple blossom in her hair
Who called me by my name and ran
And faded through the brightening air.

Though I am old with wandering
Through hollow lands and hilly lands,
I will find out where she has gone,
And kiss her lips and take her hands;
And walk among long dappled grass,
And pluck till time and times are done
The silver apples of the moon,
The golden apples of the sun.

"Introduction" *to* Songs of Innocence. *This is Blake's account of how he came to write his poems. His cloud child commanded and he obeyed. It makes a lovely picture to read or to draw.*
  "The Song of Wandering Aengus." From *Poetical Works*

by William Butler Yeats. Copyright 1906, 1934 by The Macmillan Company and used with their permission. By permission also of Mrs. William Butler Yeats and The Macmillan Company of Canada

William Shakespeare

> With hey, ho, the wind and the rain,—
> For the rain—it raineth every day.

WEATHER

Hilda Conkling

> Weather is the answer
> When I can't go out into flowery places;
> Weather is my wonder
> About the kind of morning
> Hidden behind the hills of sky.

WATER

Hilda Conkling

> The world turns softly
> Not to spill its lakes and rivers.
> The water is held in its arms
> And the sky is held in the water.
> What is water,
> That pours silver,
> And can hold the sky?

WIND AND WATER

Kate Greenaway

> Little wind, blow on the hill-top,
> Little wind, blow down the plain;
> Little wind, blow up the sunshine,
> Little wind, blow off the rain.

(Mother Goose)

Blow wind, blow, and go mill, go,
That the miller may grind his corn;
That the baker may take it,
And into bread bake it,
And bring us a loaf in the morn.

WINDY WASH DAY

Dorothy Aldis

The wash is hanging on the line
And the wind's blowing—
Dresses all so clean and fine,
Beckoning
And bowing.

Stockings twisting in a dance,
Pajamas very tripping,
And every little pair of pants
Upside down
And skipping.

A KITE

Unknown

I often sit and wish that I
Could be a kite up in the sky,
And ride upon the breeze and go
Whichever way I chanced to blow.

Christina Georgina Rossetti

Who has seen the wind?
    Neither I nor you:
But when the leaves hang trembling
    The wind is passing thro'.

Who has seen the wind?
    Neither you nor I:
But when the trees bow down their heads
    The wind is passing by.

THE WIND

Robert Louis Stevenson

I saw you toss the kites on high
And blow the birds about the sky;
And all around I heard you pass,
Like ladies' skirts across the grass—
    O wind, a-blowing all day long,
    O wind, that sings so loud a song!

I saw the different things you did,
But always you yourself you hid.
I felt you push, I heard you call,
I could not see yourself at all—
    O wind, a-blowing all day long,
    O wind, that sings so loud a song!

O you that are so strong and cold,
O blower, are you young or old?
Are you a beast of field and tree,
Or just a stronger child than me?
    O wind, a-blowing all day long,
    O wind, that sings so loud a song!

THE KITE

Harry Behn

How bright on the blue
Is a kite when it's new!

With a dive and a dip
It snaps its tail

"With hey, ho, the wind and the rain." From *King Lear*, Act III, Sc. 2
"Weather." From *Poems by a Little Girl* by Hilda Conkling. Copyright 1920 by J. B. Lippincott Company
"Water." From *Poems by a Little Girl* by Hilda Conkling. Copyright 1920 by J. B. Lippincott Company
"Little wind, blow on the hill-top." From *Under the Window* by Kate Greenaway. Frederick Warne and Company, New York and London, 1910
"Blow wind, blow, and go mill, go." *Notice the change in tempo when you come to the third line. The first two are slow and sonorous. The last three trip along briskly because of those staccato consonants. See the introduction, p. xvi, and record album* Poetry Time.

"Windy Wash Day." From *Hop, Skip and Jump* by Dorothy Aldis. Minton, Balch and Company, New York, 1934. Copyright 1934 by Dorothy Aldis
"Who has seen the wind?" From *Sing-Song* by Christina Georgina Rossetti
"The Wind." *This is a favorite wind poem and lends itself to several possible arrangements for choral speaking. See May Hill Arbuthnot*, Children and Books, *p. 215.* From *A Child's Garden of Verses* by Robert Louis Stevenson
"The Kite." From *Windy Morning* by Harry Behn. Copyright 1953 by Harry Behn. Reprinted by permission of Harcourt Brace and Company, Inc., New York

Then soars like a ship
With only a sail

As over tides
Of wind it rides,

Climbs to the crest
Of a gust and pulls,

Then seems to rest
As wind falls.

When string goes slack
You wind it back

And run until
A new breeze blows

And its wings fill
And up it goes!

How bright on the blue
Is a kite when it's new!

But a raggeder thing
You never will see

When it flaps on a string
In the top of a tree.

Unknown

When the winds blow and the seas flow?
Hey, nonny no!

T. Sturge Moore

But hark to the wind how it blows!
None comes, none goes,
None reaps or mows,
No friends turn foes,
No hedge bears sloes,
And no cock crows,
But the wind knows!

WINDY MORNING

Harry Behn

Who minds if the wind whistles and howls
    When sun makes a wall of pleasant light,
Who minds if beyond the wind owls
    Are hooting as if it still were night!

I know the night is somewhere stalking
    Singing birds, and high in tall
Far away air owls are talking,
    But I don't care if they do at all.

Inside a wall of pleasant sun,
    Inside a wall of the wind's noise
My room is still, and there's much to be done
    With paper and paste and trains and toys.

HOLIDAY

Ella Young

        Where are you going
        Little wind of May-time?

        *To the silver-branched wood
        For an hour's playtime.*

"But hark to the wind how it blows. . . ." From *Poems* by T. Sturge Moore, Macmillan & Company Ltd., 1931
"Windy Morning." From *Windy Morning* by Harry Behn. Copyright 1953 by Harry Behn. Reprinted by permission of Harcourt, Brace and Company, Inc., New York
"Holiday." *A delightful conversation to be read by two voices perhaps, or two choirs, or just read for sheer pleasure.* Used by permission of the author

O, who'll be in the naked wood
To keep you company?

Ruby-branched and silver-thorned
I'll find a wild rose-tree.

What games will you play,
Little wind?

Any game that chance sends:
I'll run in the tall tree-tops,
And dance at the branch-ends.

Whom will you take for comrade,
Little wind so gaily going?

Anyone who finds the path,
Without my showing.

WINDY NIGHTS
Robert Louis Stevenson

Whenever the moon and stars are set,
  Whenever the wind is high,
All night long in the dark and wet,
  A man goes riding by.
Late in the night when the fires are out,
Why does he gallop and gallop about?

Whenever the trees are crying aloud,
  And ships are tossed at sea,
By, on the highway, low and loud,
  By at the gallop goes he:
By at the gallop he goes, and then
By he comes back at the gallop again.

Christina Georgina Rossetti

The wind has such a rainy sound
  Moaning through the town,
The sea has such a windy sound,—
  Will the ships go down?

The apples in the orchard
  Tumble from their tree.—
Oh, will the ships go down, go down,
  In the windy sea?

WIND-WOLVES
William D. Sargent

Do you hear the cry as the pack goes by,
The wind-wolves hunting across the sky?
Hear them tongue it, keen and clear,
Hot on the flanks of the flying deer!

Across the forest, mere, and plain,
Their hunting howl goes up again!
All night they'll follow the ghostly trail,
All night we'll hear their phantom wail,

For tonight the wind-wolf pack holds sway
From Pegasus Square to the Milky Way,
And the frightened bands of cloud-deer flee
In scattered groups of two and three.

DO YOU FEAR THE WIND?
Hamlin Garland

Do you fear the force of the wind,
The slash of the rain?
Go face them and fight them,
Be savage again.
Go hungry and cold like the wolf,
Go wade like the crane:
The palms of your hands will thicken,
The skin of your cheek will tan,
You'll grow ragged and weary and swarthy,
But you'll walk like a man!

"Windy Nights." *The galloping rhythm of these lines heightens the sense of mystery and adds to the excitement as a galloping rhythm always does whether in poetry or music. If you mark the time as you say these lines, you will discover the silent beat at the end of lines 2, 4, 6, 8, 10, 12. This is like the rest in music and must be observed in reading.* From *A Child's Garden of Verses* by Robert Louis Stevenson

"The wind has such a rainy sound." From *Sing-Song* by Christina Georgina Rossetti

"Wind-Wolves." *This figure of speech may need to be talked over until the picture or idea is clear.* Reprinted from *Scholastic Magazine.* Copyright 1926, by permission of the editors

"Do You Fear the Wind?" From *Silver Pennies* compiled by Blanche Jennings Thompson. The Macmillan

STORM

Hilda Doolittle Aldington

You crash over the trees,
you crack the live branch—
the branch is white,
the green crushed,
each leaf is rent like split wood.

You burden the trees
with black drops,
you swirl and crash—
you have broken off a weighted leaf
in the wind,
it is hurled out,
whirls up and sinks,
a green stone.

Christina Georgina Rossetti

O wind, why do you never rest,
    Wandering, whistling to and fro,
Bringing rain out of the west,
    From the dim north bringing snow?

(Unknown)

White sheep, white sheep,
On a blue hill,
When the wind stops
You all stand still.
When the wind blows
You walk away slow.
White sheep, white sheep,
Where do you go?

(Mother Goose)

Rain, rain, go away,
  Come again another day;
Little Johnny wants to play.

(Mother Goose)

One misty moisty morning,
    When cloudy was the weather,
I chanced to meet an old man,
    Clothed all in leather.
He began to compliment
    And I began to grin.
How do you do? And how do you do?
    And how do you do again?

A SHOWER

Izembō (Arranged by Olive Beauprè Miller)

Shower came;
In I came;
Blue sky came!

THE RAIN

(Unknown)

Rain on the green grass,
    And rain on the tree,
And rain on the house-top,
    But not upon me!

RAIN

Robert Louis Stevenson

The rain is raining all around,
    It falls on field and tree,
It rains on the umbrellas here,
    And on the ships at sea.

Company, New York, 1925. Used by permission of Constance Garland Doyle
  "Storm." From *Sea Garden* by Hilda Doolittle Aldington. Jonathan Cape Limited, London, 1924
  "O wind, why do you never rest." From *Sing-Song* by Christina Georgina Rossetti
  "One misty moisty morning." *See the introduction, p. xviii, and record album* Poetry Time

"A Shower." From *Little Pictures of Japan*. Used by permission of the author, Olive Beauprè Miller, and the publishers, The Book House for Children, Chicago, Illinois
  "The Rain." From *Romney Gay's Picture Book of Poems*. Copyright, 1940, by Phyllis I. Britcher. Grosset and Dunlap, New York, 1940. By permission of Phyllis I. Britcher
  "Rain." From *A Child's Garden of Verses* by Robert Louis Stevenson

MUD

Polly Chase Boyden

Mud is very nice to feel
All squishy-squash between the toes!
I'd rather wade in wiggly mud
Than smell a yellow rose.

Nobody else but the rosebush knows
How nice mud feels
Between the toes.

WHO LIKES THE RAIN?

Clara Doty Bates

"I," said the duck, "I call it fun,
For I have my little red rubbers on;
They make a cunning three-toed track
In the soft, cool mud. Quack! Quack! Quack!"

SPRING RAIN

Marchette Chute

The storm came up so very quick
    It couldn't have been quicker.
I should have brought my hat along,
    I should have brought my slicker.

My hair is wet, my feet are wet,
    I couldn't be much wetter.
I fell into a river once
    But this is even better.

THE REASON

Dorothy Aldis

Rabbits and squirrels
Are furry and fat,
And all of the chickens
Have feathers and that

Is why when it's raining
They need not stay in
The way children do who have
Only their skin.

GALOSHES

Rhoda W. Bacmeister

Susie's galoshes
Makes splishes and sploshes
And slooshes and sloshes,
As Susie steps slowly
Along in the slush.

They stamp and they tramp
On the ice and concrete,
They get stuck in the muck and the mud;
But Susie likes much best to hear

The slippery slush
As it slooshes and sloshes,
And splishes and sploshes,
All round her galoshes!

from ALL AROUND THE TOWN

Phyllis McGinley

U is for Umbrellas
    That bloom in rainy weather,
Like many-colored mushrooms,
    Sprouting upward altogether.
How useful an umbrella is!
    But still I often wonder
If a roof on stormy evenings
    Isn't nicer to be under.

VERY LOVELY
Rose Fyleman

Wouldn't it be lovely if the rain came down
Till the water was quite high over all the town?
If the cabs and buses all were set afloat,
And we had to go to school in a little boat?

Wouldn't it be lovely if it still should pour
And we all went up to live on the second floor?
If we saw the butcher sailing up the hill,
And we took the letters in at the window sill?

It's been raining, raining, all the afternoon;
All these things might happen really very soon.
If we woke to-morrow and found they had be-
    gun,
Wouldn't it be glorious? *Wouldn't* it be fun?

RAIN IN THE NIGHT
Amelia Josephine Burr

Raining, raining,
All night long;
Sometimes loud, sometimes soft,
Just like a song.

There'll be rivers in the gutters
And lakes along the street.
It will make our lazy kitty
Wash his little dirty feet.

The roses will wear diamonds
Like kings and queens at court;
But the pansies all get muddy
Because they are so short.

I'll sail my boat tomorrow
In wonderful new places,
But first I'll take my watering-pot
And wash the pansies' faces.

THE UMBRELLA BRIGADE
Laura E. Richards

"Pitter patter!" falls the rain
On the school-room window-pane.
Such a plashing! such a dashing!
Will it e'er be dry again?
Down the gutter rolls a flood,
And the crossing's deep in mud;
And the puddles! oh, the puddles
Are a sight to stir one's blood!

Chorus.   But let it rain
        Tree-toads and frogs,
        Muskets and pitchforks,
        Kittens and dogs!
        Dash away! plash away!
        Who is afraid?
        Here we go,
        The Umbrella Brigade!

Pull the boots up to the knee!
Tie the hoods on merrily!
Such a hustling! such a jostling!
Out of breath with fun are we.
Clatter, clatter, down the street,
Greeting every one we meet,
With our laughing and our chaffing,
Which the laughing drops repeat.

Chorus.   So let it rain
        Tree-toads and frogs,
        Muskets and pitchforks,
        Kittens and dogs!
        Dash away! plash away!
        Who is afraid?
        Here we go,
        The Umbrella Brigade!

LITTLE RAIN

Elizabeth Madox Roberts

When I was making myself a game
Up in the garden, a little rain came.

It fell down quick in a sort of rush,
And I crawled back under the snowball bush.

I could hear the big drops hit the ground
And see little puddles of dust fly round.

A chicken came till the rain was gone;
He had just a very few feathers on.

He shivered a little under his skin,
And then he shut his eyeballs in.

Even after the rain had begun to hush
It kept on raining up in the bush.

One big flat drop came sliding down,
And a ladybug that was red and brown

Was up on a little stem waiting there
And I got some rain in my hair.

SPRING RAIN

Harry Behn

Leaves make a slow
Whispering sound
As down the drops go
Drip to the ground
  Peace, peace, says the tree.

Good wet rain!
Shout happy frogs,
Peepers and big green
Bulls in bogs,
  Lucky, lucky are we!

On a bough above,
Head under wing,
A mourning dove
Waits time to sing.
  Ah me, she sighs, ah me!

CITY RAIN

Rachel Field

Rain in the city!
  I love to see it fall
Slantwise where the buildings crowd
  Red brick and all.
Streets of shiny wetness
  Where the taxis go,
With people and umbrellas all
  Bobbing to and fro.

Rain in the city!
  I love to hear it drip
When I am cosy in my room
  Snug as any ship,
With toys spread on the table,
  With a picture book or two,
And the rain like a rumbling tune that sings
  Through everything I do.

THE RAINS OF SPRING

Lady Ise (Arranged by Olive Beaupré Miller)

The rains of spring
Which hang to the branches
Of the green willow,
Look like pearls upon a string.

IT IS RAINING

Lucy Sprague Mitchell

It is raining.

Where would you like to be in the rain?
Where would you like to be?

I'd like to be on a city street,
where the rain comes down in a driving sheet,
where it wets the houses—roof and wall—
the wagons and horses and autos and all.
That's where I'd like to be in the rain,
that's where I'd like to be.

It is raining.

Where would you like to be in the rain?
Where would you like to be?

I'd like to be in a tall tree top,
where the rain comes dripping, drop, drop, drop,
around on every side:
where it wets the farmer, the barn, the pig,
the cows, the chickens both little and big;
where it batters and beats on a field of wheat
and makes the little birds hide.

It is raining.

Where would you like to be in the rain?
Where would you like to be?

I'd like to be on a ship at sea,
where everything's wet as wet can be

and the waves are rolling high,
where sailors are pulling the ropes and singing,
and wind's in the rigging and salt spray's sting-
ing,
and round us sea gulls cry.
On a dipping skimming ship at sea—
that's where I'd like to be in the rain;
that's where I'd like to be!

APRIL RAIN SONG

Langston Hughes

Let the rain kiss you.
Let the rain beat upon your head with silver
liquid drops.
Let the rain sing you a lullaby.

The rain makes still pools on the sidewalk.
The rain makes running pools in the gutter.
The rain plays a little sleep-song on our roof at
night—

And I love the rain.

RAIN

Ella Young

Dancing dancing down the street
Comes the rain on silver feet:
O hush, O hush,
For the wind is fluting a song.

Little flute of the wind,
Little flute of the wind,
Little flute of the wind
Play on.

Silver feet of the rain
Come again, come again,
Come with a fluting song.

and the publishers, The Book House for Children, Chi-
cago, Illinois
"It Is Raining." Taken from *Another Here and Now
Story Book*, edited by Lucy Sprague Mitchell, published
and copyright, 1937, by E. P. Dutton & Co., Inc., New
York

"April Rain Song." *The music of these words is as quiet
and peaceful as a gentle rain on the roof. See the intro-
duction, p. xx.* Reprinted from *The Dream Keeper* by
Langston Hughes. By permission of Alfred A. Knopf, Inc.
Copyright 1932 by Alfred A. Knopf, Inc.
"Rain." Reprinted by permission of the author

RAIN RIDERS
Clinton Scollard

Last night I heard a *rat-tat-too;*
   'Twas not a drum-beat, that was plain;
I listened long, and then I knew
   It was the Riders of the Rain.

But with the rising of the dawn
   There was no sound of any hoofs;
The Riders of the Rain had gone
   To tramp on other children's roofs.

IN TIME OF SILVER RAIN
Langston Hughes

In time of silver rain
The earth
Puts forth new life again,
Green grasses grow
And flowers lift their heads,
And over all the plain
The wonder spreads
   Of life,
   Of life,
   Of life!

In time of silver rain
The butterflies
Lift silken wings
To catch a rainbow cry,
And trees put forth
New leaves to sing
In joy beneath the sky
As down the roadway
Passing boys and girls
Go singing, too,
In time of silver rain
   When spring
   And life
   Are new.

THE RAIN
William Henry Davies

I hear leaves drinking rain;
   I hear rich leaves on top
Giving the poor beneath
   Drop after drop;
'Tis a sweet noise to hear
These green leaves drinking near.

And when the Sun comes out,
   After this rain shall stop,
A wondrous light will fill
   Each dark, round drop;
I hope the Sun shines bright;
'Twill be a lovely sight.

FOG
Carl Sandburg

The fog comes
on little cat feet.

It sits looking
over harbor and city
on silent haunches
and then moves on.

"Rain Riders." From *St. Nicholas.* Copyright, 1922, Century Company. Reprinted by permission of Appleton-Century-Crofts, Inc.

"In Time of Silver Rain." Reprinted from *Fields of Wonder* by Langston Hughes. By permission of Alfred A. Knopf, Inc. Copyright 1947 by Langston Hughes

"The Rain." From *Collected Poems,* by William Henry Davies. Jonathan Cape & Harrison Smith, New York, 1929

"Fog." From *Chicago Poems* by Carl Sandburg. Copyright, 1916, by Henry Holt and Company, Inc. Copyright, 1944, by Carl Sandburg. Used by permission of the publishers

THE FOG

William Henry Davies

I saw the fog grow thick,
　Which soon made blind my ken;
It made tall men of boys,
　And giants of tall men.

It clutched my throat, I coughed;
　Nothing was in my head
Except two heavy eyes
　Like balls of burning lead.

And when it grew so black
　That I could know no place,
I lost all judgment then,
　Of distance and of space.

The street lamps, and the lights
　Upon the halted cars,
Could either be on earth
　Or be the heavenly stars.

A man passed by me close,
　I asked my way, he said,
'Come, follow me, my friend'—
　I followed where he led.

He rapped the stones in front,
　'Trust me' he said 'and come';
I followed like a child—
　A blind man led me home.

Christina Georgina Rossetti

Boats sail on the rivers,
　And ships sail on the seas;
But clouds that sail across the sky
　Are prettier far than these.

There are bridges on the rivers,
　As pretty as you please;
But the bow that bridges heaven,

And overtops the trees,
And builds a road from earth to sky,
Is prettier far than these.

THE RAINBOW

Walter de la Mare

I saw the lovely arch
Of Rainbow span the sky,
The gold sun burning
As the rain swept by.

In bright-ringed solitude
The showery foliage shone
One lovely moment,
And the Bow was gone.

William Wordsworth

My heart leaps up when I behold
　A rainbow in the sky:
So was it when my life began;
So is it now I am a man;
So be it when I shall grow old,
　Or let me die!

Eleanor Farjeon

The tide in the river,
The tide in the river,

"The Fog." From *The Collected Poems of W. H. Davies*. London: Jonathan Cape, Ltd., 1929. Reprinted by permission of the publishers and Mrs. H. M. Davies.

"Boats sail on the rivers." *In the last stanza, there is an accumulative pattern that keeps the reader from dropping to a conclusion until the final line.* From *Sing-Song* by Christina Georgina Rossetti

"The Rainbow." From *Collected Poems, 1901–1918*, by Walter de la Mare. Copyright, 1920, by Henry Holt and Company, Inc. Copyright, 1948, by Walter de la Mare. Reprinted by permission of the publishers

"The tide in the river." From *Gypsy and Ginger*. Copyright 1920, 1948 by Eleanor Farjeon

The tide in the river runs deep.
  I saw a shiver
  Pass over the river
As the tide turned in its sleep.

THE NOISE OF WATERS

James Joyce

All day I hear the noise of waters
  Making moan,
Sad as the sea-bird is, when going
  Forth alone,
He hears the winds cry to the waters'
  Monotone.

The grey winds, the cold winds are blowing
  Where I go.
I hear the noise of many waters
  Far below.
All day, all night, I hear them flowing
  To and fro.

T. S. Eliot

I do not know much about gods; but I think that
    the river
Is a strong brown god—sullen, untamed and in-
    tractable,
Patient to some degree, at first recognised as a
    frontier;
Useful, untrustworthy, as a conveyor of com-
    merce;
Then only a problem confronting the builder of
    bridges.
The problem once solved, the brown god is al-
    most forgotten
By the dwellers in cities—ever, however, impla-
    cable,
Keeping his seasons and rages, destroyer, re-
    minder

Of what men choose to forget. Unhonoured,
    unpropitiated
By worshippers of the machine, but waiting,
    watching and waiting.

COMPOSED UPON WESTMINSTER BRIDGE

William Wordsworth

Earth has not anything to show more fair:
Dull would he be of soul who could pass by
A sight so touching in its majesty:
This City now doth like a garment wear
The beauty of the morning; silent, bare,
Ships, towers, domes, theaters, and temples lie
Open unto the fields, and to the sky;
All bright and glittering in the smokeless air.
Never did sun more beautifully steep
In his first splendor valley, rock, or hill;
Ne'er saw I, never felt, a calm so deep!
The river glideth at his own sweet will:
Dear God! the very houses seem asleep;
And all that mighty heart is lying still!

BROOKLYN BRIDGE AT DAWN

Richard Le Gallienne

Out of the cleansing night of stars and tides,
Building itself anew in the slow dawn,
The long sea-city rises: night is gone,
Day is not yet; still merciful, she hides
Her summoning brow, and still the night-car
    glides
Empty of faces; the night-watchmen yawn
One to the other, and shiver and pass on,
Nor yet a soul over the great bridge rides.

Frail as a gossamer, a thing of air,
A bow of shadow o'er the river flung,
Its sleepy masts and lonely lapping flood;
Who, seeing thus the bridge a-slumber there,
Would dream such softness, like a picture hung,
Is wrought of human thunder, iron and blood?

THE BIG CLOCK

(*Unknown*)

Slowly ticks the big clock;
Tick-tock, tick-tock!
But Cuckoo clock ticks double quick;
Tick-a-tock-a, tick-a-tock-a,
Tick-a-tock-a, tick!

(*Mother Goose*)

Bell horses, bell horses, what time of day?
One o'clock, two o'clock, three and away.

(*Mother Goose*)

The cock doth crow
To let you know,
If you be wise,
'Tis time to rise.

ROUND THE CLOCK

(*Mother Goose*)

Cocks crow in the morn
To tell us to rise,
And he who lies late
Will never be wise;

For early to bed
And early to rise,
Is the way to be healthy
And wealthy and wise.

A CHILD'S DAY, PART II
Walter de la Mare

Softly, drowsily,
Out of sleep;
Into the world again
Ann's eyes peep;
Over the pictures
Across the walls
One little quivering
Sunbeam falls.
A thrush in the garden
Seems to say,
Wake, little Ann,
'Tis day, 'tis day!
Faint sweet breezes
The casement stir,
Breathing of pinks
And lavender.
At last from her pillow,
With cheeks bright red,
Up comes her round little
Tousled head;
And out she tumbles
From her warm bed.

SINGING-TIME
Rose Fyleman

I wake in the morning early
And always, the very first thing,
I poke out my head and I sit up in bed
And I sing and I sing and I sing.

"The Big Clock." *See record album* Poetry Time. Every effort has been made to locate the copyright owner of this poem but without success
"A Child's Day, Part II." From *A Child's Day* by Walter de la Mare. Used by permission of Henry Holt and Company, Inc. By permission also of the author and by Faber and Faber Limited
"Singing-Time." From *The Fairy Green* by Rose Fyleman. Copyright 1923 by Doubleday & Company, Inc. By permission also of Miss Rose Fyleman, The Society of Authors, and Messrs. Methuen & Co.

A SUMMER MORNING
Rachel Field

I saw dawn creep across the sky,
And all the gulls go flying by.
I saw the sea put on its dress
Of blue mid-summer loveliness,
And heard the trees begin to stir
Green arms of pine and juniper.
I heard the wind call out and say:
"Get up, my dear, it is to-day!"

THE SUN
John Drinkwater

I told the Sun that I was glad,
  I'm sure I don't know why;
Somehow the pleasant way he had
  Of shining in the sky,
Just put a notion in my head
  That wouldn't it be fun
If, walking on the hill, I said
  "I'm happy" to the Sun.

AFTERNOON ON A HILL
Edna St. Vincent Millay

I will be the gladdest thing
  Under the sun!
I will touch a hundred flowers
  And not pick one.

I will look at cliffs and clouds
  With quiet eyes,
Watch the wind bow down the grass,
  And the grass rise.

And when lights begin to show
  Up from the town,
I will mark which must be mine,
  And then start down!

"A Summer Morning." From *The Pointed People* by Rachel Field. The Macmillan Company, New York, 1930. Used by permission of Arthur S. Pederson, Trustee, Estate of Rachel Field Pederson
"The Sun." From *All About Me* by John Drinkwater. Reprinted by permission of and arrangement with Houghton Mifflin Company, the authorized publishers
"Afternoon on a Hill." From *Renascence and Other Poems*, published by Harper & Brothers. Copyright 1917, 1945 by Edna St. Vincent Millay

Kate Greenaway

In the pleasant green Garden
    We sat down to tea;
"Do you take sugar?" and
    "Do you take milk?"
She'd got a new gown on—
    A smart one of silk.
We all were as happy
    As happy could be,
On that bright Summer's day
    When she asked us to tea.

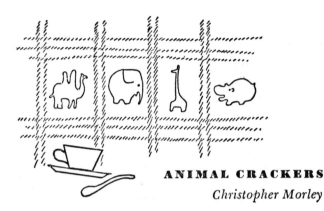

ANIMAL CRACKERS
Christopher Morley

Animal crackers, and cocoa to drink,
That is the finest of suppers, I think;
When I'm grown up and can have what I please
I think I shall always insist upon these.
What do *you* choose when you're offered a treat?
When Mother says, "What would you like best
        to eat?"
Is it waffles and syrup, or cinnamon toast?
It's cocoa and animals that *I* love most!

The kitchen's the cosiest place that I know:
The kettle is singing, the stove is aglow,
And there in the twilight, how jolly to see
The cocoa and animals waiting for me.

Daddy and Mother dine later in state,
With Mary to cook for them, Susan to wait;

But they don't have nearly as much fun as I
Who eat in the kitchen with Nurse standing by;
And Daddy once said, he would like to be me
Having cocoa and animals once more for tea!

THIS HAPPY DAY
Harry Behn

Every morning when the sun
Comes smiling up on everyone,
It's lots of fun
To say good morning to the sun.
    Good morning, Sun!

Every evening after play
When the sunshine goes away,
It's nice to say,
Thank you for this happy day,
    This happy day!

from ALL AROUND THE TOWN
Phyllis McGinley

W's for Windows.
    Watch them welcome in the night.
How they twinkle, twinkle, twinkle
    With the waning of the light!
There's nothing half so wonderful
    In all the wond'rous town
As a million winking Windows
    When the dusk is coming down.

THE PARK
James S. Tippett

I'm glad that I
    Live near a park

For in the winter
    After dark

The park lights shine
As bright and still

As dandelions
On a hill.

Elizabeth Coatsworth

Hard from the southeast blows the wind
   Promising rain.
The clouds are gathering, and dry leaves
   Tap at the pane.

Early the cows come wandering home
   To shadowy bars,
Early the candles are alight
   And a few stars.

Now is the hour that lies between
   Bright day and night,
When in the dusk the fire blooms
   In tongues of light,

And the cat comes to bask herself
   In the soft heat,
And Madame Peace draws up her chair
   To warm her feet.

SETTING THE TABLE
Dorothy Aldis

Evenings
When the house is quiet
I delight
To spread the white
Smooth cloth and put the flowers on the table.

I place the knives and forks around
Without a sound.
I light the candles.

I love to see
Their small reflected torches shine
Against the greenness of the vine
And garden.

Is that the mignonette, I wonder,
Smells so sweet?

And then I call them in to eat.

EVENING HYMN
Elizabeth Madox Roberts

The day is done;
The lamps are lit;
Woods-ward the birds are flown.
Shadows draw close,—
Peace be unto this house.

The cloth is fair;
The food is set.
God's night draw near.
Quiet and love and peace
Be to this, our rest, our place.

PRELUDE I
T. S. Eliot

The winter evening settles down
With smell of steaks in passageways.
Six o'clock.
The burnt-out ends of smoky days.
And now a gusty shower wraps
The grimy scraps
Of withered leaves about your feet
And newspapers from vacant lots;
The showers beat
On broken blinds and chimney-pots,
And at the corner of the street
A lonely cab-horse steams and stamps.
And then the lighting of the lamps.

SNOW TOWARD EVENING

Melville Cane

Suddenly the sky turned gray,
The day,
Which had been bitter and chill,
Grew intensely soft and still.
Quietly
From some invisible blossoming tree
Millions of petals cool and white
Drifted and blew,
Lifted and flew,
Fell with the falling night.

CHECK

James Stephens

The Night was creeping on the ground!
She crept and did not make a sound,

Until she reached the tree: And then
She covered it, and stole again

Along the grass beside the wall!
—I heard the rustling of her shawl

As she threw blackness everywhere
Along the sky, the ground, the air,

And in the room where I was hid!
But, no matter what she did

To everything that was without,
She could not put my candle out!

So I stared at the Night! And she
Stared back solemnly at me!

(*American Mother Goose*)

Star-light, star-bright
First star I've seen tonight;
I wish I may, I wish I might
Get the wish I wish tonight.

THE STAR

Jane Taylor

Twinkle, twinkle, little star,
How I wonder what you are!
Up above the world so high,
Like a diamond in the sky.

ESCAPE AT BEDTIME

Robert Louis Stevenson

The lights from the parlour and kitchen shone out
Through the blinds and the windows and bars;
And high overhead and all moving about,
There were thousands of millions of stars.

There ne'er were such thousands of leaves on a tree,
Nor of people in church or the Park,
As the crowds of the stars that looked down upon me,
And that glittered and winked in the dark.

The Dog, and the Plough, and the Hunter, and all,
And the Star of the Sailor, and Mars,

"Snow Toward Evening." From *January Garden* by Melville Cane, copyright, 1926 by Harcourt, Brace and Company, Inc.

"Check." From *Rocky Road to Dublin* by James Stephens. Copyright 1915, 1943 by The Macmillan Company and used with their permission. From *Collected Poems* by James Stephens. Used by permission of Mrs. James Stephens and Macmillan & Co., Ltd., London

"Star-light, star-bright." From *The American Mother Goose* compiled by Ray Wood. Copyright 1940 by J. B. Lippincott Company

"Escape at Bedtime." From *A Child's Garden of Verses* by Robert Louis Stevenson

These shone in the sky, and the pail by the wall
    Would be half full of water and stars.

They saw me at last, and they chased me with
        cries,
    And they soon had me packed into bed;
But the glory kept shining and bright in my
        eyes,
    And the stars going round in my head.

UNTIL WE BUILT
A CABIN

Aileen L. Fisher

When we lived in a city
(three flights up and down)
I never dreamed how many stars
could show above a town.

    When we moved to a village
    where lighted streets were few,
    I thought I could see ALL the stars,
    but, oh, I never knew—

        Until we built a cabin
        where hills are high and far,
        I never knew how many
                many
            stars there really are!

THE FALLING STAR

Sara Teasdale

I saw a star slide down the sky,
Blinding the north as it went by,
Too burning and too quick to hold,
Too lovely to be bought or sold,
Good only to make wishes on
And then forever to be gone.

STARS

Sara Teasdale

Alone in the night
    On a dark hill

With pines around me
    Spicy and still,

And a heaven full of stars
    Over my head,
White and topaz
    And misty red;

Myriads with beating
    Hearts of fire
That aeons
    Cannot vex or tire;

Up the dome of heaven
    Like a great hill,
I watch them marching
    Stately and still,

And I know that I
    Am honored to be
Witness
    Of so much majesty.

MOON-COME-OUT

Eleanor Farjeon

    Moon-Come-Out
    And Sun-Go-In,
    Here's a soft blanket
    To cuddle your chin.

Moon-Go-In
And Sun-Come-Out,
Throw off the blanket
And bustle about.

GOOD NIGHT

Dorothy Mason Pierce

On tip-toe comes the gentle dark
To help the children sleep
And silently, in silver paths,
The slumber fairies creep.

Then overhead, God sees that all
His candles are a-light,
And reaching loving arms to us
He bids His world Good Night.

(*Unknown*)

I see the moon,
And the moon sees me;
God bless the moon,
And God bless me.

CRESCENT MOON

Elizabeth Madox Roberts

And Dick said, "Look what I have found!"
And when we saw we danced around,
And made our feet just tip the ground.

We skipped our toes and sang, "Oh-lo.
Oh-who, oh-who, oh what do you know!
Oh-who, oh-hi, oh-loo, kee-lo!"

We clapped our hands and sang, "Oh-ee!"
It made us jump and laugh to see
The little new moon above the tree.

"Good Night." Taken from *The Susanna Winkle Book*, by Dorothy Mason Pierce, published and copyright, 1935, by E. P. Dutton & Co., Inc., New York

"Crescent Moon." *Notice how different the mood of this moon poem is from that of the De la Mare poem, "Full Moon."* From *Under the Tree* by Elizabeth Madox Roberts. Copyright 1922 by B. W. Huebsch, Inc., 1950 by Ivor S. Roberts. Reprinted by permission of The Viking Press, Inc., New York

"The White Window." From *Rocky Road to Dublin* by

THE WHITE WINDOW

James Stephens

The Moon comes every night to peep
    Through the window where I lie,
And I pretend to be asleep;
    But I watch the Moon as it goes by,
And it never makes a sound.

It stands and stares, and then it goes
    To the house that's next to me,
Stealing on its tippy-toes,
    To peep at folk asleep maybe;
And it never makes a sound.

FULL MOON

Walter de la Mare

One night as Dick lay fast asleep,
    Into his drowsy eyes
A great still light began to creep
    From out the silent skies.
It was the lovely moon's, for when
    He raised his dreamy head,

James Stephens. Copyright 1915, 1943 by The Macmillan Company and used with their permission. From *Collected Poems* by James Stephens. Used by permission of Mrs. James Stephens and Macmillan & Co., Ltd., London

"Full Moon." *Both this poem and "Silver" move with the slow serenity of the moon.* From *Collected Poems, 1901–1918,* by Walter de la Mare. Copyright, 1920, by Henry Holt and Company, Inc. Copyright, 1948, by Walter de la Mare. Reprinted by permission of the publishers

Her surge of silver filled the pane
And streamed across his bed.
So, for awhile, each gazed at each—
Dick and the solemn moon—
Till, climbing slowly on her way,
She vanished, and was gone.

SILVER

Walter de la Mare

Slowly, silently, now the moon
Walks the night in her silver shoon;
This way, and that, she peers, and sees
Silver fruit upon silver trees;
One by one the casements catch
Her beams beneath the silvery thatch;
Couched in his kennel, like a log,
With paws of silver sleeps the dog;
From their shadowy cote the white breasts peep
Of doves in a silver-feathered sleep;
A harvest mouse goes scampering by,
With silver claws, and silver eye;
And moveless fish in the water gleam,
By silver reeds in a silver stream.

LAST SONG

James Guthrie

To the Sun
Who has shone
   All day,
To the Moon
Who has gone
   Away,
To the milk-white,
Silk-white,
Lily-white Star
A fond goodnight
Wherever you are.

FINIS

Sir Henry Newbolt

Night is come,
   Owls are out;
Beetles hum
   Round about.

Children snore
   Safe in bed,
Nothing more
   Need be said.

(*Mother Goose*)

Spring is showery, flowery, bowery;
Summer: hoppy, croppy, poppy;
Autumn: wheezy, sneezy, freezy;
Winter: slippy, drippy, nippy.

ROUND THE CALENDAR

OPEN THE DOOR

Marion Edey and Dorothy Grider

Open the door and who'll come in?
  Who'll come in?
  Who'll come in?
Open the door and who'll come in,
  So early Monday morning?

My little pussycat, she'll come in,
Rubbing her fur against my shin.
She'll arch her back and she'll step right in,
  So early Monday morning.

Open the door and who'll come in?
  Who'll come in?
  Who'll come in?
Open the door and who'll come in,
  So early Tuesday morning?

My little puppy dog, he'll come in,
Mud on his paws and mud on his chin.
He'll bounce and he'll pounce as he dashes in,
   So early Tuesday morning.

Open the door and who'll come in?
   Who'll come in?
   Who'll come in?
Open the door and who'll come in,
   So early Wednesday morning?

My little Dicky bird, he'll come in,
His eyes so black and his legs so thin.
He'll fly to his cage and he'll pop right in,
   So early Wednesday morning.

Open the door and who do you see?
   Who do you see?
   Who do you see?
Open the door and who do you see,
   So early Thursday morning?

Beulah the pony is visiting me,
Nuzzling her nose against my knee,
Asking for sugar, as plain as can be,
   So early Thursday morning.

Open the door and who'll be there?
   Who'll be there?
   Who'll be there?
Open the door and who'll be there,
   So early Friday morning?

The Skillipot turtles, a tiny pair,
Their shells so hard and their heads so bare.
It takes them an hour to get anywhere
   So early Friday morning.

Open the door and what do you know?
   What do you know?
   What do you know?
Open the door and what do you know,
   So early Saturday morning?

My beautiful bunnies are white as snow,
And their pink little noses wiggle so.
Three pretty hops, and in they go,
   So early Saturday morning.

(*Mother Goose*)

   How many days has my baby to play?
     Saturday, Sunday, Monday,
   Tuesday, Wednesday, Thursday, Friday,
     Saturday, Sunday, Monday.

(*Mother Goose*)

   January brings the snow,
     Makes our feet and fingers glow.
   February brings the rain,
     Thaws the frozen lake again.
   March brings breezes loud and shrill,
     Stirs the dancing daffodil.

   April brings the primrose sweet,
     Scatters daisies at our feet.
   May brings flocks of pretty lambs,
     Skipping by their fleecy dams.
   June brings tulips, lilies, roses,
     Fills the children's hands with posies.

   Hot July brings cooling showers,
     Apricots and gillyflowers.
   August brings the sheaves of corn,
     Then the harvest home is borne.
   Warm September brings the fruit,
     Sportsmen then begin to shoot.

   Fresh October brings the pheasant,
     Then to gather nuts is pleasant.
   Dull November brings the blast,
     Then the leaves are whirling fast.
   Chill December brings the sleet,
     Blazing fire and Christmas treat.

"Open the Door." *This is charming to do with a verse choir. Let a chorus of light voices carry the "Open the door" refrain, and then let individual children say the answers.* Reprinted from *Open the Door* by Marion Edey and Dorothy Grider. Copyright 1949 by Marion Edey and Dorothy Grider. Used by permission of the publishers, Charles Scribner's Sons

"How many days has my baby to play?" *See record album* Poetry Time.

O DEAR ME!

Walter de la Mare

Here are crocuses, white, gold, grey!
    "O dear me!" says Marjorie May;
Flat as a platter the blackberry blows:
    "O dear me!" says Madeleine Rose;
The leaves are fallen, the swallows flown:
    "O dear me!" says Humphrey John;
Snow lies thick where all night it fell:
    "O dear me!" says Emmanuel.

SEPTEMBER

Edwina Fallis

A road like brown ribbon,
A sky that is blue,
A forest of green
With that sky peeping through.

Asters, deep purple,
A grasshopper's call,
Today it is summer,
Tomorrow is fall.

AUTUMN FIRES

Robert Louis Stevenson

In the other gardens
    And all up the vale,
From the autumn bonfires
    See the smoke trail!

Pleasant summer over
    And all the summer flowers.
The red fire blazes,
    The gray smoke towers.

Sing a song of seasons!
    Something bright in all!
Flowers in the summer,
    Fires in the fall!

DOWN! DOWN!

Eleanor Farjeon

    Down, down!
    Yellow and brown
The leaves are falling over the town.

AUTUMN WOODS

James S. Tippett

    I like the woods
        In autumn
When dry leaves hide the ground,
When the trees are bare
And the wind sweeps by
With a lonesome rushing sound.

    I can rustle the leaves
        In autumn
And I can make a bed
In the thick dry leaves
That have fallen
From the bare trees
Overhead.

THE CITY OF FALLING LEAVES

Amy Lowell

    Leaves fall,
    Brown leaves,
    Yellow leaves streaked with brown.
    They fall,
    Flutter,
    Fall again.

"O Dear Me!" *You might read this once or twice and never stop to think that each couplet has to do with one of the four seasons, beginning with spring.* From *Collected Poems, 1901–1918,* by Walter de la Mare. Copyright, 1920, by Henry Holt and Company, Inc. Copyright, 1948, by Walter de la Mare. Reprinted by permission of the publishers

"September." From *Sung under the Silver Umbrella.* The Macmillan Company, New York, 1935. Used by permission of the author

"Autumn Fires." From *A Child's Garden of Verses* by Robert Louis Stevenson

"Down! Down!" From *Joan's Door* by Eleanor Farjeon. Copyright 1926 by J. B. Lippincott Company

"Autumn Woods." From *A World to Know* by James S. Tippett. Copyright, 1933, Harper & Brothers

"The City of Falling Leaves." From "1777" in *Men,*

The brown leaves,
And the streaked yellow leaves,
Loosen on their branches
And drift slowly downwards.
One,
One, two, three,
One, two, five.
All Venice is a falling of Autumn leaves—
Brown,
And yellow streaked with brown.

Emily Dickinson

The morns are meeker than they were,
The nuts are getting brown;
The berry's cheek is plumper,
The rose is out of town.

The maple wears a gayer scarf,
The field a scarlet gown.
Lest I should be old-fashioned,
I'll put a trinket on.

FALL
Aileen L. Fisher

The last of October
We lock the garden gate.
(The flowers have all withered
That used to stand straight.)

The last of October
We put the swings away
And the porch looks deserted
Where we liked to play.

The last of October
The birds have all flown,
The screens are in the attic,
The sandpile's alone:

Everything is put away
Before it starts to snow—
I wonder if the ladybugs
Have any place to go!

SPLINTER
Carl Sandburg

The voice of the last cricket
across the first frost
is one kind of good-by.
It is so thin a splinter of singing.

MY BROTHER
Dorothy Aldis

My brother is inside the sheet
That gave that awful shout.
I know because those are his feet
So brown and sticking out.

And that's his head that waggles there
And his eyes peeking through—
So I can laugh, so I don't care:
"Ha!" I say. "It's you."

BLACK AND GOLD
Nancy Byrd Turner

Everything is black and gold,
 Black and gold, tonight:
Yellow pumpkins, yellow moon,
 Yellow candlelight;

Jet-black cat with golden eyes,
 Shadows black as ink,
Firelight blinking in the dark
 With a yellow blink.

Women and Ghosts by Amy Lowell. Reprinted by permission of and arrangement with Houghton Mifflin Company, the authorized publishers
"The morns are meeker than they were." From *The Poems of Emily Dickinson*. Little, Brown & Company, Boston, 1939
"Fall." From *The Coffee-Pot Face* by Aileen L. Fisher. Robert M. McBride & Company, New York, 1933

"Splinter." From *Good Morning, America*, copyright, 1928, by Carl Sandburg. Reprinted by permission of Harcourt, Brace and Company, Inc.
"My Brother." From *Hop, Skip and Jump* by Dorothy Aldis. Minton, Balch and Company, New York, 1934. Copyright 1934 by Dorothy Aldis
"Black and Gold." From *Child Life*. Child Life, Inc., Boston, October 1929. Used by permission of the author

Black and gold, black and gold,
Nothing in between—
When the world turns black and gold,
Then it's Halloween!

THEME IN YELLOW
Carl Sandburg

I spot the hills
With yellow balls in autumn.
I light the prairie cornfields
Orange and tawny gold clusters
And I am called pumpkins.
On the last of October
When dusk is fallen
Children join hands
And circle round me
Singing ghost songs
And love to the harvest moon;
I am a jack-o'-lantern
With terrible teeth
And the children know
I am fooling.

HALLOWE'EN
Harry Behn

Tonight is the night
When dead leaves fly
Like witches on switches
Across the sky,
When elf and sprite
Flit through the night
On a moony sheen.

Tonight is the night
When leaves make a sound
Like a gnome in his home
Under the ground,
When spooks and trolls
Creep out of holes
Mossy and green.

Tonight is the night
When pumpkins stare
Through sheaves and leaves
Everywhere,
When ghoul and ghost
And goblin host
Dance round their queen.
It's Hallowe'en!

THIS IS HALLOWEEN
Dorothy Brown Thompson

Goblins on the doorstep,
    Phantoms in the air,
Owls on witches' gateposts
    Giving stare for stare,
Cats on flying broomsticks,
    Bats against the moon,
Stirrings round of fate-cakes
    With a solemn spoon,
Whirling apple parings,
    Figures draped in sheets
Dodging, disappearing,
    Up and down the streets,
Jack-o'-lanterns grinning,
    Shadows on a screen,
Shrieks and starts and laughter—
    This is Halloween!

THE RIDE-BY-NIGHTS
Walter de la Mare

Up on their brooms the Witches stream,
Crooked and black in the crescent's gleam,
One foot high, and one foot low,
Bearded, cloaked, and cowled, they go.
'Neath Charlie's Wane they twitter and tweet,
And away they swarm 'neath the Dragon's feet,
With a whoop and a flutter they swing and sway,
And surge pell-mell down the Milky Way.
Between the legs of the glittering Chair

"Theme in Yellow." From *Chicago Poems* by Carl Sandburg. Copyright, 1916, by Henry Holt and Company, Inc. Copyright, 1944, by Carl Sandburg. Used by permission of the publishers
"Hallowe'en." From *The Little Hill*, copyright, 1949, by Harry Behn. Reprinted by permission of Harcourt, Brace and Company, Inc.
"This Is Halloween." From *Child Life*, October 1941.

Child Life, Inc., Boston. Used by permission of the author
"The Ride-by-Nights." *Many of the Halloween poems suggest pictures but this one does especially.* From *Collected Poems, 1901–1918*, by Walter de la Mare. Copyright, 1920, by Henry Holt and Company, Inc. Copyright, 1948, by Walter de la Mare. Reprinted by permission of the publishers
"The Last Word of a Bluebird (As Told to a Child)."

They hover and squeak in the empty air.
Then round they swoop past the glimmering
    Lion
To where Sirius barks behind huge Orion;
Up, then, and over to wheel amain
Under the silver, and home again.

THE LAST WORD OF A BLUEBIRD

(As Told to a Child)

Robert Frost

As I went out a Crow
In a low voice said 'Oh,
I was looking for you.
How do you do?
I just came to tell you
To tell Lesley (will you?)
That her little Bluebird
Wanted me to bring word
That the north wind last night
That made the stars bright
And made ice on the trough
Almost made him cough
His tail feathers off.
He just had to fly!
But he sent her Good-by,
And said to be good,
And wear her red hood,
And look for skunk tracks
In the snow with an ax—
And do everything!
And perhaps in the spring
He would come back and sing.'

This is as casual a conversation as two people talking about the weather, only it happens to be a Crow speaking! He is delivering a message the bluebird left behind him for Lesley, the poet's daughter. From *Mountain Interval* by Robert Frost. Copyright, 1916, by Henry Holt and Company, Inc. Copyright, 1943, by Robert Frost. Used by permission of the publishers

SOMETHING TOLD THE WILD GEESE

Rachel Field

Something told the wild geese
    It was time to go.
Though the fields lay golden
    Something whispered, "Snow."
Leaves were green and stirring,
    Berries, luster-glossed,
But beneath warm feathers
    Something cautioned, "Frost."
All the sagging orchards
    Steamed with amber spice,
But each wild breast stiffened
    At remembered ice.
Something told the wild geese
    It was time to fly—
Summer sun was on their wings,
    Winter in their cry.

THANKSGIVING MAGIC

Rowena Bastin Bennett

Thanksgiving Day I like to see
Our cook perform her witchery.
She turns a pumpkin into pie
As easily as you or I
Can wave a hand or wink an eye.
She takes leftover bread and muffin
And changes them to turkey stuffin'.
She changes cranberries to sauce
And meats to stews and stews to broths,
And when she mixes gingerbread
It turns into a man instead
With frosting collar 'round his throat
And raisin buttons down his coat.
Oh, some like magic made by wands,
    And some read magic out of books,
And some like fairy spells and charms
    But I like magic made by cooks!

"Something Told the Wild Geese." *This poem is also about the fall migration of birds, but it is mysterious and stirring.* From *Branches Green* by Rachel Field. Copyright 1934 by The Macmillan Company and used with their permission

"Thanksgiving Magic." From *Child Life*, November 1944. Child Life, Inc., Boston. Used by permission of the author

SELECTIONS FROM THE PSALMS

(Psalm 150)

Praise ye the Lord.
Praise God in his sanctuary:
Praise him in the firmament of his power.
Praise him for his mighty acts:
Praise him according to his excellent greatness.
Praise him with the sound of the trumpet:
Praise him with the psaltery and harp.
Praise him with the timbrel and dance:
Praise him with stringed instruments and organs.
Praise him upon the loud cymbals:
Praise him upon the high sounding cymbals.
Let every thing that hath breath praise the
    Lord.
Praise ye the Lord.

(Psalm 100)

Make a joyful noise unto the Lord, all ye lands.
Serve the Lord with gladness:
Come before his presence with singing.
Know ye that the Lord he is God:
It is he that hath made us, and not we ourselves;
We are his people, and the sheep of his pasture.
Enter into his gates with thanksgiving,
And into his courts with praise:
Be thankful unto him, and bless his name.
For the Lord is good; his mercy is everlasting;
And his truth endureth to all generations.

(Psalm 103)

Bless the Lord, O my soul:
And all that is within me, bless his holy name.
Bless the Lord, O my soul,
And forget not all his benefits:

Who forgiveth all thine iniquities;
Who healeth all thy diseases;
Who redeemeth thy life from destruction;
Who crowneth thee with loving-kindness and
    tender mercies;
Who satisfieth thy mouth with good things;
So that thy youth is renewed like the eagle's.
Bless the Lord, O my soul:
And all that is within me, bless his holy name.

(Psalm 147)

Praise ye the Lord:
For it is good to sing praises unto our God;
For it is pleasant; and praise is comely.
Great is our Lord, and of great power:
Who covereth the heaven with clouds,
Who prepareth rain for the earth,
Who maketh grass to grow upon the mountains.
He giveth to the beast his food,
And to the young ravens which cry.
He giveth snow like wool:
He scattereth the hoarfrost like ashes.
He casteth forth his ice like morsels:
Who can stand before his cold?
He sendeth out his word, and melteth them:
He causeth his wind to blow, and the waters flow.
Sing unto the Lord with thanksgiving;
Praise ye the Lord.

(Psalm 24)

The earth *is* the Lord's, and the fulness
    thereof;
The world, and they that dwell therein.
For he hath founded it upon the seas,
And established it upon the floods.
Who shall ascend into the hill of the Lord?
Or who shall stand in his holy place?

"Praise ye the Lord." Psalm 150. *When we think of the day and its name—Thanksgiving—we are immediately reminded of those matchless songs of praise and thanksgiving, the Psalms. Here are a few memorable selections, many of which are especially beautiful to speak in verse choirs. Some suggestions for casting them in this form are indicated, although there is usually more than one way of arranging them.*

A discussion of choral speaking is found on page xxiv of this book. In these notes H, M, and L indicate the high, medium, and low choirs. (Also see Chapter 10, Verse Choirs, in Children and Books *by May Hill Arbuthnot.)*

For Psalm 150 number the lines and mark for speaking in the following groups: All three choirs: line 1; M: 2, 3; H: 4, 5; M: 6, 7; L: 8, 9; H: 10, 11; L: 12; all choirs: the last line.

"Make a joyful noise unto the Lord." Psalm 100. *Number lines; cast for these groups: all choirs: line 1; H: 2, 3; L: 4, 5, 6; M: 7, 8, 9; all choirs: 10, 11*

"Bless the Lord, O my soul." Psalm 103: 1–5. *Number lines; cast for these groups: M: 1, 2; H: 3, 4; L: 5, 6; M: 7, 8; H and M: 9, 10; All: 12. Notice that after line 2 there is no conclusion until line 10. Then, lines 11 and 12 repeat the beginning and are a great swelling chorus*

He that hath clean hands, and a pure heart;
Who hath not lifted up his soul unto vanity,
Nor sworn deceitfully.
He shall receive the blessing from the Lord,
And righteousness from the God of his salvation.
This is the generation of them that seek him,
That seek thy face, O Jacob.
Lift up your heads, O ye gates;
And be ye lifted up, ye everlasting doors;
And the King of glory shall come in.
Who is this King of glory?
The Lord strong and mighty,
The Lord mighty in battle.
Lift up your heads, O ye gates;
Even lift them up, ye everlasting doors;
And the King of glory shall come in.
Who is this King of glory?
The Lord of hosts,
He *is* the King of glory.

(*Psalm 23*)

The Lord is my shepherd; I shall not want.
He maketh me to lie down in green pastures:
He leadeth me beside the still waters.
He restoreth my soul:
He leadeth me in the paths of righteousness for
    his name's sake.
Yea, though I walk through the valley of the
    shadow of death,
I will fear no evil: for thou art with me;
Thy rod and thy staff they comfort me.
Thou preparest a table before me in the presence
    of mine enemies:
Thou anointest my head with oil; my cup run-
    neth over.
Surely goodness and mercy shall follow me all
    the days of my life:
And I will dwell in the house of the Lord for
    ever.

THE MITTEN SONG
Marie Louise Allen

"Thumbs in the thumb-place,
Fingers all together!"
This is the song
We sing in mitten-weather.
When it is cold,
It doesn't matter whether
Mittens are wool,
Or made of finest leather.
This is the song
We sing in mitten-weather:
"Thumbs in the thumb-place,
Fingers all together!"

ICE
Dorothy Aldis

When it is the winter time
I run up the street
And I make the ice laugh
With my little feet—
"Crickle, crackle, crickle
Crrreeet, crrreeet, crrreeet."

FIRST SNOW
Marie Louise Allen

Snow makes whiteness where it falls.
The bushes look like popcorn-balls.
And places where I always play,
Look like somewhere else today.

of thanksgiving.
"Praise ye the Lord." Psalm 147: 1, 5, 8, 9, 16, 17, 18, 7, 20. *All choirs speak line 1; H: 2, 3; M: 4, 5, 6, 7; H: 8, 9; M: 10, 11, 12, 13; L: 14, 15, 16.*
"The earth is the Lord's." Psalm 24. *All choirs speak lines 1, 2; M: 3, 4; H: 5, 6; M: 7, 8, 9; L: 10, 11, 12, 13; M: 14, 15, 16; H: 17; L: 18, 19; M: 20, 21, 22; H: 23. This is an especially dramatic selection for choirs to speak. The question may come from the high voices or ring out clearly from one solo voice, if preferred. In that case, use two choirs for the other lines, one choir M to H and the other M to L.*

"The Lord is my shepherd." Psalm 23. *It seems best to let the sheer perfection of the Twenty-Third Psalm stand alone without verse choir arrangement.*
"The Mitten Song." From *Sung under the Silver Umbrella.* The Macmillan Company, New York, 1935. Used by permission of the author
"Ice." From *Everything and Anything* by Dorothy Aldis. Minton, Balch and Company, New York, 1927. Copyright 1925, 1926, 1927 by Dorothy Aldis
"First Snow." From *A Pocketful of Rhymes.* Harper & Brothers, New York, 1939. Used by permission of the author

FIRST SNOW

Ivy O. Eastwick

Lighter than thistledown
  Blown by a fairy,
Fine flakes of snow fall through
  Space grey and airy.

Whiter than lily that
  Blows sweet in summer,
This first snow of winter,
  This gentle newcomer.

SNOW

Dorothy Aldis

The fenceposts wear marshmallow hats
On a snowy day;
Bushes in their night gowns
Are kneeling down to pray—
And all the trees have silver skirts
And want to dance away.

SNOW

Alice Wilkins

The snow fell softly all the night.
It made a blanket soft and white.
It covered houses, flowers and ground,
But did not make a single sound!

SNOW IN THE CITY

Rachel Field

Snow is out of fashion,
  But it still comes down,
To whiten all the buildings
  In our town;
To dull the noise of traffic;

To dim each glaring light
  With star-shaped feathers
  Of frosty white.
And not the tallest building
  Halfway up the sky;
Or all the trains and busses,
  And taxis scudding by;
And not a million people,
  Not one of them at all,
Can do a thing about the snow
  But let it fall!

CYNTHIA IN THE SNOW

Gwendolyn Brooks

It SUSHES.
It hushes
The loudness in the road.
It flitter-twitters,
And laughs away from me.
It laughs a lovely whiteness,
And whitely whirs away,
To be
Some otherwhere,
Still white as milk or shirts.
So beautiful it hurts.

FALLING SNOW

(Unknown)

See the pretty snowflakes
  Falling from the sky;
On the walk and housetop
  Soft and thick they lie.

On the window-ledges
  On the branches bare;
Now how fast they gather,
  Filling all the air.

Look into the garden,
  Where the grass was green;
Covered by the snowflakes,
  Not a blade is seen.

Now the bare black bushes
  All look soft and white,
Every twig is laden—
  What a pretty sight!

Ralph Waldo Emerson

Announced by all the trumpets of the sky,
Arrives the snow, and, driving o'er the fields,
Seems nowhere to alight: the whited air
Hides hills and woods, the river and the heaven,
And veils the farm-house at the garden's end.
The sled and traveller stopped, the courier's feet
Delayed, all friends shut out, the housemates sit
Around the radiant fireplace, enclosed
In a tumultuous privacy of storm.

FOR HANUKKAH

H. N. Bialik

Father lighted candles for me;
  Like a torch the Shamash shone.
In whose honor, for whose glory?
  For Hanukkah alone.

Teacher bought a big top for me,
  Solid lead, the finest known.
In whose honor, for whose glory?
  For Hanukkah alone.

Mother made a pancake for me,
  Hot and sweet and sugar-strewn.
In whose honor, for whose glory?
  For Hanukkah alone.

Uncle had a present for me,
  An old penny for my own.
In whose honor, for whose glory?
  For Hanukkah alone.

DREIDEL SONG

Efraim Rosenzweig

Twirl about, dance about,
  Spin, spin, spin!
Turn, Dreidel, turn—
  Time to begin!

Soon it is Hanukkah—
  Fast Dreidel, fast!
For you will lie still
  When Hanukkah's past.

A SONG OF ALWAYS

Efraim Rosenzweig

The Temple is clean
  The lamp burns bright;
Judah the leader,
  Has started the light.

The sun shines by days,
  And dark is the night;
But always and always
  The lamp burns bright.

BLESSINGS FOR CHANUKAH

Jessie E. Sampter

Blessed art Thou, O God our Lord,
Who made us holy with his word,
And told us on this feast of light
To light one candle more each night.

"For Hanukkah." From *Far Over the Sea* by H. N. Bialik, translated by Jessie E. Sampter. Union of American Hebrew Congregations, Cincinnati, Ohio, 1939

"Dreidel Song." From *Now We Begin* by Marian J. and Efraim M. Rosenzweig. Union of American Hebrew Congregations, Cincinnati, Ohio, 1937

"A Song of Always." From *Now We Begin* by Marian J. and Efraim M. Rosenzweig. Union of American Hebrew Congregations, Cincinnati, Ohio, 1937

"Blessings for Chanukah." From *Around the Year in Rhymes for the Jewish Child* by Jessie E. Sampter. Bloch Publishing Company, New York, 1920

(Because when foes about us pressed
   To crush us all with death or shame,
The Lord his priests with courage blest
To strike and give his people rest
And in the House that he loved best
   Relight our everlasting flame.)

Blest are Thou, the whole world's King,
Who did so wonderful a thing
For our own fathers true and gold
At this same time in days of old!

AN OLD CHRISTMAS GREETING

(Unknown)

Sing hey! Sing hey!
For Christmas Day;
Twine mistletoe and holly,
For friendship glows
In winter snows,
And so let's all be jolly.

CHRISTMAS

(Mother Goose)

Christmas is coming, the geese are
   getting fat,
Please to put a penny in an old
   man's hat;
If you haven't got a penny a
   ha'penny will do,
If you haven't got a ha'penny, God
   bless you.

THE CHRISTMAS PUDDING

(Unknown)

Into the basin put the plums,
Stirabout, stirabout, stirabout!

Next the good white flour comes,
Stirabout, stirabout, stirabout!

Sugar and peel and eggs and spice,
Stirabout, stirabout, stirabout!

Mix them and fix them and cook them twice,
Stirabout, stirabout, stirabout!

CAROL, BROTHERS, CAROL

William Muhlenberg

Carol, brothers, carol,
Carol joyfully,
Carol the good tidings,
Carol merrily!
And pray a gladsome Christmas
For all good Christian men,
Carol, brothers, carol,
Christmas comes again.

Sir Walter Scott

Heap on more wood!—the wind is chill;
But let it whistle as it will,
We'll keep our Christmas merry still.

Christina Georgina Rossetti

But give me holly, bold and jolly,
Honest, prickly, shining holly;
Pluck me holly leaf and berry
For the day when I make merry.

BUNDLES

John Farrar

A bundle is a funny thing,
It always sets me wondering;
For whether it is thin or wide
You never know just what's inside.

Especially on Christmas week,
Temptation is so great to peek!
Now wouldn't it be much more fun
If shoppers carried things undone?

"Christmas." From *The Real Mother Goose.* Rand McNally & Company, Chicago, 1916
"The Christmas Pudding." *Five- and six-year-olds enjoy saying this in two groups, one for the narrative and the* other for the "stirabout" chorus. The latter will get more vigor into their part if they suit the action to the words.
"But give me holly, bold and jolly." From *Sing-Song* by Christina Georgina Rossetti

A VISIT FROM ST. NICHOLAS

Clement C. Moore

'Twas the night before Christmas, when all
    through the house
Not a creature was stirring, not even a mouse;
The stockings were hung by the chimney with
    care,
In hopes that St. Nicholas soon would be there;
The children were nestled all snug in their beds
While visions of sugar-plums danced in their
    heads;
And Mamma in her 'kerchief, and I in my cap,
Had just settled our brains for a long winter's
    nap,
When out on the lawn there arose such a clatter,
I sprang from my bed to see what was the matter.
Away to the window I flew like a flash,
Tore open the shutters and threw up the sash.
The moon on the breast of the new-fallen snow
Gave a lustre of midday to objects below,
When, what to my wondering eyes did appear,
But a miniature sleigh and eight tiny reindeer,
With a little old driver, so lively and quick,
I knew in a moment it must be St. Nick.
More rapid than eagles his coursers they came,
And he whistled, and shouted, and called them
    by name:
"Now, Dasher! now, Dancer! now, Prancer and
    Vixen!
On, Comet! on, Cupid! on, Donder and Blitzen!
To the top of the porch! to the top of the wall!
Now dash away! dash away! dash away, all!"
As dry leaves that before the wild hurricane fly,
When they meet with an obstacle, mount to the
    sky,
So up to the housetop the coursers they flew,
With the sleigh full of toys, and St. Nicholas too.

"Bundles." From *Songs for Parents* by John Farrar. Yale
University Press, New Haven, 1921
"A Visit from St. Nicholas." *See* Children and Books,
pp. 96–97, for the history of this famous poem.

And then, in a twinkling, I heard on the roof
The prancing and pawing of each little hoof.
As I drew in my head, and was turning around,
Down the chimney St. Nicholas came with a
    bound.
He was dressed all in fur, from his head to his
    foot,
And his clothes were all tarnished with ashes and
    soot;
A bundle of toys he had flung on his back,
And he looked like a peddler just opening his
    pack.
His eyes—how they twinkled! his dimples, how
    merry!
His cheeks were like roses, his nose like a cherry!
His droll little mouth was drawn up like a bow,
And the beard on his chin was as white as the
    snow;
The stump of a pipe he held tight in his teeth,
And the smoke, it encircled his head like a
    wreath;
He had a broad face and a little round belly
That shook, when he laughed, like a bowl full of
    jelly.
He was chubby and plump, a right jolly old elf,
And I laughed when I saw him, in spite of my-
    self;
A wink of his eye and a twist of his head,
Soon gave me to know I had nothing to dread;
He spoke not a word, but went straight to his
    work,
And filled all the stockings; then turned with a
    jerk,
And laying his finger aside of his nose,
And giving a nod, up the chimney he rose.
He sprang to his sleigh, to his team gave a
    whistle,
And away they all flew like the down of a thistle.
But I heard him exclaim, ere he drove out of
    sight,
"HAPPY CHRISTMAS TO ALL,
AND TO ALL A GOOD-NIGHT!"

HERE WE COME A-CAROLING

(An Old Christmas Carol)

Here we come a-caroling
　Among the leaves so green;
Here we come a-wand'ring
　So fair to be seen.

Love and joy come to you
And a joyful Christmas, too;
And God bless you and send
You a Happy New Year—
And God send you a Happy New Year.

We are not daily beggars
　That beg from door to door;
But we are neighbors' children
　That you have seen before.

Love and joy come to you
And a joyful Christmas, too;
And God bless you and send
You a Happy New Year—
And God send you a Happy New Year.

God bless the master of the house
　Likewise the mistress, too;
And all the little children
　That round the table go.

Love and joy come to you
And a joyful Christmas, too;
And God bless you and send
You a Happy New Year—
And God send you a Happy New Year.

CEREMONIES FOR CHRISTMAS

Robert Herrick

Come, bring with a noise,
　My merry, merry boys,
The Christmas log to the firing;

While my good dame, she
Bids ye all be free;
And drinks to your hearts' desiring.

With the last year's brand
Light the new block, and
For good success in his spending,
　On your psaltries play,
　That sweet luck may
Come while the log is a-tending.

Drink now the strong beer,
Cut the white loaf here,
The while the meat is a-shredding;
　For the rare mince-pie
　And the plums stand by
To fill the paste that's a-kneading.

IN THE WEEK WHEN CHRISTMAS COMES

Eleanor Farjeon

This is the week when Christmas comes.

Let every pudding burst with plums,
And every tree bear dolls and drums,
　In the week when Christmas comes.

Let every hall have boughs of green,
With berries glowing in between,
　In the week when Christmas comes.

Let every doorstep have a song
Sounding the dark street along,
　In the week when Christmas comes.

Let every steeple ring a bell
With a joyful tale to tell,
　In the week when Christmas comes.

"Here We Come A-Caroling." *The carols are beautiful for individual reading or for choral speaking. Although arrangements for the latter are suggested, please remember that the quiet individual reading of these songs is always desirable.*

"Here We Come A-Caroling" *is a familiar carol for singing but it also reads well. For choral speaking, half the children may speak the narrative and half the chorus. Or three solo voices may be used for the three verses while the* whole group speaks the chorus softly; or three different groups may take one chorus each.

"In the Week When Christmas Comes." *Easy and delightful for verse choirs! All the children speak the first and last lines; M, verses 1 and 6; H, verses 2 and 4; L, verses 3 and 5.* Reprinted by permission of the publishers, J. B. Lippincott Company from *Come Christmas* by Eleanor Farjeon. Copyright 1927 by J. B. Lippincott Company

Let every night put forth a star
To show us where the heavens are,
    In the week when Christmas comes.

Let every stable have a lamb
Sleeping warm beside its dam,
    In the week when Christmas comes.

This is the week when Christmas comes.

FOR CHRISTMAS DAY
Eleanor Farjeon

A carol round the ruddy hearth,
    A song outside the door—
Let Christmas Day make sure its lay
    Sounds sweetly to the poor.

A turkey in the baking-tin,
    A pudding in the pot—
Let Christmas Day the hunger stay
    In them that have not got.

Red berries on the picture-frame,
    White berries in the hall—
Let Christmas Day look twice as gay
    With evergreens for all.

A stocking on the chimneypiece,
    A present on the chair—
Let Christmas Day not pass away
    Till those who have do share.

A star upon the midnight sky,
    A shepherd looking East—
On Christmas Day let all men pray,
    And not till after feast.

SONG
Eugene Field

Why do bells for Christmas ring?
Why do little children sing?

Once a lovely, shining star,
Seen by shepherds from afar,
Gently moved until its light
Made a manger's cradle bright.

There a darling baby lay,
Pillowed soft upon the hay;
And its mother sang and smiled,
"This is Christ, the holy child!"

Therefore bells for Christmas ring,
Therefore little children sing.

CRADLE HYMN
Martin Luther

Away in a manger,
No crib for a bed,
The little Lord Jesus
Lay down his sweet head;
The stars in the heavens
Looked down where he lay,
The little Lord Jesus
Asleep in the hay.

The cattle are lowing,
The poor baby wakes,
But little Lord Jesus
No crying he makes.
I love thee, Lord Jesus,
Look down from the sky,
And stay by my cradle
Till morning is nigh.

"For Christmas Day." *The second couplet of each verse is in the nature of a warning or reminder, but speak it gravely and gently, or it will sound too moralistic and lugubrious. The low choir might carry the second couplet in verses 1, 2, 3, and 4; H: the first couplet in verses 2 and 4; M: the first couplet in verses 1, 3, and 5; and everyone the last couplet.* Reprinted by permission of the publishers, J. B. Lippincott Company, from *Eleanor Farjeon's Poems for Children.* Copyright, 1951, by Eleanor Farjeon

"Song." *A solo voice, light and clear, asks the question in the first two lines; M to L: verse 2; M to H: verse 3; the last couplet may be spoken by all or by a low, warm solo voice.* Reprinted from *Sharps and Flats* by Eugene Field; copyright 1900, 1928 by Julia Sutherland Field; used by permission of the publishers, Charles Scribner's Sons

LONG, LONG AGO

(Unknown)

Winds through the olive trees
  Softly did blow,
Round little Bethlehem
  Long, long ago.

Sheep on the hillside lay
  Whiter than snow;
Shepherds were watching them,
  Long, long ago.

Then from the happy sky,
  Angels bent low,
Singing their songs of joy,
  Long, long ago.

For in a manger bed,
  Cradled we know,
Christ came to Bethlehem,
  Long, long ago.

A CHRISTMAS FOLK-SONG

Lizette Woodworth Reese

The little Jesus came to town;
The wind blew up, the wind blew down;
Out in the street the wind was bold;
Now who would house Him from the cold?

Then opened wide the stable door,
Fair were the rushes on the floor;
The Ox put forth a hornèd head:
"Come, little Lord, here make Thy bed."

Up rose the Sheep were folded near:
"Thou Lamb of God, come, enter here."
He entered there to rush and reed,
Who was the Lamb of God indeed.

The little Jesus came to town;
With ox and sheep He laid Him down;

Peace to the byre, peace to the fold,
For that they housed Him from the cold!

A CHRISTMAS CAROL

Gilbert K. Chesterton

The Christ-child lay on Mary's lap,
  His hair was like a light.
(O weary, weary were the world,
  But here is all aright.)

The Christ-child lay on Mary's breast,
  His hair was like a star.
(O stern and cunning are the kings,
  But here the true hearts are.)

The Christ-child lay on Mary's heart,
  His hair was like a fire.
(O weary, weary is the world,
  But here the world's desire.)

The Christ-child stood at Mary's knee,
  His hair was like a crown,
And all the flowers looked up at Him
And all the stars looked down.

THE SHEPHERD AND THE KING

Eleanor Farjeon

The Shepherd and the King,
The Angel and the Ass,
They heard Sweet Mary sing
When her joy was come to pass;
They heard Sweet Mary sing
To the Baby on her knee;
Sing again, Sweet Mary,
And we will sing with thee!
  Earth, bear a berry!
  Heaven, bear a light!
  Man, make you merry
  On Christmas Night.

"A Christmas Folk Song." From *The Selected Poems of Lizette Woodworth Reese*. Copyright 1926 by Lizette Woodworth Reese, and reprinted by permission of Rinehart & Company, Inc., Publishers

"A Christmas Carol." *Each verse has a refrain and a narrative. These may be variously distributed: Verse 1: High, refrain: Medium; verse 2: High, refrain: Low; verse 3: High, refrain: Low, verse 4: Medium, refrain: High; or all may speak the refrain softly and tenderly. Taken from The Wild Knight and Other Poems, by G. K. Chesterton,*

The Oxen in the stall,
The Sheep upon the hill,
They are waking all
To hear Sweet Mary still.
The Baby is a Child,
And the Child is running free;
Sing again, Sweet Mary,
And we will sing with thee!
   Earth, bear a berry!
   Heaven, bear a light!
   Man, make you merry
   On Christmas night.

The People in the land,
So many million strong,
All silently do stand
To hear Sweet Mary's song.
The Child He is a Man,
And the Man hangs on a tree.
Sing again, Sweet Mary,
And we will sing with thee!
   Earth, bear a berry!
   Heaven, bear a light!
   Man, make you merry
   On Christmas night.

The Stars that are so old,
The Grass that is so young,
They listen in the cold
To hear Sweet Mary's tongue.
The Man's the Son of God,
And in Heaven walketh He.
Sing again, Sweet Mary,
And we will sing with thee!
   Earth, bear a berry!
   Heaven, bear a light!
   Man, make you merry
   On Christmas night.

William Shakespeare

Some say, that ever 'gainst that season comes
Wherein our Savior's birth is celebrated,
The bird of dawning singeth all night long:
So hallow'd and so gracious is the time.

published by E. P. Dutton & Co., Inc. Reprinted by permission of the publishers and Miss Collins, Executrix.
"The Shepherd and the King." Reprinted by permission of the publishers, J. B. Lippincott Company from *Eleanor Farjeon's Poems for Children.* Copyright, 1951, by Eleanor Farjeon

CHRISTMAS IN THE WOODS
Frances M. Frost

Tonight when the hoar frost falls on the wood,
And the rabbit cowers, and the squirrel is cold,
And the horned owl huddles against a star,
And the drifts are deep, and the year is old,
All shy creatures will think of Him.
The shivering mouse, the hare, the wild young
    fox,
The doe with the startled fawn,
Will dream of gentleness and a Child:

The buck with budding horns will turn
His starry eyes to a silver hill tonight,
The chipmunk will awake and stir
And leave his burrow for the chill, dark mid-
    night,
And all timid things will pause and sigh, and
    sighing, bless
That Child who loves the trembling hearts,
The shy hearts of the wilderness.

GLADDE THINGS
(*Unknown*)

   Of gladde things there be four, ay four:
   A Larke above ye olde nest blithely singing,
   A wild Rose clinging
   In safety to a rock, a Shepherd bringing
   A Lambe found in his arms,
   And Christmasse Bells a-ringing.

CHRISTMAS CAROL
(*Unknown*)

   God bless the master of this house,
     The mistress also,
   And all the little children,
     That round the table go,
   And all your kin and kinsmen
     That dwell both far and near;
   I wish you a Merry Christmas
     And a Happy New Year.

"Some say, that ever 'gainst that season comes." From *Hamlet,* Act I, Sc. 1
"Christmas in the Woods." From *Christmas in the Woods* by Frances M. Frost. Copyright, 1942, by Frances M. Frost

NEW YEAR'S DAY

Rachel Field

Last night, while we were fast asleep,
  The old year went away.
It can't come back again because
  A new one's come to stay.

Elizabeth Coatsworth

Cold winter now is in the wood,
The moon wades deep in snow.
Pile balsam boughs about the sills,
And let the fires glow!

The cows must stand in the dark barn,
The horses stamp all day.
Now shall the housewife bake her pies
And keep her kitchen gay.

The cat sleeps warm beneath the stove,
The dog on paws outspread;
But the brown deer with flinching hide
Seeks for a sheltered bed.

The fox steps hungry through the brush,
The lean hawk coasts the sky.
"Winter is in the wood!" the winds
In the warm chimney cry.

WINTER NIGHT

Mary Frances Butts

Blow, wind, blow!
  Drift the flying snow!
Send it twirling, whirling overhead!
  There's a bedroom in a tree
  Where, snug as snug can be,
The squirrel nests in his cozy bed.

Shriek, wind, shriek!
  Make the branches creak!
Battle with the boughs till break o' day!

In a snow-cave warm and tight,
  Through the icy winter night
The rabbit sleeps the peaceful hours away.

Call, wind, call,
  In entry and in hall,
Straight from off the mountain white and wild!
  Soft purrs the pussy-cat,
  On her little fluffy mat,
And beside her nestles close her furry child.

Scold, wind, scold,
  So bitter and so bold!
Shake the windows with your tap, tap, tap!
  With half-shut dreamy eyes
  The drowsy baby lies
Cuddled closely in his mother's lap.

STOPPING BY WOODS ON A SNOWY EVENING

Robert Frost

Whose woods these are I think I know.
His house is in the village though;
He will not see me stopping here
To watch his woods fill up with snow.

My little horse must think it queer
To stop without a farmhouse near
Between the woods and frozen lake
The darkest evening of the year.

He gives his harness bells a shake
To ask if there is some mistake.
The only other sound's the sweep
Of easy wind and downy flake.

The woods are lovely, dark and deep.
But I have promises to keep,
And miles to go before I sleep,
And miles to go before I sleep.

"New Year's Day." From *A Little Book of Days* by Rachel Field. Copyright 1927 by Doubleday & Company

"Cold winter now is in the wood." *A study in contrasts—indoors and outdoors in winter!* From *Away Goes Sally* by Elizabeth Coatsworth. Copyright 1934 by The Macmillan Company and used with their permission

"Winter Night." From *The Outlook.* The Outlook Publishing Company, New York, 1897. Every effort has been made to locate the copyright owner of this poem but without success

"Stopping by Woods on a Snowy Evening." From *New Hampshire* by Robert Frost. Copyright, 1923, by Henry Holt and Company, Inc. Used by permission of the publishers

VELVET SHOES
Elinor Wylie

Let us walk in the white snow
 In a soundless space;
With footsteps quiet and slow,
 At a tranquil pace,
 Under veils of white lace.

I shall go shod in silk,
 And you in wool,
White as a white cow's milk,
 More beautiful
 Than the breast of a gull.

We shall walk through the still town
 In a windless peace;
We shall step upon white down,
 Upon silver fleece,
 Upon softer than these.

We shall walk in velvet shoes:
 Wherever we go
Silence will fall like dews
 On white silence below.
 We shall walk in the snow.

WINTER NIGHT
Collister Hutchison

A tree may be laughter in the spring
Or a promise
Or conceit.

In the summer it may be anything
Lazy and warm with life,
Complete.

In the fall
It is the answer
To a long-forgotten call.

But on a lonely winter night
In still air
When it takes the shape of a candle flame
Springing dark from a hill all white,
It is a dare.

WAITING
Harry Behn

Dreaming of honeycombs to share
With her small cubs, a mother bear
Sleeps in a snug and snowy lair.

Bees in their drowsy, drifted hive
Sip hoarded honey to survive
Until the flowers come alive.

Sleeping beneath the deep snow
Seeds of honeyed flowers know
When it is time to wake and grow.

A SURE SIGN
Nancy Byrd Turner

Here's the mail, sort it quick—
Papers, letters, notes,
Postcard scenes,
Magazines;
Our hearts are in our throats.
Something there,
White and square,
Sealed with wax, and bumpy—
At the edges flat and thin,
In the middle lumpy.

"Velvet Shoes." *Read this aloud slowly and you discover that it has the quiet softness of snow itself.* Reprinted from *Collected Poems of Elinor Wylie* by Elinor Wylie. By permission of Alfred A. Knopf, Inc. Copyright 1921, 1932 by Alfred A. Knopf, Inc.

"Winter Night." By Collister Hutchison from *Toward Daybreak.* Copyright, 1950, by Hazel Collister Hutchison

"Waiting." From *The Little Hill*, copyright, 1949, by Harry Behn. Reprinted by permission of Harcourt, Brace and Company, Inc.

"A Sure Sign." From *The Youth's Companion.* Used by permission of the author

When you feel the envelope,
Do your fingers trace
Something narrow,
Like an arrow?
Or a part
Of a heart?
Or a Cupid's face?
Is your name across the back
In a crooked line?
Hurry, then; that's a sign
Someone's sent a valentine!

A VALENTINE

Eleanor Hammond

Frost flowers on the window glass,
Hopping chickadees that pass,
Bare old elms that bend and sway,
Pussy willows, soft and gray,

Silver clouds across the sky,
Lacy snowflakes flitting by,
Icicles like fringe in line—
That is Outdoor's valentine!

MY VALENTINE

Mary Catherine Parsons

I have a little valentine
  That some one sent to me.
It's pink and white and red and blue,
  And pretty as can be.

Forget-me-nots are round the edge,
  And tiny roses, too;
And such a lovely piece of lace—
  The very palest blue.

And in the center there's a heart,
  As red as red can be!

And on it's written all in gold,
  "To You, with Love from Me."

HEARTS WERE MADE TO GIVE AWAY

Annette Wynne

Hearts were made to give away
  On Valentine's good day;
Wrap them up in dainty white,
Send them off the thirteenth night,
Any kind of heart that's handy—
  Hearts of lace, and hearts of candy,
  Hearts all trimmed with ribbands fine
  Send for good St. Valentine.
Hearts were made to give away
On Valentine's dear day.

I'LL WEAR A SHAMROCK

Mary Carolyn Davies

St. Patrick's Day is with us,
  The day when all that's seen
To right and left and everywhere
  Is green, green, green!

And Irish tunes they whistle
  And Irish songs they sing,
To-day each Irish lad walks out
  As proud as any king.

I'll wear a four-leaf shamrock
  In my coat, the glad day through,
For my father and mother are Irish
  And I am Irish, too!

WISE JOHNNY

Edwina Fallis

  Little Johnny-jump-up said,
    "It must be spring,

I just saw a lady-bug
And heard a robin sing."

(Mother Goose)

Daffadowndilly
   Has come up to town,
In a yellow petticoat
   And a green gown.

DAFFODILS

Kikuriō

In spite of cold and chills
That usher in the early spring
We have the daffodils.

Christina Georgina Rossetti

Growing in the vale
   By the uplands hilly,
Growing straight and frail,
   Lady Daffadowndilly.

In a golden crown,
And a scant green gown
   While the spring blows chilly,
Lady Daffadown,
   Sweet Daffadowndilly.

E. Wyndham Tennant

I saw green banks of daffodil,
   Slim poplars in the breeze,
Great tan-brown hares in gusty March
   A-courting on the leas;
And meadows with their glittering
     streams, and silver scurrying dace,
   Home—what a perfect place!

"Growing in the vale." From *Sing-Song* by Christina Georgina Rossetti
"I saw green banks of daffodil. . . ." From *Home Thoughts in Laventi* by E. Wyndham Tennant. London: Oxford University Press. By permission of the Estate of the Author
"Spring." From *The Little Hill*, copyright, 1949, by Harry Behn. Reprinted by permission of Harcourt, Brace

William Shakespeare

    . . . daffodils,
That come before the swallow dares, and take
The winds of March with beauty . . .

SPRING

Harry Behn

The last snow is going,
Brooks are overflowing,
And a sunny wind is blowing
   Swiftly along.

Through the sky birds are blowing,
On earth green is showing,
You can feel earth growing
   So quiet and strong.

A sunny wind is blowing,
Farmer's busy sowing,
Apple trees are snowing,
   And shadows grow long.

Now the wind is slowing,
Cows begin lowing,
Evening clouds are glowing
   And dusk is full of song.

from THE SONG OF SONGS

For, lo, the winter is past,
The rain is over and gone;
The flowers appear on the earth;
The time of the singing of birds is come,
And the voice of the turtle is heard in our land.

ROBIN'S SONG

E. L. M. King

   Robin's song is crystal clear
   Cold as an icicle,

and Company, Inc.
"For, lo, the winter is past." The Song of Songs, 2:11, 12. *"The voice of the turtle" refers to the bird, the turtle dove.*
"Robin's Song." From *Fifty Country Rhymes for Children* by E. L. M. King. Copyright, 1926, by D. Appleton and Company. Reprinted by permission of Appleton-Century-Crofts, Inc.

Sharp as a spear.
I have seen Spring lift her head,
Snowdrops a-shivering,
Winter dead.

CROCUSES

Jōsa

The sunrise tints the dew;
The yellow crocuses are out,
And I must pick a few.

WRITTEN IN MARCH

William Wordsworth

The Cock is crowing,
The stream is flowing,
The small birds twitter,
The lake doth glitter,
The green field sleeps in the sun;
The oldest and youngest
Are at work with the strongest;
The cattle are grazing,
Their heads never raising;
There are forty feeding like one!

Like an army defeated
The snow hath retreated,
And now doth fare ill
On the top of the bare hill;
The ploughboy is whooping—anon—anon:
There's joy in the mountains;
There's life in the fountains;
Small clouds are sailing,
Blue sky prevailing;
The rain is over and gone!

I WILL GO WITH MY FATHER A-PLOUGHING

Joseph Campbell

I will go with my Father a-ploughing
To the Green Field by the sea,

And the rooks and crows and seagulls
Will come flocking after me.
I will sing to the patient horses
With the lark in the shine of the air,
And my Father will sing the Plough-Song
That blesses the cleaving share.

I will go with my Father a-sowing
To the Red Field by the sea,
And blackbirds and robins and thrushes
Will come flocking after me.
I will sing to the striding sowers
With the finch on the flowering sloe,
And my Father will sing the Seed-Song
That only the wise men know.

I will go with my Father a-reaping
To the Brown Field by the sea,
And the geese and pigeons and sparrows
Will come flocking after me.
I will sing to the weary reapers
With the wren in the heat of the sun,
And my Father will sing the Scythe-Song
That joys for the harvest done.

SEEDS

Walter de la Mare

The seeds I sowed—
For weeks unseen—
Have pushed up pygmy
Shoots of green;
So frail you'd think
The tiniest stone
Would never let
A glimpse be shown.

But no; a pebble
Near them lies,
At least a cherry-stone
In size,
Which that mere sprout
Has heaved away,
To bask in sun,
And see the day.

SPRING

William Blake

Sound the flute!
Now it's mute;
Birds delight,
Day and night,
Nightingale
In the dale,
Lark in sky,—
Merrily,
Merrily, merrily, to welcome in the year.

Little Boy,
Full of joy;
Little Girl,
Sweet and small;
Cock does crow,
So do you;
Merry voice,
Infant noise,
Merrily, merrily, to welcome in the year.

Little Lamb,
Here I am;
Come and lick
My white neck;
Let me pull
Your soft Wool;
Let me kiss
Your soft face;
Merrily, merrily, we welcome in the year.

MEETING THE EASTER BUNNY

Rowena Bastin Bennett

On Easter morn at early dawn
 before the cocks were crowing,
I met a bob-tail bunnykin
 and asked where he was going,
" 'Tis in the house and out the house
 a-tipsy, tipsy-toeing,
'Tis round the house and 'bout the house
 a-lightly I am going."

Table by Rowena Bastin Bennett. Follett Publishing Company, Chicago, 1930
 "The Day Before April." From *Youth Riding* by Mary Carolyn Davies. The Macmillan Company, New York, 1919.

"But what is that of every hue
 you carry in your basket?"
" 'Tis eggs of gold and eggs of blue;
 I wonder that you ask it.
'Tis chocolate eggs and bonbon eggs
 and eggs of red and gray,
For every child in every house
 on bonny Easter Day."
He perked his ears and winked his eye
 and twitched his little nose;
He shook his tail—what tail he had—
 and stood up on his toes.
"I must be gone before the sun;
 the east is growing gray;
'Tis almost time for bells to chime."—
 So he hippety-hopped away.

THE DAY BEFORE APRIL

Mary Carolyn Davies

The day before April
 Alone, alone,
I walked in the woods
 And I sat on a stone.

I sat on a broad stone
 And sang to the birds.
The tune was God's making
 But I made the words.

APRIL

Sara Teasdale

The roofs are shining from the rain,
 The sparrows twitter as they fly,
And with a windy April grace
 The little clouds go by.

Yet the back-yards are bare and brown
 With only one unchanging tree—
I could not be so sure of Spring
 Save that it sings in me.

Used by permission of A. H. Davies
 "April." From *Rivers to the Sea* by Sara Teasdale. Copyright 1915, 1943 by The Macmillan Company and used with their permission

EASTER

Hilda Conkling

On Easter morn
Up the faint cloudy sky
I hear the Easter bell,
   Ding dong . . . ding dong . . .
Easter morning scatters lilies
On every doorstep;
Easter morning says a glad thing
Over and over.
Poor people, beggars, old women
Are hearing the Easter bell . . .
   Ding dong . . . ding dong . . .

EASTER

Joyce Kilmer

The air is like a butterfly
  With frail blue wings.
The happy earth looks at the sky
  And sings.

LILIES

Shikō (Arranged by Olive Beauprè Miller)

I thought I saw white clouds, but no!—
  Bending across the fence,
  White lilies in a row!

THE FALL OF
THE PLUM BLOSSOMS

Rankō

I came to look, and lo!
The plum tree petals scatter down,
  A fall of purest snow.

Christina Georgina Rossetti

Oh, fair to see
Bloom-laden cherry tree,

Arrayed in sunny white:
  An April day's delight,
Oh, fair to see!

Oh, fair to see
Fruit-laden cherry tree,
  With balls of shining red
  Decking a leafy head,
Oh, fair to see!

THE IRIS

Gasetsu

   Ere yet the sun is high,
  All blue the iris blossoms wave,
   The colour of the sky.

William Shakespeare

  Under the greenwood tree
  Who loves to lie with me,
  And turn his merry note
  Unto the sweet bird's throat,
Come hither, come hither, come hither:
  Here shall he see
  No enemy
But winter and rough weather.

TREES

Harry Behn

  Trees are the kindest things I know,
  They do no harm, they simply grow

  And spread a shade for sleepy cows,
  And gather birds among their boughs.

  They give us fruit in leaves above,
  And wood to make our houses of,

  And leaves to burn on Hallowe'en,
  And in the Spring new buds of green.

"Easter." Reprinted by permission of the publishers, J. B. Lippincott Company from *Poems by a Little Girl* by Hilda Conkling. Copyright 1920 by J. B. Lippincott Company

"Easter." From *Poems, Essays and Letters* by Joyce Kilmer. Copyright 1914, 1917, 1918 by Doubleday & Company, Inc.

"Lilies." From *Little Pictures of Japan*. Used by permission of the author, Olive Beauprè Miller, and the publishers, The Book House for Children, Chicago, Illinois

"The Fall of the Plum Blossoms." From *A Year of Japanese Epigrams* compiled by W. N. Porter. By permission of Oxford University Press, London

"Oh, fair to see." *See the introduction, p. xviii.* From *Sing-Song* by Christina Georgina Rossetti

"The Iris." From *A Year of Japanese Epigrams* compiled

They are the first when day's begun
To touch the beams of morning sun,

They are the last to hold the light
When evening changes into night,

And when a moon floats on the sky
They hum a drowsy lullaby

Of sleepy children long ago . . .
Trees are the kindest things I know.

WHAT DO WE PLANT?

Henry Abbey

What do we plant when we plant the tree?
We plant the ship, which will cross the sea.
We plant the mast to carry the sails;
We plant the planks to withstand the gales—
The keel, the keelson, and beam and knee;
We plant the ship when we plant the tree.

What do we plant when we plant the tree?
We plant the houses for you and me.
We plant the rafters, the shingles, the floors,
We plant the studding, the lath, the doors,
The beams and siding, all parts that be;
We plant the house when we plant the tree.

What do we plant when we plant the tree?
A thousand things that we daily see;
We plant the spire that out-towers the crag,
We plant the staff for our country's flag,
We plant the shade, from the hot sun free;
We plant all these when we plant the tree.

THE FLAG GOES BY

Henry Holcomb Bennett

Hats off!
Along the street there comes
A blare of bugles, a ruffle of drums,
A flash of color beneath the sky:

Hats off!
The flag is passing by!

Blue and crimson and white it shines,
Over the steel-tipped, ordered lines.
Hats off!
The colors before us fly;
But more than the flag is passing by.

Sea-fights and land-fights, grim and great,
Fought to make and to save the State:
Weary marches and sinking ships;
Cheers of victory on dying lips;

Days of plenty and years of peace;
March of a strong land's swift increase;
Equal justice, right and law,
Stately honor and reverend awe;

Sign of a nation, great and strong
To ward her people from foreign wrong:
Pride and glory and honor,—all
Live in the colors to stand or fall.

Hats off!
Along the street there comes
A blare of bugles, a ruffle of drums;
And loyal hearts are beating high:
Hats off!
The flag is passing by!

Christina Georgina Rossetti

The days are clear,
  Day after day,
When April's here,
  That leads to May,
And June
Must follow soon:
  Stay, June, stay!—
If only we could stop the moon
And June!

by W. N. Porter. By permission of Oxford University Press, London
  "Under the greenwood tree." *This song always suggests Robin Hood and his merry men.* From *As You Like It*, Act II, Sc. 5
  "Trees." From *The Little Hill*, copyright, 1949, by Harry Behn. Reprinted by permission of Harcourt, Brace and Company, Inc.
  "What Do We Plant?" From *The Poems of Henry Abbey*. D. Appleton and Company, New York, 1904
  "The Flag Goes By." Used with the kind permission of Martha Trimble Bennett
  "The days are clear." From *Sing-Song* by Christina Georgina Rossetti

Christina Georgina Rossetti

There is but one May in the year,
    And sometimes May is wet and cold;
There is but one May in the year
    Before the year grows old.

Yet though it be the chilliest May,
    With least of sun and most of showers,
Its wind and dew, its night and day,
    Bring up the flowers.

DANDELION

Hilda Conkling

O little soldier with the golden helmet,
What are you guarding on my lawn?
You with your green gun
And your yellow beard,
Why do you stand so stiff?
There is only the grass to fight!

DANDELIONS

Frances M. Frost

Over the climbing meadows
Where swallow-shadows float,
These are the small gold buttons
On earth's green, windy coat.

MILLIONS OF STRAWBERRIES

Genevieve Taggard

Marcia and I went over the curve,
Eating our way down
Jewels of strawberries we didn't deserve,
Eating our way down.
Till our hands were sticky, and our lips painted,
And over us the hot day fainted,

And we saw snakes,
And got scratched,
And a lust overcame us for the red unmatched
Small buds of berries,
Till we lay down—
Eating our way down—
And rolled in the berries like two little dogs,
Rolled
In the late gold.
And gnats hummed,
And it was cold,
And home we went, home without a berry,
Painted red and brown,
Eating our way down.

SPRINKLING

Dorothy Mason Pierce

Sometimes in the summer
When the day is hot
Daddy takes the garden hose
And finds a shady spot;
Then he calls me over,
Looks at my bare toes
And says, "Why, you need sprinkling,
You thirsty little rose!"

THE LITTLE ROSE TREE

Rachel Field

Every rose on the little tree
Is making a different face at me!

Some look surprised when I pass by,
And others droop—but they are shy.

These two whose heads together press
Tell secrets I could never guess.

Some have their heads thrown back to sing,
And all the buds are listening.

I wonder if the gardener knows,
Or if he calls each just a rose?

FOURTH OF JULY NIGHT

Dorothy Aldis

Pin wheels whirling round
Spit sparks upon the ground,
And rockets shoot up high
And blossom in the sky—
Blue and yellow, green and red
Flowers falling on my head,
And I don't ever have to go
To bed, to bed, to bed!

"Fourth of July Night." From *Hop, Skip and Jump* by Dorothy Aldis. Minton, Balch and Company, New York, 1934. Copyright 1934 by Dorothy Aldis.

Christina Georgina Rossetti

What is pink? a rose is pink
By the fountain's brink.
What is red? a poppy's red
In its barley bed.
What is blue? the sky is blue
Where the clouds float thro'.
What is white? a swan is white
Sailing in the light.
What is yellow? pears are yellow,
Rich and ripe and mellow.
What is green? the grass is green,
With small flowers between.
What is violet? clouds are violet
In the summer twilight.
What is orange? why, an orange,
Just an orange!

"What is pink? a rose is pink." From *Sing-Song* by Christina Georgina Rossetti

HAPPY THOUGHT

Robert Louis Stevenson

The world is so full of a number of things,
I'm sure we should all be as happy as kings.

I AM

Hilda Conkling

I am willowy boughs
For coolness;
I am gold-finch wings
For darkness;
I am a little grape
Thinking of September,
I am a very small violet
Thinking of May.

LESSON FROM A SUN-DIAL

(from the German adapted by Louis Untermeyer)

Ignore dull days; forget the showers;
Keep count of only shining hours.

OF QUARRELS

Arthur Guiterman

No Quarrel ever Stirred
Before the Second Word.

WISDOM AND BEAUTY

OF GIVING

Arthur Guiterman

Not what you Get, but what you Give
Is that which proves your Right to Live.

SHORT SERMON

(from the German adapted by Louis Untermeyer)

To give—and forgive—
Is a good way to live.

OF COURTESY

Arthur Guiterman

Good Manners may in Seven Words be found:
Forget Yourself and think of Those Around.

GOOD ADVICE

(from the German adapted by Louis Untermeyer)

Don't shirk
Your work
For the sake of a dream;
A fish
In the dish
Is worth ten in the stream.

MOTTO

(from the German adapted by Louis Untermeyer)

However they talk, whatever they say,
Look straight at the task without dismay—
And if you can do it, do it today.

DAY-DREAMER

(from the German adapted by Louis Untermeyer)

Too much thought:
Too little wrought.

Elizabeth Coatsworth

He who has never known hunger
Has never known how good
The taste of bread may be,
The kindliness of food.

COLLECTION OF PROVERBS

(Proverbs 16:32)

He that is slow to anger is better than the
mighty;
And he that ruleth his spirit than he that taketh
a city.

(Proverbs 15:1)

A soft answer turneth away wrath:
But grievous words stir up anger.

(Ecclesiastes 11:1)

Cast thy bread upon the waters:
For thou shalt find it after many days.

(II Timothy 1:7)

For God hath not given us the spirit of fear;
But of power, and of love, and of a sound mind.

(Isaiah 40:31)

But they that wait upon the Lord shall renew
their strength;
They shall mount up with wings as eagles;

The poems in this section have to be thought about, talked about, or tucked away in memory to reread or say again. Here are manners, morals, and dreams to be savored thoughtfully. These poems are for children old enough to wonder about life and to be touched by beauty.

"Happy Thought." From *A Child's Garden of Verses* by Robert Louis Stevenson

"I Am." From *Poems by a Little Girl* by Hilda Conkling. Copyright 1920 by J. B. Lippincott Company

"Lesson from a Sun-Dial." From *Rainbow in the Sky* edited by Louis Untermeyer, copyright, 1935, by Harcourt, Brace and Company, Inc.

"Of Quarrels." Taken from *A Poet's Proverbs*, by Arthur Guiterman, published and copyright, 1924, by E. P. Dutton & Co., Inc., New York

"Of Giving." Taken from *A Poet's Proverbs*, by Arthur Guiterman, published and copyright, 1924, by E. P. Dutton & Co., Inc., New York

"Short Sermon." From *Rainbow in the Sky* edited by Louis Untermeyer, copyright, 1935, by Harcourt, Brace and Company, Inc.

"Of Courtesy." Taken from *A Poet's Proverbs*, by Arthur Guiterman, published and copyright, 1924, by E. P. Dutton & Co., Inc., New York

"Good Advice." From *Rainbow in the Sky* edited by Louis Untermeyer, copyright, 1935, by Harcourt, Brace and Company, Inc.

"Motto." From *Rainbow in the Sky* edited by Louis Untermeyer, copyright, 1935, by Harcourt, Brace and Company, Inc.

"Day-Dreamer." From *Rainbow in the Sky* edited by Louis Untermeyer, copyright, 1935, by Harcourt, Brace and Company, Inc.

"He who has never known hunger." From *The Fair American* by Elizabeth Coatsworth. Copyright 1940 by The Macmillan Company and used with their permission

They shall run, and not be weary;
And they shall walk, and not faint.

(*Philippians 4:8*)

Whatsoever things are true,
Whatsoever things are honest,
Whatsoever things are just,
Whatsoever things are pure,
Whatsoever things are lovely,
Whatsoever things are of good report;
If there be any virtue,
And if there be any praise,
I will think on these things.

FRET NOT THYSELF
BECAUSE OF EVILDOERS

(*Psalm 37*)

Fret not thyself because of evildoers,
Neither be thou envious against the workers of
    iniquity.
For they shall soon be cut down like the grass,
And wither as the green herb.
I have seen the wicked in great power,
And spreading himself like a green bay tree.
Yet he passed away, and, lo, he was not:
Yea, I sought him, but he could not be found.
Trust in the Lord, and do good;
So shalt thou dwell in the land,
And verily thou shalt be fed.

T. S. Eliot

The world turns and the world changes,
But one thing does not change.
In all of my years, one thing does not change.
However you disguise it, this thing does not
    change:
The perpetual struggle of Good and Evil.

"Fret not thyself because of evildoers." Psalm 37 : 1, 2,
35, 36, 3
"The world turns and the world changes." *See the introduction, p. xx.* From "The Rock" in *Collected Poems 1909–1935* by T. S. Eliot, copyright, 1936, by Harcourt,

Christina Georgina Rossetti

An emerald is as green as grass;
    A ruby red as blood;
A sapphire shines as blue as heaven;
    A flint lies in the mud.

A diamond is a brilliant stone,
    To catch the world's desire;
An opal holds a fiery spark;
    But a flint holds fire.

THE LITTLE BOY LOST
William Blake

"Father, father, where are you going?
    Oh, do not walk so fast!
Speak, father, speak to your little boy,
    Or else I shall be lost."

The night was dark, no father was there,
    The child was wet with dew;
The mire was deep, and the child did weep,
    And away the vapour flew.

THE LITTLE BOY FOUND
William Blake

The little boy lost in the lonely fen,
    Led by the wandering light,
Began to cry, but God, ever nigh,
    Appeared like his father, in white.

He kissed the child, and by the hand led,
    And to his mother brought,
Who in sorrow pale, through the lonely dale,
    The little boy weeping sought.

Brace and Company, Inc. Reprinted by permission of
Harcourt, Brace and Company, Inc., and Faber and Faber,
Limited
"An emerald is as green as grass." From *Sing-Song* by
Christina Georgina Rossetti

THE PILGRIM

John Bunyan

Who would true valour see,
  Let him come hither!
One here will constant be,
  Come wind, come weather;
There's no discouragement
Shall make him once relent
His firm-avowed intent
  To be a Pilgrim.

Whoso beset him round
  With dismal stories,
Do but themselves confound;
  His strength the more is.
No lion can him fright;
He'll with a giant fight;
But he will have a right
  To be a Pilgrim.

Nor enemy, nor friend,
  Can daunt his spirit;
He knows he at the end
  Shall Life inherit:—
Then, fancies, fly away;
He'll not fear what men say:
He'll labour, night and day,
  To be a Pilgrim.

Elizabeth Coatsworth

Violets, daffodils,
Roses and thorn
Were all in the garden
Before you were born.

Daffodils, violets,
Green thorn and roses
Your grandchildren's children
Will hold to their noses.

A CHARM FOR SPRING FLOWERS

Rachel Field

Who sees the first marsh marigold
Shall count more wealth than hands can hold.

Who bends a knee where violets grow
A hundred secret things shall know.

Who finds hepatica's dim blue
Shall have his dearest wish come true.

Who spies on lady-slippers fair
Shall keep a heart as light as air.

But whosoever toucheth not
One petal, sets no root in pot,

He shall be blessed of earth and sky
Till under them he, too, shall lie.

Emily Dickinson

I'm nobody! Who are you?
Are you nobody too?
Then there's a pair of us—don't tell!
They'd banish us, you know.

How dreary to be somebody!
How public, like a frog
To tell your name the livelong day
To an admiring bog.

NIGHT

Sara Teasdale

Stars over snow,
  And in the west a planet
Swinging below a star—
  Look for a lovely thing and you will
    find it,
It is not far—
  It never will be far.

LOVELINESS

Hilda Conkling

Loveliness that dies when I forget
Comes alive when I remember.

BE LIKE THE BIRD

Victor Hugo

Be like the bird, who
Halting in his flight
On limb too slight
Feels it give way beneath him,
Yet sings
Knowing he hath wings.

I NEVER SAW A MOOR

Emily Dickinson

I never saw a moor,
I never saw the sea;
Yet know I how the heather looks,
And what a wave must be.

I never spoke with God,
Nor visited in heaven;
Yet certain am I of the spot
As if the chart were given.

A BLACKBIRD SUDDENLY

Joseph Auslander

Heaven is in my hand, and I
Touch a heart-beat of the sky,
Hearing a blackbird's cry.

Strange, beautiful, unquiet thing,
Lone flute of God, how can you sing
Winter to spring?

You have outdistanced every voice and word,
And given my spirit wings until it stirred
Like you—a bird!

DUST OF SNOW

Robert Frost

The way a crow
Shook down on me
The dust of snow
From a hemlock tree

Has given my heart
A change of mood
And saved some part
Of a day I had rued.

I HEARD A BIRD SING

Oliver Herford

I heard a bird sing
  In the dark of December
A magical thing
  And sweet to remember.

"We are nearer to Spring
  Than we were in September,"
I heard a bird sing
  In the dark of December.

DAYS
Karle Wilson Baker

Some days my thoughts are just cocoons—all
cold, and dull and blind,
They hang from dripping branches in the grey
woods of my mind;
And other days they drift and shine—such free
and flying things!
I find the gold-dust in my hair, left by their
brushing wings.

THE COIN
Sara Teasdale

Into my heart's treasury
I slipped a coin
That time cannot take
Nor a thief purloin,—
Oh, better than the minting
Of a gold-crowned king
Is the safe-kept memory
Of a lovely thing.

LEISURE
William Henry Davies

What is this life if, full of care,
We have no time to stand and stare.

No time to stand beneath the boughs
And stare as long as sheep or cows.

No time to see, when woods we pass,
Where squirrels hide their nuts in grass.

No time to see, in broad daylight,
Streams full of stars, like stars at night.

No time to turn at Beauty's glance,
And watch her feet, how they can dance.

No time to wait till her mouth can
Enrich that smile her eyes began.

A poor life this if, full of care,
We have no time to stand and stare.

BEAUTY
E-Yeh-Shure'

Beauty is seen
In the sunlight,
The trees, the birds,
Corn growing and people working
Or dancing for their harvest.

Beauty is heard
In the night,
Wind sighing, rain falling,
Or a singer chanting
Anything in earnest.

Beauty is in yourself.
Good deeds, happy thoughts
That repeat themselves
In your dreams,
In your work,
And even in your rest.

Elizabeth Coatsworth

Swift things are beautiful:
Swallows and deer,
And lightning that falls
Bright-veined and clear,
Rivers and meteors,

University Press, New Haven, 1919
"The Coin." From *Flame and Shadow* by Sara Teasdale.
Copyright 1920, 1948 by The Macmillan Company and
used with their permission
"Leisure." From *Collected Poems* by William Henry
Davies. Jonathan Cape & Harrison Smith, New York, 1929

"Beauty." From *I Am a Pueblo Indian Girl* by E-Yeh-
Shure', copyright 1939 by William Morrow and Company,
Inc. By permission of William Morrow and Company, Inc.
"Swift things are beautiful." From *Away Goes Sally* by
Elizabeth Coatsworth. Copyright 1934 by The Macmillan
Company and used with their permission

Wind in the wheat,
The strong-withered horse,
The runner's sure feet.

And slow things are beautiful:
The closing of day,
The pause of the wave
That curves downward to spray,
The ember that crumbles,
The opening flower,
And the ox that moves on
In the quiet of power.

HOLD FAST YOUR DREAMS

Louise Driscoll

Within your heart
Keep one still, secret spot
Where dreams may go,
And sheltered so,
May thrive and grow—
Where doubt and fear are not.
Oh, keep a place apart
Within your heart,
For little dreams to go.

HEAVEN

Langston Hughes

Heaven is
The place where
Happiness is
Everywhere.

T. S. Eliot

If humility and purity be not in the heart, they
are not in the home: and if they are not
in the home, they are not in the City.

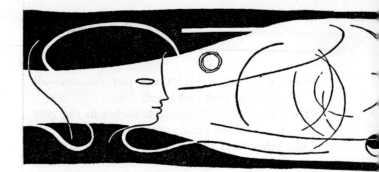

THE CREATION

James Weldon Johnson

And God stepped out on space,
And he looked around and said:
I'm lonely—
I'll make me a world.

And as far as the eye of God could see
Darkness covered everything,
Blacker than a hundred midnights
Down in a cypress swamp.

Then God smiled,
And the light broke,
And the darkness rolled up on one side,
And the light stood shining on the other,
And God said: That's good!

Then God reached out and took the light in his
    hands,
And God rolled the light in his hands
Until he made the sun;
And he set that sun a-blazing in the heavens.
And the light that was left from making the sun
God gathered it up in a shining ball
And flung it against the darkness,
Spangling the night with the moon and stars.
Then down between
The darkness and the light

He hurled the world;
And God said: That's good!

Then God himself stepped down—
And the sun was on his right hand,
And the moon was on his left;
The stars were clustered about his head,
And the earth was under his feet.
And God walked, and where he trod
His footsteps hollowed the valleys out
And bulged the mountains up.

Then he stopped and saw
That the earth was hot and barren.
So God stepped over to the edge of the world
And he spat out the seven seas—
He batted his eyes, and the lightnings flashed—
He clapped his hands, and the thunders rolled—
And the waters above the earth came down,
The cooling waters came down.

Then the green grass sprouted,
And the little red flowers blossomed,
The pine tree pointed his finger to the sky,
And the oak spread out his arms,
The lakes cuddled down in the hollows of the
    ground,
And the rivers ran down to the sea;
And God smiled again,
And the rainbow appeared,
And curled itself around his shoulder.

Then God raised his arm and waved his hand,
Over the sea and over the land,
And he said: Bring forth! Bring forth!
And quicker than God could drop his hand,
Fishes and fowls
And beasts and birds
Swam the rivers and the seas,
Roamed the forests and the woods,

And split the air with their wings.
And God said: That's good!

Then God walked around,
And God looked around
On all that he had made.
He looked at his sun,
And he looked at his moon,
And he looked at his little stars;
He looked on his world
With all its living things,
And God said: I'm lonely still.

Then God sat down—
On the side of a hill where he could think;
By a deep, wide river he sat down;
With his head in his hands,
God thought and thought,
Till he thought: I'll make me a man!

Up from the bed of the river
God scooped the clay;
And by the bank of the river
He kneeled him down;
And there the great God Almighty
Who lit the sun and fixed it in the sky,
Who flung the stars to the most far corner of the
    night,
Who rounded the earth in the middle of his
    hand;
This great God,
Like a mammy bending over her baby,
Kneeled down in the dust
Toiling over a lump of clay
Till he shaped it in his own image;

Then into it he blew the breath of life,
And man became a living soul.
Amen. Amen.

WISDOM
Langston Hughes

I stand most humbly
Before man's wisdom,
Knowing we are not
Really wise:

If we were
We'd open up the kingdom
And make earth happy
As the dreamed of skies.

Walt Whitman

I believe a leaf of grass is no less than the jour-
    ney-work of the stars,
And the pismire is equally perfect, and a grain of
    sand, and the egg of the wren,
And the tree-toad is a chef-d'oeuvre for the high-
    est,
And the running blackberry would adorn the
    parlors of heaven,
And the narrowest hinge in my hand puts to
    scorn all machinery,
And the cow crunching with depress'd head sur-
    passes any statue,
And a mouse is miracle enough to stagger sextil-
    lions of infidels.

Elizabeth Coatsworth

How gray the rain
And gray the world
And gray the rain clouds overhead,
When suddenly
Some cloud is furled
And there is gleaming sun instead!

The raindrops drip
Prismatic light,
And trees and meadows burn in green,
And arched in air
Serene and bright
The rainbow all at once is seen.

Serene and bright
The rainbow stands
That was not anywhere before,
And so may joy
Fill empty hands
When someone enters through a door.

Elizabeth Coatsworth

The warm of heart shall never lack a fire
However far he roam.
Although he live forever among strangers
He cannot lack a home.

For strangers are not strangers to his spirit,
And each house seems his own,
And by the fire of his loving-kindness
He cannot sit alone.

HOUSE BLESSING
Arthur Guiterman

Bless the four corners of this house,
    And be the lintel blest;
And bless the heart and bless the board
    And bless each place of rest;
And bless the door that opens wide
    To stranger as to kin;
And bless each crystal window-pane
    That lets the starlight in;
And bless the rooftree overhead
    And every sturdy wall.
The peace of man, the peace of God,
    The peace of Love on all!

WHO HATH A BOOK
Wilbur D. Nesbit

Who hath a book
    Hath friends at hand,
And gold and gear
    At his command;
And rich estates,
    If he but look,

Are held by him
Who hath a book.

Who hath a book
Hath but to read
And he may be
A king, indeed.
His kingdom is
His inglenook—
All this is his
Who hath a book.

TO THE WAYFARER

Unknown

A Poem Fastened to Trees in the Portuguese Forests

Ye who pass by and would raise your hand
against me, hearken ere you harm me.

I am the heat of your hearth on the cold winter
nights, the friendly shade screening you
from summer sun, and my fruits are refresh-
ing draughts, quenching your thirst as you
journey on.

I am the beam that holds your house, the board
of your table, the bed on which you lie, the
timber that builds your boat.

I am the handle of your hoe, the door of your
homestead, the wood of your cradle, and the
shell of your coffin.

I am the bread of kindness and the flower of
beauty.
Ye who pass by, listen to my prayer: harm me
not.

THE SPLENDOR FALLS ON CASTLE WALLS

Alfred, Lord Tennyson

The splendor falls on castle walls
And snowy summits old in story;
The long light shakes across the lakes,
And the wild cataract leaps in glory.
Blow, bugle, blow, set the wild echoes flying,
Blow, bugle; answer, echoes, dying, dying, dying.

O hark, O hear! how thin and clear,
And thinner, clearer, farther going!
O sweet and far from cliff and scar
The horns of Elfland faintly blowing!
Blow, let us hear the purple glens replying,
Blow, bugle; answer, echoes, dying, dying, dying.

O love, they die in yon rich sky,
They faint on hill or field or river;
Our echoes roll from soul to soul,
And grow forever and forever.
Blow, bugle, blow, set the wild echoes flying,
And answer, echoes, answer, dying, dying, dying.

Emily Dickinson

Hope is the thing with feathers
That perches in the soul,
And sings the tune without the words,
And never stops at all,

And sweetest in the gale is heard;
And sore must be the storm
That could abash the little bird
That kept so many warm.

I've heard it in the chillest land,
And on the strangest sea;
Yet, never, in extremity,
It asked a crumb of me.

A WORD

Emily Dickinson

A word is dead
When it is said,
Some say.

I say it just
Begins to live
That day.

THE WONDERFUL WORLD

William Brighty Rands

Great, wide, beautiful, wonderful World,
With the wonderful water round you curled,

And the wonderful grass upon your breast,
World, you are beautifully dressed.

MY LAND IS FAIR FOR ANY EYES TO SEE

Jesse Stuart

My land is fair for any eyes to see—
Now look, my friends—look to the east and west!
You see the purple hills far in the west—
Hills lined with pine and gum and black-oak
    tree—
Now to the east you see the fertile valley!
This land is mine, I sing of it to you—
My land beneath the skies of white and blue.
This land is mine, for I am part of it.
I am the land, for it is part of me—
We are akin and thus our kinship be!
It would make me a brother to the tree!
And far as eyes can see this land is mine.
Not for one foot of it I have a deed—
To own this land I do not need a deed—
They all belong to me—gum, oak, and pine.

THE DAY WILL BRING SOME LOVELY THING

Grace Noll Crowell

"The day will bring some lovely thing,"
I say it over each new dawn:
"Some gay, adventurous thing to hold
Against my heart when it is gone."

And so I rise and go to meet
The day with wings upon my feet.

I come upon it unaware—
Some sudden beauty without name:
A snatch of song—a breath of pine—
A poem lit with golden flame;
High tangled bird notes—keenly thinned—
Like flying color on the wind.

No day has ever failed me quite—
Before the grayest day is done,
I come upon some misty bloom
Or a late line of crimson sun.
Each night I pause—remembering
Some gay, adventurous, lovely thing.

GOOD NIGHT

Victor Hugo

Good night! good night!
Far flies the light;
But still God's love
Shall flame above,
Making all bright.
Good night! Good night!

"My Land is Fair for Any Eyes to See." From *Man with a Bull-Tongue Plough* by Jesse Stuart. New York: E. P. Dutton & Co., Inc., 1934. By permission of the author
"The Day Will Bring Some Lovely Thing." From *Silver in the Sun* by Grace Noll Crowell. Harper & Brothers, New York

BIBLIOGRAPHY

POETS CHILDREN ENJOY

Although some of the books listed here are now out of print, they are included because they may still be available in libraries.

ALDIS, DOROTHY, *All Together: A Child's Treasury of Verse*, Putnam, 1952.

ALLEN, MARIE LOUISE, *A Pocketful of Poems*, Harper, 1957.

BARUCH, DOROTHY, *I Like Machinery*, Harper, 1933.

BEHN, HARRY, *The Little Hill*, Harcourt, Brace, 1949.
Windy Morning, Harcourt, Brace, 1953.
The Wizard in the Well, Harcourt, Brace, 1956.

BENÉT, ROSEMARY and STEPHEN VINCENT, *A Book of Americans*, Rinehart, 1933.

BROOKS, GWENDOLYN, *Bronzeville Boys and Girls*, Harper, 1956.

CHUTE, MARCHETTE, *Rhymes About the City*, Macmillan, 1946.

CIARDI, JOHN, *The Reason for the Pelican*, Lippincott, 1959.

CONKLING, HILDA, *Poems by a Little Girl*, Stokes, 1920.

DE LA MARE, WALTER, *Rhymes and Verses; Collected Poems for Children*, Holt, 1947.

FARJEON, ELEANOR, *Poems for Children*, Lippincott, 1951.
The Children's Bells, Walck, 1960.

FIELD, EUGENE, *Poems of Childhood*, Scribner's, 1904, 1925.
A Scribner's Illustrated Classic, n.d. The last is the one now in print.

FIELD, RACHEL, *Taxis and Toadstools*, Doubleday, 1926.
Poems, Macmillan, 1957.

FROST, FRANCES M., *The Little Whistler*, Whittlesey House, 1949.
The Little Naturalist, Whittlesey House, 1959.

FROST, ROBERT, *You Come Too; Favorite Poems for Young Readers*, Holt, 1959.

FYLEMAN, ROSE, *Fairies and Chimneys*, Doubleday, 1920.

GREENAWAY, KATE, *Under the Window*, Warne, n.d.

LEAR, EDWARD, *The Complete Nonsense Book*, Dodd, Mead, 1942.

LINDSAY, VACHEL, *Johnny Appleseed and Other Poems*, Macmillan, 1928.

MC CORD, DAVID, *Far and Few: Rhymes of the Never Was and Always Is*, Little, Brown, 1952.

MC GINLEY, PHYLLIS, *All Around the Town* (a city alphabet), Lippincott, 1948.

MILNE, A. A., *The World of Christopher Robin*, Dutton, 1958. (*When We Were Very Young* and *Now We Are Six* combined in one volume.)

RICHARDS, LAURA E., *Tirra Lirra; Rhymes Old and New*, Little, Brown, 1955.

RILEY, JAMES WHITCOMB, *Rhymes of Childhood*, Bobbs-Merrill, 1891.

ROBERTS, ELIZABETH MADOX, *Under the Tree*, Viking, 1922.

ROSSETTI, CHRISTINA, *Sing-Song*, Macmillan, 1924.

SANDBURG, CARL, *Early Moon*, Harcourt, Brace, 1930.

SMITH, WILLIAM JAY, *Laughing Time*, Little, Brown, 1955.
Boy Blue's Book of Beasts, Little, Brown, 1957.

STARBIRD, KAYE, *Speaking of Cows*, Lippincott, 1960.

STEARNS, MONROE, *Ring-A-Ling*, Lippincott, 1959.

STEVENSON, ROBERT LOUIS, *A Child's Garden of Verses*, Oxford, 1947.

TEASDALE, SARA, *Stars To-Night*, Macmillan, 1930.

TIPPETT, JAMES, *I Live in a City*, Harper, 1927.

WYNNE, ANNETTE, *For Days and Days*, Stokes, 1919.

MOTHER GOOSE EDITIONS OF SPECIAL INTEREST

Marguerite de Angeli's Book of Nursery and Mother Goose Rhymes, ill. by Marguerite de Angeli, Doubleday, 1954.

Ring o' Roses; A Nursery Rhyme Picture Book, ill. by L. Leslie Brooke, Warne, n.d.

LANGSTAFF, JOHN, *Frog Went A'Courtin'*, ill. by Feodor Rojankovsky, Harcourt, Brace, 1955.

LANGSTAFF, JOHN, ed., *Over in the Meadow*, ill. by Feodor Rojankovsky, Harcourt, Brace, 1957. Single nursery rhymes with music.

LINES, KATHLEEN, ed., *Lavender's Blue*, ill. by Harold Jones, Watts, 1954.

OPIE, IONA and PETER, eds., *The Oxford Nursery Rhyme Book*, ill. from old chapbooks with additional pictures by Joan Hassal, Oxford, 1955.

The Tall Book of Mother Goose, ill. by Feodor Rojankovsky, Harper, 1942.

Mother Goose, ill. by Tasha Tudor, Oxford, 1944.

The Real Mother Goose, ill. by Blanche Fisher Wright, Rand McNally, 1916, with later editions.

A FEW SUPPLEMENTARY ANTHOLOGIES

ADSHEAD, GLADYS L. and DUFF, ANNIS, *An Inheritance of Poetry*, Houghton, Mifflin, 1948. Chiefly for adolescents.

ASSOCIATION FOR CHILDHOOD EDUCATION, *Sung Under the Silver Umbrella*, Macmillan, 1935. For children 4 to 9.

BREWTON, JOHN E., *Under the Tent of the Sky*, Macmillan, 1937. The best of the author's many anthologies.

COLE, WILLIAM, ed., *Humorous Poetry for Children*, ill. by Ervine Metzl, World, 1955.
Story Poems New and Old, ill. by Walter Buehr, World, 1957. Fresh material in both these areas.
Poems of Magic and Spells, ill. by Peggy Bacon, World, 1960. A collection of ninety poems of mystery about strange people or things. Ages 9 and up.

DE LA MARE, WALTER, ed., *Come Hither*, ill. by Warren Chappell, Knopf, 1957. An entrancing collection.

FERRIS, HELEN, *Favorite Poems Old and New*, ill. by Leonard Weisgard, Doubleday, 1957. A varied selection of over 700 poems for children of all ages.

HUFFARD, GRACE T. and others, *My Poetry Book*, Winston, rev. ed., 1956. A large collection, well selected.

MC DONALD, GERALD D., *A Way of Knowing*, A Collection of Poems for Boys, ill. by Clare and John Ross, Crowell, 1959. In spite of the subtitle, girls will like this collection of vigorous poetry as well as the boys do.

PLOTZ, HELEN, ed., *Imagination's Other Place; Poems of Science and Mathematics*, ill. by Clare Leighton, Crowell, 1955. For older children, youth, and adults, this is a superb collection of poems.

READ, HERBERT, ed., *This Way Delight*, ill. by Juliet Kepes, Pantheon, 1956. A small, choice collection of authentic poetry from the Elizabethans to Dylan Thomas.

THOMPSON, BLANCHE, *Silver Pennies*, Macmillan, 1925. *More Silver Pennies*, Macmillan, 1938. Small collections of choice modern poetry for children and youth.

UNTERMEYER, LOUIS, *The Golden Treasury of Poetry*, ill. by Joan Walsh Anglund, Golden Press, 1959. A large, attractively illustrated collection of poetry, chiefly from the older poets. The comments add much to the text.

ADULT POETRY REFERENCES

ABERCROMBIE, LASCELLES, *Poetry; Its Music and Meaning*, Oxford, 1932. A detailed analysis of the elements involved in the music of poetry and the relation of music to meaning. Difficult reading but rewarding.

ARBUTHNOT, MAY HILL, *Children and Books*, 1957. Chapters 4–10 are about poets and poetry, including a discussion of verse choirs and various helps in using poetry with children.

ARNSTEIN, FLORA, *Adventure into Poetry*, Stanford University Press, 1951. A teacher's careful record of her step-by-step procedures in conducting an experiment in creative writing with a group of elementary-school children. Sound literary taste, endless patience and tact make this an invaluable study.

AUSLANDER, JOSEPH and HILL, FRANK ERNEST, *The Winged Horse; The Story of the Poets and Their Poetry*, Doubleday, 1927. Written for young people, this book is good reading for adults.

DUFF, ANNIS, *"Bequest of Wings"; A Family's Pleasures with Books*, Viking, 1944. Charming account of introducing two children to books, especially poetry. Good!

EASTMAN, MAX, *The Enjoyment of Poetry*, Scribner's, new ed., 1951. Good reading; note especially the chapters on "Poetic People," which includes children, and "Practical Values of Poetry."

ERSKINE, JOHN, *The Kinds of Poetry and Other Essays*, Bobbs-Merrill, 1920. Read the fine chapter on "The Teaching of Poetry."

HIGHET, GILBERT, *The Powers of Poetry*, Oxford, 1960. A brief introduction to the oral-aural aspects of poetry, with delightful chapters on poets and types of poetry.

ISAACS, J., *The Background of Modern Poetry*, Dutton, 1952. Scholarly first aid to adults who find modern poetry hard to take.

OPIE, IONA and PETER, *The Oxford Dictionary of Nursery Rhymes*, Oxford, 1951. An exhaustive study of the origins and variants of nursery rhymes. A treasure of sources for students of this field.

SOME SOURCES OF BIOGRAPHIES

BALFOUR, GRAHAM, *The Life of Robert Louis Stevenson*, Scribner's, 1915.

BARNES, WALTER, *The Children's Poets*, World Book Company, 1924. Interesting notes about the older poets of childhood.

DAVIDSON, ANGUS, *Edward Lear, Landscape Painter and Non-Sense Poet*, Dutton, 1939.

FARJEON, ELEANOR, *Portrait of a Family*, Stokes, 1936.

KUNITZ, STANLEY J., *British Authors of the 19th Century*, Wilson, 1936.

KUNITZ, STANLEY J. and HAYCROFT, HOWARD, *American Authors*, 1600–1900, Wilson, 1938. A biographical dictionary of American literature, complete in one volume.

KUNITZ, STANLEY J. and HAYCROFT, HOWARD, *The Junior Book of Authors*, 2nd ed. revised, Wilson, 1951. Includes biographical or autobiographical sketches of authors of both classic and contemporary juvenile literature.

KUNITZ, STANLEY J. and HAYCROFT, HOWARD, *Twentieth Century Authors*, Wilson, 1942. A biographical dictionary of modern literature. Gives information about writers of this century of all nations. First suppl. 1955.

LENNON, FLORENCE BECKER, *Victoria Through the Looking-Glass*, Simon & Schuster, 1945. A fine biography of Lewis Carroll.

MILNE, A. A., *Autobiography*, Dutton, 1939.

NEWCOMB, COVELLE, *The Secret Door: The Story of Kate Greenaway*, Dodd, Mead, 1946. A fictionalized biography of Kate Greenaway, a good source of stories to tell to children.

BOOKS ON VERSE CHOIRS

ABNEY, LOUISE, *Choral Speaking Arrangements for the Upper Grades*, Expression, 1952.

ADAMS, HILDA and CROASDELL, ANNE, eds., *A Poetry Speaking Anthology*, Books I, II, III, Methuen, 1938. This single volume contains three small books on Infant Work, Junior Work, and Senior Work, corresponding to the middle grades, upper grades, and high school.

ARBUTHNOT, MAY HILL, *Children and Books*, Scott, Foresman, 1957. Chapter 10, "Verse Choirs."

BROWN, HELEN A. and HELTMAN, HARRY J., eds., *Choral Readings for Fun and Recreation*, Westminster Press, 1956.

DE WITT, MARGUERITE E., ed., *Practical Methods in Choral Speaking*, Expression, 1936. A compilation of papers by American teachers covering methods from the primary grades through the university.

GULLAN, MARJORIE, *The Speech Choir*, Harper, 1937. This is one of the most useful of Miss Gullan's books, because it is both an anthology and a methods text. It contains American poetry as well as English ballads, with detailed descriptions of the presentations.

HAMM, AGNES C., *Choral Speaking Technique*, 3rd ed., Tower Press, 1951.

HICKS, HELEN GERTRUDE, *The Reading Chorus*, Noble & Noble, 1939.

KEPPIE, ELIZABETH, *The Teaching of Choric Speech*, Expression, 1932. Beginners like this small book because of its detailed directions for a step-by-step development. The methods follow the much too formal procedures of the earliest books in the field.

KEPPIE, ELIZABETH E. and others, *Speech Improvement Through Choral Speaking*, Expression Co., 1942.

INDEX OF AUTHORS AND TITLES

INDEX OF FIRST LINES